Study and Solutions Guide for

COLLEGE ALGEBRA

SECOND EDITION

Larson/Hostetler

Dianna L. Zook

The Pennsylvania State University
The Behrend College

D. C. Heath and Company

Lexington, Massachusetts   Toronto

International Standard Book Number: 0-669-16275-2

3   4   5   6   7   8   9   0

TO THE STUDENT

The *Study and Solutions Guide for College Algebra* is a supplement to the text by Roland E. Larson and Robert P. Hostetler.

As a mathematics instructor, I often have students come to me with questions about the assigned homework. When I ask to see their work, the reply often is "I didn't know where to start." The purpose of the *Study Guide* is to provide brief summaries of the topics covered in the textbook and enough detailed solutions to problems so that you will be able to work the remaining exercises.

A special thanks to Linda M. Bollinger for typing this guide. Also I would like to thank my husband Edward L. Schlindwein for his support during the several months I worked on this project.

If you have any corrections or suggestions for improving this *Study Guide*, I would appreciate hearing from you.

Good luck with your study of algebra.

Dianna L. Zook
The Pennsylvania State University
Erie, Pennsylvania 16563

CONTENTS

CHAPTER 1

Review of Fundamental Concepts of Algebra

SECTION 1.1

The Real Number System

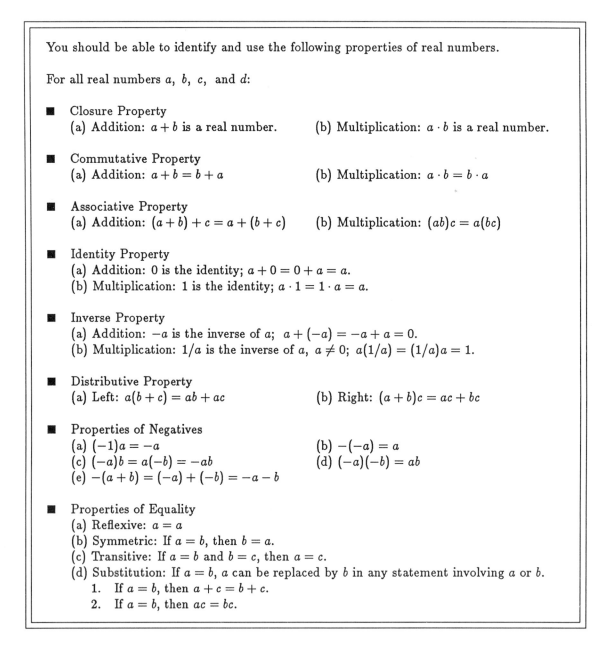

You should be able to identify and use the following properties of real numbers.

For all real numbers a, b, c, and d:

- **Closure Property**
  (a) Addition: $a + b$ is a real number.   (b) Multiplication: $a \cdot b$ is a real number.

- **Commutative Property**
  (a) Addition: $a + b = b + a$ (b) Multiplication: $a \cdot b = b \cdot a$

- **Associative Property**
  (a) Addition: $(a + b) + c = a + (b + c)$ (b) Multiplication: $(ab)c = a(bc)$

- **Identity Property**
  (a) Addition: 0 is the identity; $a + 0 = 0 + a = a$.
  (b) Multiplication: 1 is the identity; $a \cdot 1 = 1 \cdot a = a$.

- **Inverse Property**
  (a) Addition: $-a$ is the inverse of a; $a + (-a) = -a + a = 0$.
  (b) Multiplication: $1/a$ is the inverse of a, $a \neq 0$; $a(1/a) = (1/a)a = 1$.

- **Distributive Property**
  (a) Left: $a(b + c) = ab + ac$ (b) Right: $(a + b)c = ac + bc$

- **Properties of Negatives**
  (a) $(-1)a = -a$ (b) $-(-a) = a$
  (c) $(-a)b = a(-b) = -ab$ (d) $(-a)(-b) = ab$
  (e) $-(a + b) = (-a) + (-b) = -a - b$

- **Properties of Equality**
  (a) Reflexive: $a = a$
  (b) Symmetric: If $a = b$, then $b = a$.
  (c) Transitive: If $a = b$ and $b = c$, then $a = c$.
  (d) Substitution: If $a = b$, a can be replaced by b in any statement involving a or b.
    1. If $a = b$, then $a + c = b + c$.
    2. If $a = b$, then $ac = bc$.

- Cancellation Laws
  - (a) If $a + c = b + c$, then $a = b$.
  - (b) If $ac = bc$, then $a = b$, $c \neq 0$.

- Subtraction: $a - b = a + (-b)$

- Division: $a \div b = a(1/b) = a/b$, $b \neq 0$

- Properties of Fractions $(b \neq 0, d \neq 0)$
  - (a) Equivalent Fractions: $a/b = c/d$ if and only if $ad = bc$.
  - (b) Rule of Signs: $-a/b = a/-b = -(a/b)$ and $-a/-b = a/b$
  - (c) Equivalent Fractions: $a/b = ac/bc$, $c \neq 0$
  - (d) Addition and Subtraction
    1. Like Denominators: $(a/b) \pm (c/b) = (a \pm c)/b$
    2. Unlike Denominators: $(a/b) \pm (c/d) = (ad \pm bc)/bd$
  - (e) Multiplication: $(a/b) \cdot (c/d) = ac/bd$
  - (f) Division: $(a/b) \div (c/d) = (a/b) \cdot (d/c) = ad/bc$ if $c \neq 0$.

- Properties of Zero
  - (a) $a \pm 0 = a$
  - (b) $a \cdot 0 = 0$
  - (c) $0 \div a = 0/a = 0$, $a \neq 0$
  - (d) If $ab = 0$, then $a = 0$ or $b = 0$.
  - (e) $a/0$ is undefined.

- Definition of Absolute Value:

$$|a| = \begin{cases} a, & \text{if } a \geq 0 \\ -a, & \text{if } a < 0 \end{cases}$$

- Properties of Absolute Value
  - (a) $|-a| = |a|$
  - (b) $|ab| = |a||b|$
  - (c) $|a/b| = |a|/|b|$, $b \neq 0$

- Distance Between Two Points on the Real Line
  $d(a, b) = |b - a| = |a - b|$

Solutions to Selected Exercises

7. Identify the property illustrated in the equation $2(x+3) = 2x + 6$.

Solution:

By the Distributive Property, we have

$$2(x+3) = 2 \cdot x + 2 \cdot 3 = 2x + 6.$$

15. Identify the properties illustrated in the equation $x(3y) = (x \cdot 3)y = (3x)y$.

Solution:

$$
\begin{aligned}
x(3y) &= (x \cdot 3)y \quad &&\text{by the Associative Property of Multiplication} \\
&= (3x)y \quad &&\text{by the Commutative Property of Multiplication}
\end{aligned}
$$

19. Use the properties of zero to evaluate, if possible, the following expression. If the expression is undefined, state why.

$$\frac{8}{-9 + (6+3)}$$

Solution:

$$\frac{8}{-9 + (6+3)} = \frac{8}{-9 + 9} = \frac{8}{0}$$

which is undefined since the denominator is zero.

23. Perform the indicated operations: $10 - 6 - 2$.

Solution:

$$10 - 6 - 2 = (10 - 6) - 2 = 4 - 2 = 2$$

27. Perform the indicated operation:

$$2\left(\frac{77}{-11}\right).$$

Solution:

$$2\left(\frac{77}{-11}\right) = 2(-7) = -14$$

35. Perform the indicated operations:

$$\frac{4}{5} \times \frac{1}{2} \times \frac{3}{4}.$$

Solution:

$$\frac{4}{5} \times \frac{1}{2} \times \frac{3}{4} = \frac{1}{5} \times \frac{1}{2} \times \frac{3}{1} = \frac{3}{10}$$

39. Perform the indicated operation: $12 \div \frac{1}{4}$.

Solution:

$$12 \div \frac{1}{4} = 12 \times \frac{4}{1} = 12 \times 4 = 48$$

45. Plot the two real numbers $\frac{5}{6}$ and $\frac{2}{3}$ on the number real line and place the appropriate inequality sign between them.

Solution:

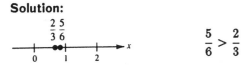

$$\frac{5}{6} > \frac{2}{3}$$

47. Use inequality notation to denote the expression "x is negative".

Solution:

"x is negative" can be written as $x < 0$.

51. Use inequality notation to denote the expression "the annual rate of inflation, R, is expected to be at least 3.5% but no more than 6%".

Solution:

The expression "the annual rate of inflation, R, is expected to be at least 3.5% but no more than 6%" can be written

$$3.5\% \leq R \leq 6\%$$

or

$$0.035 \leq R \leq 0.06$$

59. Find the distance between the points $-\frac{5}{2}$ and 0 on the real line.

Solution:

$$d\left(-\frac{5}{2}, \, 0\right) = \left| 0 - \left(-\frac{5}{2}\right) \right| = \left| \frac{5}{2} \right| = \frac{5}{2}$$

63. Find the distance between the points 9.34 and −5.65 on the real line.

Solution:

$$d(9.34,\ -5.65) = |9.34 - (-5.65)|$$
$$= |9.34 + 5.65|$$
$$= |14.99| = 14.99$$

67. Use absolute value notation to describe the expression "the distance between z and $\frac{3}{2}$ is greater than 1".

Solution:
Since

$$d(z,\ \tfrac{3}{2}) = |z - \tfrac{3}{2}| \quad \text{and} \quad d(z,\ \tfrac{3}{2}) > 1$$

we have

$$|z - \tfrac{3}{2}| > 1.$$

71. Let m and n be any two integers. Then $2m$ and $2n$ are even integers and $(2m+1)$ and $(2n+1)$ are odd integers.

(a) Prove that the sum of two even integers is even.
(b) Prove that the sum of two odd integers is even.
(c) Prove that the product of an even integer with *any* integer is even.

Solution:

(a) The sum of two even integers can be written as

$$2m + 2n = 2(m + n)$$

which is even.

(b) The sum of two odd integers can be written as

$$(2m + 1) + (2n + 1) = 2m + 2n + 2 = 2(m + n + 1)$$

which is even.

(c) Let n be any integer. The product of an even integer with n can be written as

$$(2m)n = 2(mn)$$

which is even.

73. One worker can assemble a component in seven days and a second worker can do the same task in five days. If they work together, what fraction of a component can they assemble in two days?

Solution:
One worker assembles 1/7 of a component each day. The other worker assembles 1/5 of a component each day. Together, in two days, they assemble

$$2\left(\frac{1}{7} + \frac{1}{5}\right) = 2\left(\frac{5+7}{35}\right) = 2\left(\frac{12}{35}\right) = \frac{24}{35}$$

of a component.

77. (a) Use a calculator to order the following real numbers, from smallest to largest.

$$\frac{7071}{5000}, \ \frac{584}{413}, \ \sqrt{2}, \ \frac{47}{33}, \ \frac{127}{90}$$

(b) Which of the rational numbers in part (a) is closest to $\sqrt{2}$?

Solution:

(a) $\dfrac{7071}{5000} = 1.4142$

$\dfrac{584}{413} = 1.414043584$

$\sqrt{2} = 1.414213562$

$\dfrac{47}{33} = 1.42\overline{42}$

$\dfrac{127}{90} = 1.41\overline{1}$

$$\frac{127}{90} < \frac{584}{413} < \frac{7071}{5000} < \sqrt{2} < \frac{47}{33}$$

(b) $\dfrac{7071}{5000}$ is closest to $\sqrt{2}$.

SECTION 1.2

Integer Exponents

■ You should know the properties of exponents.

(a) $a^1 = a$ (b) $a^0 = 1,\ a \neq 0$

(c) $a^m a^n = a^{m+n}$ (d) $a^m/a^n = a^{m-n}$

(e) $a^{-n} = 1/a^n$ (f) $(a^m)^n = a^{m \cdot n}$

(g) $(ab)^n = a^n b^n$ (h) $(a/b)^n = a^n/b^n$

■ You should be able to write numbers in scientific notation, $c \times 10^n$, where $1 \leq c < 10$ and n is an integer.

■ You should be able to use your calculator to evaluate expressions involving exponents.

Solutions to Selected Exercises

3. Evaluate the expression.

$$\frac{5^5}{5^2}$$

Solution:

$$\frac{5^5}{5^2} = 5^{5-2} = 5^3 = 125$$

7. Evaluate the expression $(2^3 \cdot 3^2)^2$.

Solution:

$$(2^3 \cdot 3^2)^2 = (8 \cdot 9)^2 = 72^2 = 5184$$

13. Evaluate the expression.

$$\frac{4 \cdot 3^{-2}}{2^{-2} \cdot 3^{-1}}$$

Solution:

$$\frac{4 \cdot 3^{-2}}{2^{-2} \cdot 3^{-1}} = \frac{4 \cdot 2^2 \cdot 3^1}{3^2} = \frac{4 \cdot 4}{3} = \frac{16}{3}$$

21. Evaluate $6x^0 - (6x)^0$ when $x = 10$.

Solution:

$$6(10)^0 - (6 \cdot 10)^0 = 6 \cdot 1 - (60)^0 = 6 - 1 = 5$$

25. Simplify $5x^4(x^2)$.

Solution:

$$5x^4(x^2) = 5x^{4+2} = 5x^6$$

29. Simplify $6y^2(2y^4)^2$.

Solution:

$$6y^2(2y^4)^2 = 6y^2(2)^2(y^4)^2 = 6y^2(4)(y^8) = 24y^{10}$$

35. Simplify

$$\frac{12(x+y)^3}{9(x+y)}.$$

Solution:

$$\frac{12(x+y)^3}{9(x+y)} = \frac{3 \cdot 4(x+y)^{3-1}}{3 \cdot 3} = \frac{4(x+y)^2}{3}$$

41. Simplify $(-2x^2)^3(4x^3)^{-1}$.

Solution:

$$(-2x^2)^3(4x^3)^{-1} = \frac{(-2x^2)^3}{4x^3} = \frac{-8x^6}{4x^3} = -2x^3$$

47. Simplify $(4a^{-2}b^3)^{-3}$.

Solution:

$$(4a^{-2}b^3)^{-3} = (4)^{-3}(a^{-2})^{-3}(b^3)^{-3} = 4^{-3}a^6b^{-9} = \frac{a^6}{4^3b^9} = \frac{a^6}{64b^9}$$

51. Simplify

$$\left(\frac{a^{-2}}{b^{-2}}\right)\left(\frac{b}{a}\right)^3.$$

Solution:

$$\left(\frac{a^{-2}}{b^{-2}}\right)\left(\frac{b}{a}\right)^3 = \left(\frac{b^2}{a^2}\right)\left(\frac{b^3}{a^3}\right) = \frac{b^5}{a^5}$$

55. Write 0.00000435 in scientific notation.

Solution:

$$0.00000435 = 4.35 \times 10^{-6}$$

59. Write $1,637,000,000$ in scientific notation.

Solution:

$$1,637,000,000 = 1.637 \times 10^9$$

63. Write 6.21×10^0 in decimal form.

Solution:

$$6.21 \times 10^0 = 6.21 \times 1 = 6.21$$

67. Write 3.798×10^{-8} in decimal form.

Solution:

$$3.798 \times 10^{-8} = 0.00000003798$$

69. Use a calculator to evaluate the following. Round your answers to three decimal places.

(a) $2400(1 + 0.06)^{20}$

(b) $750\left(1 + \dfrac{0.11}{365}\right)^{800}$

Solution:

(a) $2400(1 + 0.06)^{20} = 2400(1.06)^{20} = 7697.125$

$$2400 \;\boxed{\times}\; 1.06 \;\boxed{y^x}\; 20 \;\boxed{=}$$

(b) $750\left(1 + \dfrac{0.11}{365}\right)^{800} = 954.448$

$$750 \;\boxed{\times}\; \boxed{(}\; 1 \;\boxed{+}\; .11 \;\boxed{\div}\; 365 \;\boxed{)}\; \boxed{y^x}\; 800 \;\boxed{=}$$

73. Use a calculator to evaluate the following. Round your answers to three decimal places.

(a) $(0.000345)(8,980,000,000)$

(b) $\dfrac{67,000,000 + 93,000,000}{0.0052}$

Solution:

(a) $(0.000345)(8,980,000,000) = (3.45 \times 10^{-4})(8.98 \times 10^{9}) = 3,098,100$

       3.45 $\boxed{\text{EE}}$ 4 $\boxed{+/-}$ $\boxed{\times}$ 8.98 $\boxed{\text{EE}}$ 9 $\boxed{=}$

(b) $\dfrac{67,000,000 + 93,000,000}{0.0052} = \dfrac{(6.7 \times 10^{7}) + (9.3 \times 10^{7})}{5.2 \times 10^{-3}} \approx 3.077 \times 10^{10}$

       $\boxed{(}$ 6.7 $\boxed{\text{EE}}$ 7 $\boxed{+}$ 9.3 $\boxed{\text{EE}}$ 7 $\boxed{)}$ $\boxed{\div}$ 5.2 $\boxed{\text{EE}}$ 3 $\boxed{+/-}$ $\boxed{=}$

75. The speed of light is $11,160,000$ miles per minute. The distance from the sun to the earth is $93,000,000$ miles. Find the time it takes for light to travel from the sun to the earth.

Solution:

$$\dfrac{93,000,000 \text{ miles}}{11,160,000 \text{ miles/minute}} = 8\tfrac{1}{3} \text{ minutes}$$

77. The amount A after t years in a savings account earning an annual interest rate of r compounded n times per year is $A = P(1 + \frac{r}{n})^{nt}$ where P is the original principal. Complete the following table for \$500 deposited in an account earning 12% compounded daily. [Note that $r = 0.12$ implies an interest rate of 12%.]

[*Hint:* If you have a programmable calculator, try using the programming feature to complete the table.]

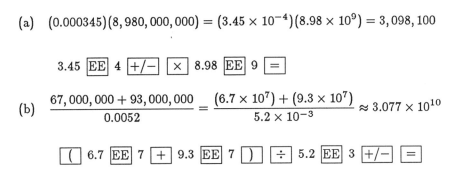

t	5	10	20
A	$500\left(1 + \dfrac{0.12}{365}\right)^{365 \times 5}$ $= \$910.97$	$500\left(1 + \dfrac{0.12}{365}\right)^{365 \times 10}$ $= \$1659.73$	$500\left(1 + \dfrac{0.12}{365}\right)^{365 \times 20}$ $= \$5509.41$

t	30	40	50
A	$500\left(1 + \dfrac{0.12}{365}\right)^{365 \times 30}$ $= \$18,288.29$	$500\left(1 + \dfrac{0.12}{365}\right)^{365 \times 40}$ $= \$60,707.30$	$500\left(1 + \dfrac{0.12}{365}\right)^{365 \times 50}$ $= \$201,515.58$

SECTION 1.3

Radicals and Rational Exponents

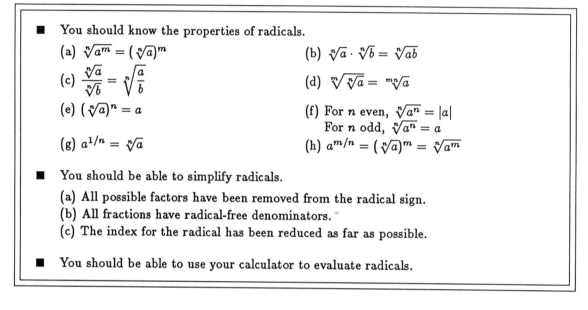

- You should know the properties of radicals.
  - (a) $\sqrt[n]{a^m} = (\sqrt[n]{a})^m$
  - (b) $\sqrt[n]{a} \cdot \sqrt[n]{b} = \sqrt[n]{ab}$
  - (c) $\dfrac{\sqrt[n]{a}}{\sqrt[n]{b}} = \sqrt[n]{\dfrac{a}{b}}$
  - (d) $\sqrt[m]{\sqrt[n]{a}} = \sqrt[mn]{a}$
  - (e) $(\sqrt[n]{a})^n = a$
  - (f) For n even, $\sqrt[n]{a^n} = |a|$
    For n odd, $\sqrt[n]{a^n} = a$
  - (g) $a^{1/n} = \sqrt[n]{a}$
  - (h) $a^{m/n} = (\sqrt[n]{a})^m = \sqrt[n]{a^m}$

- You should be able to simplify radicals.
  - (a) All possible factors have been removed from the radical sign.
  - (b) All fractions have radical-free denominators.
  - (c) The index for the radical has been reduced as far as possible.

- You should be able to use your calculator to evaluate radicals.

Solutions to Selected Exercises

3. Find the radical form for $32^{1/5} = 2$.

Solution:
Radical Form: $\sqrt[5]{32} = 2$

7. Find the rational exponent form for $\sqrt[3]{-216} = -6$.

Solution:
Rational Exponent Form: $(-216)^{1/3} = -6$

13. Evaluate $\sqrt{36}$ without using a calculator.

Solution:

$$\sqrt{36} = 6 \text{ since } (6)^2 = 36.$$

17. Evaluate $4/\sqrt{64}$ without using a calculator.

Solution:

$$\frac{4}{\sqrt{64}} = \frac{4}{8} = \frac{1}{2}$$

21. Evaluate $\sqrt[4]{562^4}$ without using a calculator.

Solution:

$$\sqrt[4]{562^4} = 562 \text{ since } \sqrt[n]{a^n} = |a| \text{ and } |562| = 562.$$

25. Simplify $\sqrt{8}$ by removing all possible factors from the radical.

Solution:

$$\sqrt{8} = \sqrt{4 \cdot 2} = \sqrt{4}\sqrt{2} = 2\sqrt{2}$$

29. Simplify $\sqrt{75x^2y^{-4}}$ by removing all possible factors from the radical.

Solution:

$$\sqrt{75x^2y^{-4}} = \sqrt{\frac{75x^2}{y^4}} = \sqrt{\frac{25 \cdot 3x^2}{y^4}} = \frac{5|x|\sqrt{3}}{y^2}$$

33. Rewrite $8/\sqrt[3]{2}$ by rationalizing the denominator. Simplify your answer.

Solution:

$$\frac{8}{\sqrt[3]{2}} = \frac{8}{\sqrt[3]{2}} \cdot \frac{\sqrt[3]{2}}{\sqrt[3]{2}} \cdot \frac{\sqrt[3]{2}}{\sqrt[3]{2}} = \frac{8(\sqrt[3]{2})^2}{(\sqrt[3]{2})^3} = \frac{8\sqrt[3]{2^2}}{2} = 4\sqrt[3]{4}$$

37. Rewrite the following by rationalizing the denominator. Simplify your answer.

$$\frac{3}{\sqrt{5} + \sqrt{6}}$$

Solution:

$$\frac{3}{\sqrt{5} + \sqrt{6}} = \frac{3}{\sqrt{5} + \sqrt{6}} \cdot \frac{\sqrt{5} - \sqrt{6}}{\sqrt{5} - \sqrt{6}} = \frac{3(\sqrt{5} - \sqrt{6})}{5 - 6}$$
$$= -3(\sqrt{5} - \sqrt{6}) = 3(\sqrt{6} - \sqrt{5})$$

41. Rewrite the following by rationalizing the numerator. Simplify your answer.

$$\frac{\sqrt{5}+\sqrt{3}}{3}$$

Solution:

$$\frac{\sqrt{5}+\sqrt{3}}{3} = \frac{\sqrt{5}+\sqrt{3}}{3} \cdot \frac{\sqrt{5}-\sqrt{3}}{\sqrt{5}-\sqrt{3}} = \frac{5-3}{3(\sqrt{5}-\sqrt{3})} = \frac{2}{3(\sqrt{5}-\sqrt{3})}$$

47. Combine and simplify $2\sqrt{50} + 12\sqrt{8}$.

Solution:

$$2\sqrt{50} + 12\sqrt{8} = 2\sqrt{25 \cdot 2} + 12\sqrt{4 \cdot 2}$$
$$= 2(5)\sqrt{2} + 12(2)\sqrt{2}$$
$$= 10\sqrt{2} + 24\sqrt{2}$$
$$= 34\sqrt{2}$$

51. Combine and simplify $\sqrt{5x^2 y}\sqrt{3y}$.

Solution:

$$\sqrt{5x^2 y}\sqrt{3y} = \sqrt{15x^2 y^2} = |x|y\sqrt{15}$$

55. Write $\sqrt{x}\sqrt[3]{x}$ as a single radical.

Solution:

$$\sqrt{x}\sqrt[3]{x} = x^{1/2}x^{1/3} = x^{1/2+1/3} = x^{3/6+2/6} = x^{5/6} = \left(\sqrt[6]{x}\right)^5 = \sqrt[6]{x^5}$$

59. Write $\sqrt{\sqrt[4]{2x}}$ as a single radical.

Solution:

$$\sqrt{\sqrt[4]{2x}} = \left((2x)^{1/4}\right)^{1/2} = (2x)^{1/8} = \sqrt[8]{2x}$$

63. Use fractional exponents to reduce the index of $\sqrt[6]{(x+1)^4}$.

Solution:

$$\sqrt[6]{(x+1)^4} = (x+1)^{4/6} = (x+1)^{2/3} = \sqrt[3]{(x+1)^2}$$

67. Use a calculator to approximate $\sqrt[6]{125}$. Round your answer to four decimal places.

Solution:

$\sqrt[6]{125} \approx 2.2361$

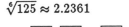 125 $\boxed{y^x}$ $\boxed{(}$ 1 $\boxed{\div}$ 6 $\boxed{)}$ $\boxed{=}$

Note: You may get an error if you raise a negative number to a power on your calculator. To use the $\boxed{y^x}$ key when your base is negative, omit the sign and then give the result the appropriate sign.

73. Fill in the blank with $<$, $>$, or $=$ by finding the decimal approximation.

$$5 \underline{\hspace{1cm}} \sqrt{3^2 + 2^2}$$

Solution:

$$\sqrt{3^2 + 2^2} = \sqrt{9 + 4} = \sqrt{13} \approx 3.6056$$

Therefore, $5 > \sqrt{3^2 + 2^2}$.

77. To find uniform depreciation by the declining balance method, we use the formula $R = N[1 - (S/C)^{1/N}]$ where R is the rate factor each year, N is the useful life of the item, C is the original cost, and S is the salvage value. Calculate R (to two decimal places) for each of the following.

(a) $N = 8$, $C = \$10,400$, $S = \$1,500$
(b) $N = 4$, $C = \$11,200$, $S = \$3,200$

Solution:

(a) $R = 8\left[1 - \left(\dfrac{1500}{10400}\right)^{1/8}\right] \approx 1.72$

8 $\boxed{\times}$ $\boxed{(}$ 1 $\boxed{-}$ $\boxed{(}$ 1500 $\boxed{\div}$ 10,400 $\boxed{)}$ $\boxed{y^x}$ $\boxed{(}$ 1 $\boxed{\div}$ 8 $\boxed{)}$ $\boxed{)}$ $\boxed{=}$

(b) $R = 4\left[1 - \left(\dfrac{3200}{11200}\right)^{1/4}\right] \approx 1.08$

4 $\boxed{\times}$ $\boxed{(}$ 1 $\boxed{-}$ $\boxed{(}$ 3200 $\boxed{\div}$ 11,200 $\boxed{)}$ $\boxed{y^x}$ .25 $\boxed{)}$ $\boxed{=}$

SECTION 1.4

Polynomials and Special Products

■ Given a polynomial in x, $a_n x^n + a_{n-1} x^{n-1} + \ldots + a_1 x + a_0$, where $a_n \neq 0$, you should be able to identify the following:

(a) Degree: n
(b) Terms: $a_n x^n$, $a_{n-1} x^{n-1}$, ..., $a_1 x$, a_0
(c) Coefficients: a_n, a_{n-1}, ..., a_1, a_0
(d) Leading coefficient: a_n

■ You should be able to add and subtract polynomials.

■ You should be able to multiply polynomials by either

(a) The Distributive Law or
(b) The Vertical Method.

■ You should know the special binomial products.

(a) $(ax + b)(cx + d) = acx^2 + adx + bcx + bd$
$$= acx^2 + (ad + bc)x + bd$$
(b) $(u \pm v)^2 = u^2 \pm 2uv + v^2$
(c) $(u + v)(u - v) = u^2 - v^2$
(d) $(u \pm v)^3 = u^3 \pm 3u^2 v + 3uv^2 \pm v^3$

■ You should be able to determine the degree of a polynomial in more than one variable.

(a) The degree of a *term* is the sum of the powers.
(b) The degree of the *polynomial* is the highest degree.

Solutions to Selected Exercises

5. Find the degree and the leading coefficient of

$$4x^5 + 6x^4 - 3x^3 + 10x^2 - x - 1.$$

Solution:
For $4x^5 + 6x^4 - 3x^3 + 10x^2 - x - 1$, we have the following.

Degree: 5
Leading Coefficient: 4

7. Simplify $(6x + 5) - (8x + 15)$.

Solution:

$$(6x + 5) - (8x + 15) = 6x + 5 - 8x - 15 = 6x - 8x + 5 - 15 = -2x - 10$$

11. Simplify $(15x^2 - 6) - (-8x^3 - 14x^2 - 17)$.

Solution:

$$(15x^2 - 6) - (-8x^3 - 14x^2 - 17) = 15x^2 - 6 + 8x^3 + 14x^2 + 17$$
$$= 8x^3 + 29x^2 + 11$$

13. Simplify $5z - [3z - (10z + 8)]$.

Solution:

$$5z - [3z - (10z + 8)] = 5z - [3z - 10z - 8]$$
$$= 5z - [-7z - 8]$$
$$= 5z + 7z + 8$$
$$= 12z + 8$$

19. Simplify $(-2x)(-3x)(5x + 2)$.

Solution:

$$(-2x)(-3x)(5x + 2) = 6x^2(5x + 2) = 6x^2(5x) + 6x^2(2) = 30x^3 + 12x^2$$

23. Find the product.

$$(3x - 5)(2x + 1)$$

Solution:

$$(3x - 5)(2x + 1) = 6x^2 + 3x - 10x - 5 = 6x^2 - 7x - 5$$

27. Find the product.

$$(2x - 5y)^2$$

Solution:

$$(2x - 5y)^2 = (2x)^2 - 2(2x)(5y) + (5y)^2 = 4x^2 - 20xy + 25y^2$$

29. Find the product.

$$[(x-3)+y]^2$$

Solution:

$$
\begin{aligned}
[(x-3)+y]^2 &= (x-3)^2 + 2(x-3)y + y^2 \\
&= x^2 - 6x + 9 + 2xy - 6y + y^2 \\
&= x^2 + 2xy + y^2 - 6x - 6y + 9
\end{aligned}
$$

35. Find the product.

$$(m-3+n)(m-3-n)$$

Solution:

$$
\begin{aligned}
(m-3+n)(m-3-n) &= [(m-3)+n][(m-3)-n] \\
&= (m-3)^2 - n^2 \\
&= m^2 - 6m + 9 - n^2 \\
&= m^2 - n^2 - 6m + 9
\end{aligned}
$$

41. Find the product.

$$(2x-y)^3$$

Solution:

$$
\begin{aligned}
(2x-y)^3 &= (2x)^3 - 3(2x)^2 y + 3(2x)y^2 - y^3 \\
&= 8x^3 - 12x^2 y + 6xy^2 - y^3
\end{aligned}
$$

45. Find the product.

$$(4r^3 - 3s^2)^2$$

Solution:

$$
\begin{aligned}
(4r^3 - 3s^2)^2 &= (4r^3)^2 - 2(4r^3)(3s^2) + (3s^2)^2 \\
&= 16r^6 - 24r^3 s^2 + 9s^4
\end{aligned}
$$

49. Find the product.

$$(x^2 + 9)(x^2 - x - 4)$$

Solution:

$$(x^2 + 9)(x^2 - x - 4) = (x^2 + 9)x^2 - (x^2 + 9)x - (x^2 + 9)4$$
$$= (x^4 + 9x^2) - (x^3 + 9x) - (4x^2 + 36)$$
$$= x^4 + 9x^2 - x^3 - 9x - 4x^2 - 36$$
$$= x^4 - x^3 + 5x^2 - 9x - 36$$

55. Find the product.

$$(x^2 + 2x + 5)(2x^2 - x - 1)$$

Solution:
By the Vertical Method we have

$$
\begin{array}{r}
2x^2 - \ x \ - \ 1 \\
x^2 + 2x \ + \ 5 \\
\hline
2x^4 - \ x^3 - \ \ x^2 \\
4x^3 - \ 2x^2 - 2x \\
10x^2 - 5x - 5 \\
\hline
2x^4 + 3x^3 + \ 7x^2 - 7x - 5
\end{array}
$$

61. Find the product.

$$(x + \sqrt{5})(x - \sqrt{5})(x + 4)$$

Solution:

$$(x + \sqrt{5})(x - \sqrt{5})(x + 4) = (x^2 - 5)(x + 4) \qquad \text{Special Product}$$
$$= x^3 + 4x^2 - 5x - 20$$

63. The probability of three successes and two failures in a certain experiment is given by $10p^3(1 - p)^2$. Find this product.

Solution:

$$10p^3(1 - p)^2 = 10p^3(1 - 2p + p^2)$$
$$= 10p^3(p^2 - 2p + 1)$$
$$= 10p^5 - 20p^4 + 10p^3$$

SECTION 1.5

Factoring

- ■ You should be able to factor out all common factors, the first step in factoring.

- ■ You should be able to factor the following special polynomial forms.

  (a) $u^2 - v^2 = (u + v)(u - v)$

  (b) $u^2 \pm 2uv + v^2 = (u \pm v)^2$

  (c) $mx^2 + nx + r = (ax + b)(cx + d)$, where $m = ac$, $r = bd$, $n = ad + bc$

  Note: Not all trinomials can be factored (using real coefficients).

  (d) $u^3 \pm v^3 = (u \pm v)(u^2 \mp uv + v^2)$

- ■ You should be able to factor by grouping.

Solutions to Selected Exercises

5. Remove the common factor: $(x - 1)^2 + 6(x - 1)$.

Solution:

$$(x - 1)^2 + 6(x - 1) = (x - 1)[(x - 1) + 6] = (x - 1)(x + 5)$$

9. Factor $16y^2 - 9$.

Solution:

$$16y^2 - 9 = (4y)^2 - (3)^2 = (4y + 3)(4y - 3)$$

11. Factor $(x - 1)^2 - 4$.

Solution:

$$(x - 1)^2 - 4 = [(x - 1) + 2][(x - 1) - 2] = (x + 1)(x - 3)$$

15. Factor $4t^2 + 4t + 1$.

Solution:

$$4t^2 + 4t + 1 = (2t)^2 + 2(2t)(1) + (1)^2 = (2t + 1)^2$$

21. Factor $s^2 - 5s + 6$.

Solution:

$$s^2 - 5s + 6 = (s - 2)(s - 3) \text{ since } (-2)(-3) = 6 \text{ and } (-2) + (-3) = -5.$$

25. Factor $x^2 - 30x + 200$.

Solution:

$$x^2 - 30x + 200 = (x - 10)(x - 20) \text{ since } (-10)(-20) = 200 \text{ and } (-10) + (-20) = -30.$$

29. Factor $9z^2 - 3z - 2$.

Solution:

$$9z^2 - 3z - 2 = (3z + 1)(3z - 2)$$

35. Factor $y^3 + 64$.

Solution:

$$y^3 + 64 = y^3 + 4^3 = (y + 4)(y^2 - 4y + 16)$$

39. Factor $x^3 - x^2 + 2x - 2$ by grouping.

Solution:

$$x^3 - x^2 + 2x - 2 = x^2(x - 1) + 2(x - 1) = (x - 1)(x^2 + 2)$$

43. Factor $6 + 2x - 3x^3 - x^4$ by grouping.

Solution:

$$6 + 2x - 3x^3 - x^4 = 2(3 + x) - x^3(3 + x) = (3 + x)(2 - x^3)$$

45. Completely factor $x^3 - 4x^2$.

Solution:

$$x^3 - 4x^2 = x^2(x - 4)$$

49. Completely factor $1 - 4x + 4x^2$.

Solution:

$$1 - 4x + 4x^2 = (1 - 2x)^2$$

53. Completely factor $9x^2 + 10x + 1$.

Solution:

$$9x^2 + 10x + 1 = (9x + 1)(x + 1)$$

57. Completely factor $2(x+1)(x-3)^2 - 3(x+1)^2(x-3)$.

Solution:

$$\begin{aligned}
2(x+1)(x-3)^2 - 3(x+1)^2(x-3) &= (x+1)(x-3)[2(x-3) - 3(x+1)] \\
&= (x+1)(x-3)[2x - 6 - 3x - 3] \\
&= (x+1)(x-3)(-x-9) \\
&= -(x+1)(x-3)(x+9)
\end{aligned}$$

61. Completely factor $x^4 - 4x^3 + x^2 - 4x$.

Solution:

$$\begin{aligned}
x^4 - 4x^3 + x^2 - 4x &= x^3(x-4) + x(x-4) \\
&= (x-4)(x^3 + x) \\
&= (x-4)x(x^2 + 1) \\
&= x(x-4)(x^2 + 1)
\end{aligned}$$

65. Completely factor $(x^2 + 1)^2 - 4x^2$.

Solution:

$$\begin{aligned}
(x^2 + 1)^2 - 4x^2 &= [(x^2 + 1) + 2x][(x^2 + 1) - 2x] \\
&= (x^2 + 2x + 1)(x^2 - 2x + 1) \\
&= (x+1)^2(x-1)^2
\end{aligned}$$

69. Completely factor $x^6 - 64$.

Solution:

$$\begin{aligned}
x^6 - 64 &= (x^2)^3 - (4)^3 \\
&= (x^2 - 4)(x^4 + 4x^2 + 16) \\
&= (x+2)(x-2)(x^4 + 4x^2 + 16)
\end{aligned}$$

Alternate Solution:

$$\begin{aligned}
x^6 - 64 &= (x^3)^2 - (8)^2 \\
&= (x^3 + 8)(x^3 - 8) \\
&= (x+2)(x^2 - 2x + 4)(x-2)(x^2 + 2x + 4) \\
&= (x+2)(x-2)(x^2 - 2x + 4)(x^2 + 2x + 4)
\end{aligned}$$

71. Factor $x^3 + 6x^2 + 12x + 8$ by using the formula

$$(x + a)^3 = x^3 + 3x^2 a + 3xa^2 + a^3.$$

Solution:

$$x^3 + 6x^2 + 12x + 8 = x^3 + 3x^2(2) + 3x(2)^2 + (2)^3$$
$$= (x + 2)^3$$

73. Factor $x^5 - 10x^4 + 40x^3 - 80x^2 + 80x - 32$ by using the formula

$$(x + a)^5 = x^5 + 5x^4 a + 10x^3 a^2 + 10x^2 a^3 + 5xa^4 + a^5.$$

Solution:

$$x^5 - 10x^4 + 40x^3 - 80x^2 + 80x - 32$$
$$= x^5 + 5x^4(-2) + 10x^3(-2)^2 + 10x^2(-2)^3 + 5x(-2)^4 + (-2)^5$$
$$= (x + (-2))^5$$
$$= (x - 2)^5$$

SECTION 1.6

Fractional Expressions

- ■ You should know that a rational expression is the quotient of two polynomials.

- ■ You should be able to simplify rational expressions by reducing them to lowest terms. This may involve factoring both the numerator and the denominator.

- ■ You should be able to add, subtract, multiply, and divide rational expressions.

- ■ You should be able to simplify compound fractions by either
  (a) Combining Fractions or
  (b) Rationalizing Fractions.

Solutions to Selected Exercises

3. Fill in the missing numerator so that the two fractions are equivalent.

$$\frac{x+1}{x} = \frac{(\qquad)}{x(x-2)}$$

Solution:

$$\frac{x+1}{x} = \frac{x+1}{x} \cdot \frac{x-2}{x-2}$$
$$= \frac{(x+1)(x-2)}{x(x-2)}, \quad x \neq 2$$

9. Reduce to lowest terms.

$$\frac{3xy}{xy+x}$$

Solution:

$$\frac{3xy}{xy+x} = \frac{3xy}{x(y+1)} = \frac{3y}{y+1}$$

13. Reduce to lowest terms.

$$\frac{x^3 + 5x^2 + 6x}{x^2 - 4}$$

Solution:

$$\frac{x^3 + 5x^2 + 6x}{x^2 - 4} = \frac{x(x+2)(x+3)}{(x+2)(x-2)} = \frac{x(x+3)}{x-2}$$

17. Reduce to lowest terms.

$$\frac{2 - x + 2x^2 - x^3}{x - 2}$$

Solution:

$$\frac{2 - x + 2x^2 - x^3}{x - 2} = \frac{(2-x) + x^2(2-x)}{x - 2}$$

$$= \frac{(2-x)(1+x^2)}{x - 2}$$

$$= \frac{-(x-2)(x^2+1)}{x - 2}$$

$$= -(x^2 + 1)$$

19. Reduce to lowest terms.

$$\frac{z^3 - 8}{z^2 + 2z + 4}$$

Solution:

$$\frac{z^3 - 8}{z^2 + 2z + 4} = \frac{(z-2)(z^2 + 2z + 4)}{z^2 + 2z + 4} = z - 2$$

23. Simplify

$$\frac{(x-9)(x+7)}{x+1} \cdot \frac{x}{9-x}.$$

Solution:

$$\frac{(x-9)(x+7)}{x+1} \cdot \frac{x}{9-x} = -\frac{(9-x)(x+7)x}{(x+1)(9-x)} = -\frac{x(x+7)}{x+1}$$

27. Simplify

$$\frac{t^2 - t - 6}{t^2 + 6t + 9} \cdot \frac{t+3}{t^2 - 4}.$$

Solution:

$$\frac{t^2 - t - 6}{t^2 + 6t + 9} \cdot \frac{t+3}{t^2 - 4} = \frac{(t+2)(t-3)}{(t+3)(t+3)} \cdot \frac{t+3}{(t+2)(t-2)} = \frac{t-3}{(t+3)(t-2)}$$

29. Simplify

$$\frac{x^2 + xy - 2y^2}{x^3 + x^2y} \cdot \frac{x}{x^2 + 3xy + 2y^2}.$$

Solution:

$$\frac{x^2 + xy - 2y^2}{x^3 + x^2y} \cdot \frac{x}{x^2 + 3xy + 2y^2} = \frac{(x+2y)(x-y)}{x^2(x+y)} \cdot \frac{x}{(x+2y)(x+y)} = \frac{x-y}{x(x+y)^2}$$

33. Simplify

$$\frac{\dfrac{(xy)^2}{(x+y)^2}}{\dfrac{xy}{(x+y)^3}}.$$

Solution:

$$\frac{\dfrac{(xy)^2}{(x+y)^2}}{\dfrac{xy}{(x+y)^3}} = \frac{(xy)^2}{(x+y)^2} \div \frac{xy}{(x+y)^3} = \frac{(xy)^2}{(x+y)^2} \cdot \frac{(x+y)^3}{xy} = xy(x+y)$$

37. Simplify

$$6 - \frac{5}{x+3}.$$

Solution:

$$6 - \frac{5}{x+3} = \frac{6(x+3)}{x+3} - \frac{5}{x+3} = \frac{6(x+3) - 5}{x+3}$$

$$= \frac{6x + 18 - 5}{x+3} = \frac{6x + 13}{x+3}$$

43. Simplify

$$\frac{1}{x^2 - x - 2} - \frac{x}{x^2 - 5x + 6} \, .$$

Solution:

$$\frac{1}{x^2 - x - 2} - \frac{x}{x^2 - 5x + 6} = \frac{1}{(x-2)(x+1)} - \frac{x}{(x-2)(x-3)}$$

$$= \frac{(x-3) - x(x+1)}{(x+1)(x-2)(x-3)}$$

$$= \frac{-x^2 - 3}{(x+1)(x-2)(x-3)} = -\frac{x^2 + 3}{(x+1)(x-2)(x-3)}$$

49. Simplify

$$\frac{\left(\dfrac{x+3}{x-3}\right)^2}{\dfrac{1}{x+3} + \dfrac{1}{x-3}} \, .$$

Solution:
(a) Combining method:

$$\frac{\left(\dfrac{x+3}{x-3}\right)^2}{\dfrac{1}{x+3} + \dfrac{1}{x-3}} = \frac{\dfrac{(x+3)^2}{(x-3)^2}}{\dfrac{(x-3)+(x+3)}{(x+3)(x-3)}}$$

$$= \frac{(x+3)^2}{(x-3)^2} \cdot \frac{(x+3)(x-3)}{2x} = \frac{(x+3)^3}{2x(x-3)}$$

(b) Rationalizing method:

$$\frac{\dfrac{(x+3)^2}{(x-3)^2}}{\dfrac{1}{x+3} + \dfrac{1}{x-3}} \cdot \frac{(x+3)(x-3)^2}{(x+3)(x-3)^2} = \frac{(x+3)^3}{(x-3)^2 + (x+3)(x-3)}$$

$$= \frac{(x+3)^3}{(x^2 - 6x + 9) + (x^2 - 9)}$$

$$= \frac{(x+3)^3}{2x^2 - 6x}$$

$$= \frac{(x+3)^3}{2x(x-3)}$$

55. Rationalize the denominator of

$$\frac{3}{\sqrt{x+1}}.$$

Solution:

$$\frac{3}{\sqrt{x+1}} = \frac{3}{\sqrt{x+1}} \cdot \frac{\sqrt{x+1}}{\sqrt{x+1}} = \frac{3\sqrt{x+1}}{x+1}$$

59. Rationalize the numerator of

$$\frac{\sqrt{x+2} - \sqrt{x}}{2}.$$

Solution:

$$\frac{\sqrt{x+2} - \sqrt{x}}{2} = \frac{\sqrt{x+2} - \sqrt{x}}{2} \cdot \frac{\sqrt{x+2} + \sqrt{x}}{\sqrt{x+2} + \sqrt{x}}$$

$$= \frac{(x+2) - x}{2(\sqrt{x+2} + \sqrt{x})} = \frac{2}{2(\sqrt{x+2} + \sqrt{x})}$$

$$= \frac{1}{\sqrt{x+2} + \sqrt{x}}$$

63. Simplify

$$\frac{\dfrac{t^2}{\sqrt{t^2+1}} - \sqrt{t^2+1}}{t^2}.$$

Solution:

$$\frac{\dfrac{t^2}{\sqrt{t^2+1}} - \sqrt{t^2+1}}{t^2} = \frac{\dfrac{t^2}{\sqrt{t^2+1}} - \sqrt{t^2+1}}{t^2} \cdot \frac{\sqrt{t^2+1}}{\sqrt{t^2+1}}$$

$$= \frac{t^2 - (t^2+1)}{t^2\sqrt{t^2+1}}$$

$$= -\frac{1}{t^2\sqrt{t^2+1}}$$

67. Simplify

$$\frac{-x^3(1-x^2)^{-1/2} - 2x(1-x^2)^{1/2}}{x^4} \, .$$

Solution:

$$\frac{-x^3(1-x^2)^{-1/2} - 2x(1-x^2)^{1/2}}{x^4} = \frac{-x^3(1-x^2)^{-1/2} - 2x(1-x^2)^{1/2}}{x^4} \cdot \frac{(1-x^2)^{1/2}}{(1-x^2)^{1/2}}$$

$$= \frac{-x^3 - 2x(1-x^2)}{x^4(1-x^2)^{1/2}}$$

$$= \frac{-x^3 - 2x + 2x^3}{x^4(1-x^2)^{1/2}}$$

$$= \frac{x^3 - 2x}{x^4(1-x^2)^{1/2}}$$

$$= \frac{x(x^2 - 2)}{x^4(1-x^2)^{1/2}}$$

$$= \frac{x^2 - 2}{x^3(1-x^2)^{1/2}}$$

SECTION 1.7

Algebraic Errors and Some Algebra of Calculus

■ You should be able to recognize and avoid the common algebraic errors listed in this section.
■ You should be able to "unsimplify" algebraic expressions by the following methods:

(a) Unusual Factoring
(b) Inserting Required Factors
(c) Rewriting with Negative Exponents
(d) Writing a Fraction as a Sum of Terms

Solutions to Selected Exercises

3. Find and correct any errors in $5z + 3(x - 2) = 5z + 3x - 2$.

Solution:

$$5z + 3(x - 2) = 5z + 3x - 6 \quad \text{By the Distributive Law}$$
$$\neq 5z + 3x - 2$$

5. Find and correct any errors in

$$-\frac{x - 3}{x - 1} = \frac{3 - x}{1 - x}.$$

Solution:

$$-\frac{x - 3}{x - 1} = \frac{-(x - 3)}{x - 1}$$
$$= \frac{3 - x}{x - 1} \qquad \text{Only the numerator is multiplied by } (-1).$$
$$\neq \frac{3 - x}{1 - x}$$

11. Find and correct any errors in $\sqrt{x+9} = \sqrt{x} + 3$.

Solution:

$$\sqrt{x+9} \neq \sqrt{x} + 3$$

The root of a sum does not equal the sum of the roots.

$$\sqrt{x} + 3 = \sqrt{(\sqrt{x}+3)^2} = \sqrt{x + 6\sqrt{x} + 9} \neq \sqrt{x+9}$$

$\sqrt{x+9}$ cannot be simplified.

15. Find and correct any errors in $\dfrac{1}{x+y^{-1}} = \dfrac{y}{x+1}$.

Solution:

$$\frac{1}{x+y^{-1}} = \frac{1}{x+(1/y)} \cdot \frac{y}{y} = \frac{y}{xy+1} \neq \frac{y}{x+1}$$

19. Find and correct any errors in $\sqrt[3]{x^3 + 7x^2} = x^2\sqrt[3]{x+7}$.

Solution:

$$\sqrt[3]{x^3 + 7x^2} = \sqrt[3]{x^2(x+7)} = \sqrt[3]{x^2}\sqrt[3]{x+7} \neq x^2\sqrt[3]{x+7}$$

Radicals apply to every factor of the radicand.

23. Find and correct any errors in $\dfrac{1}{2y} = (1/2)y$.

Solution:

$$\frac{1}{2y} = \frac{1}{2}\cdot\frac{1}{y} = \left(\frac{1}{2}\right)\frac{1}{y} \neq \left(\frac{1}{2}\right)y$$

Use the definition for multiplying fractions.

27. Insert the required factor in the parentheses.

$$\frac{2}{3}x^2 + \frac{1}{3}x + 5 = \frac{1}{3}(\quad)$$

Solution:

$$\frac{2}{3}x^2 + \frac{1}{3}x + 5 = \frac{2}{3}x^2 + \frac{1}{3}x + \frac{15}{3} = \frac{1}{3}(2x^2 + x + 15)$$

31. Insert the required factor in the parentheses.

$$x(2x^2 + 15) = (\quad)(2x^2 + 15)(2x)$$

Solution:

$$x(2x^2 + 15) = \left(\frac{1}{2}\right)(2x)(2x^2 + 15) = \left(\frac{1}{2}\right)(2x^2 + 15)(2x)$$

35. Insert the required factor in the parentheses.

$$\frac{1}{\sqrt{x}(1 + \sqrt{x})^2} = (\quad)\frac{1}{(1 + \sqrt{x})^2}\left(\frac{1}{2\sqrt{x}}\right)$$

Solution:

$$\frac{1}{\sqrt{x}(1 + \sqrt{x})^2} = \frac{1}{\sqrt{x}} \cdot \frac{1}{(1 + \sqrt{x})^2} = (2)\left(\frac{1}{2\sqrt{x}}\right)\frac{1}{(1 + \sqrt{x})^2}$$

$$= (2)\frac{1}{(1 + \sqrt{x})^2}\left(\frac{1}{2\sqrt{x}}\right)$$

39. Insert the required factor in the parentheses.

$$\frac{3}{x} + \frac{5}{2x^2} - \frac{3}{2}x = (\quad)(6x + 5 - 3x^3)$$

Solution:

$$\frac{3}{x} + \frac{5}{2x^2} - \frac{3}{2}x = \frac{6x}{2x^2} + \frac{5}{2x^2} - \frac{3x^3}{2x^2} = \left(\frac{1}{2x^2}\right)(6x + 5 - 3x^3)$$

43. Insert the required factor in the parentheses.

$$\frac{x^2}{1/12} - \frac{y^2}{2/3} = \frac{12x^2}{(\quad)} - \frac{3y^2}{(\quad)}$$

Solution:

$$\frac{x^2}{1/12} - \frac{y^2}{2/3} = x^2\left(\frac{12}{1}\right) - y^2\left(\frac{3}{2}\right) = \frac{12x^2}{1} - \frac{3y^2}{2}$$

47. Insert the required factor in the parentheses.

$$3(2x + 1)x^{1/2} + 4x^{3/2} = x^{1/2}(\quad)$$

Solution:

$$3(2x+1)x^{1/2} + 4x^{3/2} = 3(2x+1)x^{1/2} + 4xx^{1/2}$$
$$= x^{1/2}[3(2x+1) + 4x]$$
$$= x^{1/2}(10x + 3)$$

51. Insert the required factor in the parentheses.

$$\frac{1}{10}(2x+1)^{5/2} - \frac{1}{6}(2x+1)^{3/2} = \frac{(2x+1)^{3/2}}{15}(\quad)$$

Solution:

$$\frac{1}{10}(2x+1)^{5/2} - \frac{1}{6}(2x+1)^{3/2} = \frac{3}{30}(2x+1)^{3/2}(2x+1) - \frac{5}{30}(2x+1)^{3/2}$$
$$= \frac{1}{30}(2x+1)^{3/2}[3(2x+1) - 5]$$
$$= \frac{1}{30}(2x+1)^{3/2}(6x - 2)$$
$$= \frac{1}{30}(2x+1)^{3/2}2(3x - 1)$$
$$= \frac{1}{15}(2x+1)^{3/2}(3x - 1)$$

55. Write the following as a sum of two or more terms.

$$\frac{4x^3 - 7x^2 + 1}{x^{1/3}}$$

Solution:

$$\frac{4x^3 - 7x^2 + 1}{x^{1/3}} = \frac{4x^3}{x^{1/3}} - \frac{7x^2}{x^{1/3}} + \frac{1}{x^{1/3}}$$
$$= 4x^{3-1/3} - 7x^{2-1/3} + \frac{1}{x^{1/3}}$$
$$= 4x^{8/3} - 7x^{5/3} + \frac{1}{x^{1/3}}$$

59. Write the following as a sum of two or more terms.

$$\frac{x^2 + 4x + 8}{x^4 + 1}$$

Solution:

$$\frac{x^2 + 4x + 8}{x^4 + 1} = \frac{x^2}{x^4 + 1} + \frac{4x}{x^4 + 1} + \frac{8}{x^4 + 1}$$

REVIEW EXERCISES FOR CHAPTER 1

Solutions to Selected Exercises

1. Describe the *error* and make the necessary correction.

$$\frac{7}{16} + \frac{3}{16} = \frac{10}{32}$$

Solution:
Do not add the denominators.

$$\frac{7}{16} + \frac{3}{16} = \frac{10}{16} = \frac{5}{8} \neq \frac{10}{32}$$

5. Describe the *error* and make the necessary correction.

$$4\left(\frac{3}{7}\right) = \frac{12}{28}$$

Solution:
Use the definition for multiplying fractions.

$$4\left(\frac{3}{7}\right) = \frac{4}{1} \cdot \frac{3}{7} = \frac{12}{7} \neq \frac{12}{28}$$

9. Describe the *error* and make the necessary correction.

$$\frac{x-1}{1-x} = 1$$

Solution:
Cancel only common factors.

$$\frac{x-1}{1-x} = \frac{-(1-x)}{1-x} = -1 \neq 1$$

13. Describe the error and make the necessary correction for $(2x)^4 = 2x^4$.

Solution:
Apply the exponent to both factors in the parentheses.

$$(2x)^4 = 2^4 x^4 = 16x^4 \neq 2x^4$$

17. Describe the error and make the necessary correction for $(3^4)^4 = 3^8$.

Solution:

Multiply the exponents.

$$(3^4)^4 = 3^{4 \times 4} = 3^{16} \neq 3^8$$

21. Perform the indicated operations for $-10(7-5)$.

Solution:

$$-10(7-5) = -10(2) = -20$$

25. Perform the indicated operations for $|-3| + 4(-2) - 6$.

Solution:

$$|-3| + 4(-2) - 6 = 3 - 8 - 6 = -11$$

29. Perform the indicated operations for $6[4 - 2(6+8)]$.

Solution:

$$6[4 - 2(6+8)] = 6[4 - 2(14)] = 6[4 - 28] = 6[-24] = -144$$

31. Perform the indicated operations for

$$\left(\frac{3^2}{5^2}\right)^{-3}.$$

Solution:

$$\left(\frac{3^2}{5^2}\right)^{-3} = \left(\frac{9}{25}\right)^{-3} = \left(\frac{25}{9}\right)^{3} = \frac{15,625}{729}$$

35. Perform the indicated operations for $(3 \times 10^4)^2$.

Solution:

$$(3 \times 10^4)^2 = 3^2 \times (10^4)^2 = 9 \times 10^8$$

39. Use absolute value notation to describe the statement "the distance between y and -30 is less than 5".

Solution:

$$d(y, \ -30) = |y - (-30)| = |y + 30|$$

Since $d(y, \ -30)$ is less than 5, we have $|y + 30| < 5$.

43. Perform the indicated operations and/or simplify $\sqrt[3]{x}(3 + 4\sqrt[3]{x^2})$.

Solution:

$$\sqrt[3]{x}(3 + 4\sqrt[3]{x^2}) = x^{1/3}(3 + 4x^{2/3})$$
$$= 3x^{1/3} + 4x^{1/3+2/3}$$
$$= 3\sqrt[3]{x} + 4x$$

47. Perform the indicated operations and/or simplify $(x^2 - 2x + 1)(x^3 - 1)$.

Solution:

$$(x^2 - 2x + 1)(x^3 - 1) = (x^2 - 2x + 1)x^3 - (x^2 - 2x + 1)(1)$$
$$= x^5 - 2x^4 + x^3 - x^2 + 2x - 1$$

51. Perform the indicated operations and/or simplify $(y^2 - y)(y^2 + 1)(y^2 + y + 1)$.

Solution:

$$(y^2 - y)(y^2 + 1)(y^2 + y + 1) = (y^4 - y^3 + y^2 - y)(y^2 + y + 1)$$

By the Vertical Method we have

$$
\begin{array}{l}
y^4 - y^3 + y^2 - \ y \\
\underline{\qquad y^2 + y \ + \ 1} \\
y^6 - y^5 + y^4 - y^3 \\
\ \ + y^5 - y^4 + y^3 - y^2 \\
\ \ \ \ \ \ + y^4 - y^3 + y^2 - y \\
\underline{\qquad\qquad\qquad\qquad} \\
y^6 \qquad + y^4 - y^3 \qquad - y
\end{array}
$$

55. Perform the indicated operations and/or simplify.

$$\frac{x^2 - 4}{x^4 - 2x^2 - 8} \cdot \frac{x^2 + 2}{x^2}$$

Solution:

$$\frac{x^2 - 4}{x^4 - 2x^2 - 8} \cdot \frac{x^2 + 2}{x^2} = \frac{x^2 - 4}{(x^2 - 4)(x^2 + 2)} \cdot \frac{x^2 + 2}{x^2} = \frac{1}{x^2}$$

59. Perform the indicated operations and/or simplify.

$$x - 1 + \frac{1}{x + 2} + \frac{1}{x - 1}$$

Solution:

$$x - 1 + \frac{1}{x+2} + \frac{1}{x-1} = \frac{x(x+2)(x-1) - (x+2)(x-1) + (x-1) + (x+2)}{(x+2)(x-1)}$$

$$= \frac{(x^3 + x^2 - 2x) - (x^2 + x - 2) + (2x+1)}{(x+2)(x-1)}$$

$$= \frac{x^3 - x + 3}{(x+2)(x-1)}$$

65. Perform the indicated operations and/or simplify.

$$\frac{1}{x-2} + \frac{1}{(x-2)^2} + \frac{1}{x+2}$$

Solution:

$$\frac{1}{x-2} + \frac{1}{(x-2)^2} + \frac{1}{x+2} = \frac{(x-2)(x+2) + (x+2) + (x-2)^2}{(x+2)(x-2)^2}$$

$$= \frac{(x^2 - 4) + (x+2) + (x^2 - 4x + 4)}{(x+2)(x-2)^2}$$

$$= \frac{2x^2 - 3x + 2}{(x+2)(x-2)^2}$$

69. Perform the indicated operations and/or simplify.

$$\frac{\dfrac{x^2(5x-6)}{2x+3}}{\dfrac{5x}{2x+3}}$$

Solution:

$$\frac{\dfrac{x^2(5x-6)}{2x+3}}{\dfrac{5x}{2x+3}} = \frac{x^2(5x-6)}{2x+3} \cdot \frac{2x+3}{5x} = \frac{x(5x-6)}{5}$$

73. Simplify the compound fraction.

$$\frac{\dfrac{3a}{(a^2/x) - 1}}{\dfrac{a}{x} - 1}$$

Solution:

$$\frac{\dfrac{3a}{(a^2/x)-1}}{\dfrac{a}{x}-1} = \frac{\left[\dfrac{3a}{(a^2/x)-1}\right]\dfrac{x}{x}}{\dfrac{a-x}{x}} = \frac{3ax}{a^2-x}\cdot\frac{x}{a-x} = \frac{3ax^2}{(a^2-x)(a-x)}$$

77. Insert the missing factors for $x^3 - x = x($ $)($ $)$.

Solution:

$$x^3 - x = x(x^2-1) = x(x+1)(x-1)$$

83. Insert the missing factor for $x^4 - 2x^2 + 1 = (x+1)^2($ $)^2$.

Solution:

$$x^4 - 2x^2 + 1 = (x^2-1)^2 = [(x+1)(x-1)]^2 = (x+1)^2(x-1)^2$$

87. Insert the missing factor for $x^3 - x^2 + 2x - 2 = (x-1)($ $)$.

Solution:

$$x^3 - x^2 + 2x - 2 = x^2(x-1) + 2(x-1) = (x-1)(x^2+2)$$

91. Calculate 15^4 in two ways. First, use the exponential key $\boxed{y^x}$. Second, enter 15 and press the square key $\boxed{x^2}$ twice. Why do these two methods give the same result?

Solution:

Since $(15^2)^2 = 15^4$, the two methods will give the same result: $15^4 = 50,625$.

95. Use a calculator to complete the following table.

n	1	10	10^2	10^4	10^6	10^{10}
$\dfrac{5}{\sqrt{n}}$						

What number is $5/\sqrt{n}$ approaching as n increases without bound?

Solution:

n	1	10	10^2	10^4	10^6	10^{10}
$\dfrac{5}{\sqrt{n}}$	5	1.5811	0.5	0.05	0.005	0.00005

As $n \to \infty$, $\dfrac{5}{\sqrt{n}} \to 0$.

Practice Test for Chapter 1

1. Evaluate $\dfrac{42 - 20}{4 - 15}$.

2. Evaluate $\dfrac{x}{z} - \dfrac{z}{y}$.

3. The distance between x and 7 is no more than 4. Use absolute value notation to describe this expression.

4. Evaluate $10(-x)^3$ for $x = 5$.

5. Simplify $(-4x^3)(2x^{-5})\left(\dfrac{1}{16}x\right)$.

6. Change 0.0000412 to scientific notation.

7. Evaluate $125^{2/3}$.

8. Simplify $\sqrt[4]{64x^7y^9}$.

9. Rationalize the denominator and simplify $\dfrac{6}{\sqrt{12}}$.

10. Simplify $3\sqrt{80} - 7\sqrt{500}$.

11. Simplify $(8x^4 - 9x^2 + 2x - 1) - (3x^3 + 5x + 4)$.

12. Multiply $(x - 3)(x^2 + x - 7)$.

13. Multiply $[(x - 2) - y]^2$.

14. Factor $16x^4 - 1$.

15. Factor $6x^2 + 5x - 4$.

16. Factor $x^3 - 64$.

17. Combine and simplify $-\dfrac{3}{x} + \dfrac{x}{x^2 + 2}$.

18. Combine and simplify $\dfrac{x - 3}{4x} \div \dfrac{x^2 - 9}{x^2}$.

19. Simplify $\dfrac{1 - (1/x)}{1 - \dfrac{1}{1 - (1/x)}}$.

20. Factor the expression $\dfrac{1}{3}(x - 1)^{5/2} - \dfrac{1}{6}(x - 1)^{1/2}$ so that at least one factor is a polynomial with integer coefficients.

CHAPTER 2

Algebraic Equations and Inequalities

SECTION 2.1

Linear Equations

- You should know how to solve linear equations. $ax + b = 0$

- An identity is an equation whose solution consists of every real number in its domain.

- To solve an equation you can:

  (a) Add or subtract the same quantity from both sides.
  (b) Multiply or divide both sides by the same nonzero quantity.

- To solve an equation that can be simplified to a linear equation:

  (a) Remove all symbols of grouping and all fractions.
  (b) Combine like terms.
  (c) Solve by algebra.
  (d) Check the answer.

- A "solution" that does not satisfy the original equation is called an extraneous solution.

Solutions to Selected Exercises

3. Determine whether the given value of x is a solution of the equation $3x^2 + 2x - 5 = 2x^2 - 2$.

(a) $x = -3$ (b) $x = 1$

(c) $x = 4$ (d) $x = -5$

Solution:

(a) $3(-3)^2 + 2(-3) - 5 \stackrel{?}{=} 2(-3)^2 - 2$

$$16 = 16$$

$x = -3$ is a solution.

(b) $3(1)^2 + 2(1) - 5 \stackrel{?}{=} 2(1)^2 - 2$

$$0 = 0$$

$x = 1$ is a solution.

(c) $3(4)^2 + 2(4) - 5 \stackrel{?}{=} 2(4)^2 - 2$

$$51 \neq 30$$

$x = 4$ is not a solution.

(d) $3(-5)^2 + 2(-5) - 5 \stackrel{?}{=} 2(-5)^2 - 2$

$$60 \neq 48$$

$x = -5$ is not a solution.

11. Solve the equation $7 - 2x = 15$.

Solution:

$$
\begin{aligned}
7 - 2x &= 15 \\
-2x &= 8 \qquad && \text{Subtract 7 from both sides.} \\
x &= -4 \qquad && \text{Divide both sides by } -2.
\end{aligned}
$$

15. Solve the equation $2(x + 5) - 7 = 3(x - 2)$.

Solution:

$$
\begin{aligned}
2(x + 5) - 7 &= 3(x - 2) \\
2x + 10 - 7 &= 3x - 6 \\
2x + 3 &= 3x - 6 \\
-x + 3 &= -6 \\
-x &= -9 \\
x &= 9
\end{aligned}
$$

19. Solve the equation $\dfrac{5x}{4} + \dfrac{1}{2} = x - \dfrac{1}{2}$.

Solution:

$$
\begin{aligned}
\frac{5x}{4} + \frac{1}{2} &= x - \frac{1}{2} \\
4\left(\frac{5x}{4} + \frac{1}{2}\right) &= 4\left(x - \frac{1}{2}\right) \\
5x + 2 &= 4x - 2 \\
x + 2 &= -2 \\
x &= -4
\end{aligned}
$$

23. Solve the equation $0.25x + 0.75(10 - x) = 3$.

Solution:

$$
\begin{aligned}
0.25x + 0.75(10 - x) &= 3 \\
100[0.25x + 0.75(10 - x)] &= 100(3) \\
25x + 75(10 - x) &= 300 \\
25x + 750 - 75x &= 300 \\
-50x + 750 &= 300 \\
-50x &= -450 \\
x &= 9
\end{aligned}
$$

25. Solve the equation $x + 8 = 2(x - 2) - x$, if possible.

Solution:

$$x + 8 = 2(x - 2) - x$$
$$x + 8 = 2x - 4 - x$$
$$x + 8 = x - 4$$
$$8 = -4 \qquad \text{Not possible}$$

Thus, the equation has no solution.

29. Solve the equation

$$\frac{5x - 4}{5x + 4} = \frac{2}{3} .$$

Solution:

$$\frac{5x - 4}{5x + 4} = \frac{2}{3}$$
$$3(5x - 4) = 2(5x + 4) \qquad \text{Cross multiply}$$
$$15x - 12 = 10x + 8$$
$$5x = 20$$
$$x = 4$$

33. Solve the equation

$$\frac{1}{x - 3} + \frac{1}{x + 3} = \frac{10}{x^2 - 9} .$$

Solution:

$$\frac{1}{x - 3} + \frac{1}{x + 3} = \frac{10}{x^2 - 9}$$
$$\frac{(x + 3) + (x - 3)}{(x - 3)(x + 3)} = \frac{10}{x^2 - 9}$$
$$(x^2 - 9)\left(\frac{2x}{x^2 - 9}\right) = \left(\frac{10}{x^2 - 9}\right)(x^2 - 9)$$
$$2x = 10$$
$$x = 5$$

37. Solve the equation

$$\frac{7}{2x+1} - \frac{8x}{2x-1} = -4 \,.$$

Solution:

$$\frac{7}{2x+1} - \frac{8x}{2x-1} = -4$$

$$(2x+1)(2x-1)\left[\frac{7}{2x+1} - \frac{8x}{2x-1}\right] = -4(2x+1)(2x-1)$$

$$7(2x-1) - 8x(2x+1) = -4(4x^2 - 1)$$

$$14x - 7 - 16x^2 - 8x = -16x^2 + 4$$

$$-16x^2 + 6x - 7 = -16x^2 + 4$$

$$6x - 7 = 4$$

$$6x = 11$$

$$x = \frac{11}{6}$$

41. Solve the equation $(x+2)^2 + 5 = (x+3)^2$.

Solution:

$$(x+2)^2 + 5 = (x+3)^2$$

$$x^2 + 4x + 4 + 5 = x^2 + 6x + 9$$

$$4x + 9 = 6x + 9$$

$$4x = 6x$$

$$-2x = 0$$

$$x = 0$$

45. Solve the equation $(2x+1)^2 = 4(x^2 + x + 1)$, if possible.

Solution:

$$(2x+1)^2 = 4(x^2 + x + 1)$$

$$4x^2 + 4x + 1 = 4x^2 + 4x + 4$$

$$1 = 4 \qquad \text{Not possible}$$

Thus, the equation has no solution.

51. Determine whether the equation $x^2 - 8x + 5 = (x-4)^2 - 11$ is conditional or an identity.

Solution:

$$x^2 - 8x + 5 = (x-4)^2 - 11$$
$$= x^2 - 8x + 16 - 11$$
$$= x^2 - 8x + 5 \qquad \text{Identity}$$

55. Determine whether the following equation is conditional or an identity.

$$3 + \frac{1}{x+1} = \frac{4x}{x+1}$$

Solution:

$$3 + \frac{1}{x+1} = \frac{4x}{x+1}$$
$$\frac{3x+4}{x+1} = \frac{4x}{x+1}$$
$$3x + 4 = 4x$$
$$x = 4 \qquad \text{Conditional}$$

57. Use a calculator to solve $0.275x + 0.725(500 - x) = 300$. Round your answer to three decimal places.

Solution:

$$0.275x + 0.725(500 - x) = 300$$
$$0.275x + 362.5 - 0.725x = 300$$
$$-0.45x = -62.5$$
$$x \approx 138.889$$

61. Use a calculator to solve $(x + 5.62)^2 + 10.83 = (x + 7)^2$. Round your answer to three decimal places.

Solution:

$$(x + 5.62)^2 + 10.83 = (x + 7)^2$$
$$x^2 + 11.24x + 31.5844 + 10.83 = x^2 + 14x + 49$$
$$-6.5856 = 2.76x$$
$$x \approx -2.386$$

65. Evaluate

$$\frac{2 - 1.63254}{(2.58)(0.135)}$$

in two ways. (a) Calculate entirely on your calculator by storing intermediate results, and then round your answer to two decimal places. (b) Round both the numerator and the denominator to two decimal places before dividing, and then round the final answer to two decimal places. Does the second method introduce an additional round–off error?

Solution:

(a) $\dfrac{2 - 1.63254}{(2.58)(0.135)} = \dfrac{0.36746}{0.3483}$

$\qquad\qquad\qquad = 1.055010049$

$\qquad\qquad\qquad \approx 1.06$

(b) $\dfrac{2 - 1.63254}{(2.58)(0.135)} \approx \dfrac{0.37}{0.35} = 1.057142857$

$\qquad\qquad\qquad\qquad \approx 1.06$

No substantial round–off error was introduced in this case.

SECTION 2.2

Applications

Solutions to Selected Exercises

5. Solve for C.

$$S = C + RC$$

Solution:

$$S = C + RC$$
$$S = C(1 + R)$$
$$\frac{S}{1 + R} = C$$

9. Solve for b.

$$A = \frac{1}{2}(a + b)h$$

Solution:

$$A = \frac{1}{2}(a+b)h$$

$$2A = (a+b)h$$

$$\frac{2A}{h} = a+b$$

$$\frac{2A}{h} - a = b$$

$$b = \frac{2A - ah}{h}$$

11. Solve for r.

$$V = \frac{1}{3}\pi h^2(3r - h)$$

Solution:

$$V = \frac{1}{3}\pi h^2(3r - h)$$

$$3V = \pi h^2(3r - h)$$

$$\frac{3V}{\pi h^2} = 3r - h$$

$$\frac{3V}{\pi h^2} + h = 3r$$

$$\frac{3V + \pi h^3}{\pi h^2} = 3r$$

$$r = \frac{3V + \pi h^3}{3\pi h^2}$$

15. Solve for m_2.

$$F = \alpha\frac{m_1 m_2}{r^2}$$

Solution:

$$F = \alpha\frac{m_1 m_2}{r^2}$$

$$\frac{F}{\alpha} = \frac{m_1 m_2}{r^2}$$

$$\frac{Fr^2}{\alpha} = m_1 m_2$$

$$m_2 = \frac{Fr^2}{\alpha m_1}$$

21. Solve for r.

$$S = \frac{rL - a}{r - 1}$$

Solution:

$$S = \frac{rL - a}{r - 1}$$
$$S(r - 1) = rL - a$$
$$Sr - S = rL - a$$
$$Sr - rL = S - a$$
$$r(S - L) = S - a$$
$$r = \frac{S - a}{S - L}$$

25. Write an algebraic expression for the sum of two consecutive natural numbers.

Solution:

Let S be the sum, n the first natural number and $n + 1$ the next natural number. Then we have

$$S = n + (n + 1)$$
$$S = 2n + 1$$

29. Write an algebraic expression for the perimeter of a rectangle whose width is x and whose length is twice the width.

Solution:

Let P be the perimeter, x the width and $2x$ the length. Then we have

$$P = 2L + 2W$$
$$P = 2(2x) + 2x$$
$$P = 4x + 2x$$
$$P = 6x$$

33. One number is five times another number. The difference between the two numbers is 148. Find the numbers.

Solution:

Let $x =$ one number and $5x =$ other number.

$$5x - x = 148$$
$$4x = 148$$
$$x = 37, \quad 5x = 185$$

Thus, the two numbers are 37 and 185.

37. Jean was 30 years old when her daughter Ruth was born.

   (a) How old will Ruth be when her age is one-third that of Jean's age?

   (b) How old will Ruth be when Ruth's and Jean's combined ages total 100?

Solution:

Let x = Ruth's age and $x + 30$ = Jean's age.

(a) $x = \frac{1}{3}(x + 30)$

     $3x = x + 30$

     $2x = 30$

      $x = 15$ years old

(b) $x + (x + 30) = 100$

       $2x + 30 = 100$

         $2x = 70$

          $x = 35$ years old

41. To get an A in a course a student must have an average of at least 90 on four tests that have 100 points each. A student's scores on the first three tests were 87, 92, and 84. What must the student score on the fourth test to get an A for the course?

Solution:

Let x = score on fourth test. Then

$$\frac{87 + 92 + 84 + x}{4} = 90$$

$$\frac{263 + x}{4} = 90$$

$$263 + x = 360$$

$$x = 97$$

45. What is 0.045% of 2,650,000?

Solution:

$$x = 0.045\% \times 2,650,000$$

$$x = (0.00045)(2,650,000)$$

$$x = 1192.5$$

49. 70 is 40% of what number?

Solution:

$70 = 40\% \times$ number

$$\text{number} = \frac{70}{40\%} = \frac{70}{0.40} = 175$$

55. Two families meet at a park for a picnic. At the end of the day, one family travels east at an average speed of 42 miles per hour and the other travels west at an average speed of 50 miles per hour. Both families have approximately 160 miles to travel.

   (a) Find the time it takes each family to get home.
   (b) Find the time that will have elapsed when they are 100 miles apart.
   (c) Find the distance the eastbound family has to travel after the westbound family has arrived home.

   Solution:

   (a) Time for the first family: $t_1 = \dfrac{d}{r_1} = \dfrac{160}{42} \approx 3.8$ hr

   Time for the other family: $t_2 = \dfrac{d}{r_2} = \dfrac{160}{50} = 3.2$ hr

   (b) $t = \dfrac{d}{r} = \dfrac{100}{42 + 50} = \dfrac{100}{92} \approx 1.1$ hr

   (c) $d = rt = 42 \left(\dfrac{160}{42} - \dfrac{160}{50} \right) = 25.6$ mi

59. Radio waves travel at the same speed as light, 3.0×10^8 meters per second. Find the time required for a radio wave to travel from mission control in Houston to NASA astronauts on the surface of the moon, 3.86×10^8 meters away.

   Solution:

   $$d = rt$$
   $$3.86 \times 10^8 = (3.0 \times 10^8)t$$
   $$t = \frac{3.86 \times 10^8}{3.0 \times 10^8} \approx 1.29 \text{ sec}$$

63. Denise invests $12,000$ in two funds paying $10\frac{1}{2}\%$ and 13% simple interest. The total annual interest is 1447.50. How much is invested in each fund?

   Solution:

   Let $x =$ amount in the $10\frac{1}{2}\%$ fund and $12,000 - x =$ amount in the 13% fund. Then

   $$I = P_1 r_1 (1 \text{ yr}) + P_2 r_2 (1 \text{ yr})$$
   $$I = 10\tfrac{1}{2}\% x + 13\%(12,000 - x) = 1447.50$$
   $$0.105x + 0.13(12,000 - x) = 1447.50$$
   $$0.105x + 1560 - 0.13x = 1447.50$$
   $$112.5 = 0.025x$$
   $$x = \frac{112.5}{0.025} = \$4,500$$
   $$12,000 - x = \$7,500$$

67. A company has fixed costs of $10,000 per month, and variable costs of $8.50 per unit manufactured. The company has $85,000 available to cover the monthly costs. How many units can they manufacture? (*Fixed costs* are those that occur regardless of the level of production. *Variable costs* depend on the level of production.)

Solution:

$$\text{Total cost} = \text{fixed cost} + (\text{variable cost} \times \text{number of units})$$

$$85,000 = 10,000 + 8.50x$$

$$75,000 = 8.50x$$

$$x = 8823.5 \quad \text{or} \quad 8823 \text{ units}$$

71. Using the values from the following table, determine the amounts of Solutions 1 and 2, respectively, needed to obtain the desired amount and concentration of the final mixture.

	Concentration of Solution 1	Concentration of Solution 2	Concentration of Final Solution	Amount of Final Solution
(a)	10%	30%	25%	100 gallons
(b)	25%	50%	30%	5 liters
(c)	15%	45%	30%	10 quarts
(d)	70%	90%	75%	25 gallons

Solution:

(a) $0.10x + 0.30(100 - x) = 0.25(100)$

$$0.10x + 30 - 0.30x = 25$$

$$5 = 0.20x$$

$$x = 25 \text{ gal}, \quad 100 - x = 75 \text{ gal}$$

(b) $0.25x + 0.50(5 - x) = 0.30(5)$

$$0.25x + 2.5 - 0.50x = 1.5$$

$$1 = 0.25x$$

$$x = 4 \text{ L}, \quad 5 - x = 1 \text{ L}$$

(c) $0.15x + 0.45(10 - x) = 0.30(10)$

$$0.15x + 4.5 - 0.45x = 3$$

$$1.5 = 0.3x$$

$$x = 5 \text{ qt}, \quad 10 - x = 5 \text{ qt}$$

(d) $0.70x + 0.90(25 - x) = 0.75(25)$

$$0.70x + 22.5 - 0.90x = 18.75$$

$$3.75 = 0.20x$$

$$x = 18.75 \text{ gal}, \quad 25 - x = 6.25 \text{ gal}$$

SECTION 2.3

Quadratic Equations

■ You should be able to factor a quadratic.

■ You should be able to complete the square on any quadratic.

Solutions to Selected Exercises

5. Write the equation $(x-3)^2 = 2$ in standard quadratic form. Identify the constants a, b, and c.

Solution:

$$(x-3)^2 = 2$$
$$x^2 - 6x + 9 = 2$$
$$x^2 - 6x + 7 = 0$$
$$a = 1, \ b = -6, \ c = 7$$

9. Write the following equation in standard quadratic form. Identify the constants a, b, and c.

$$\frac{3x^2 - 10}{5} = 12x$$

Solution:

$$\frac{3x^2 - 10}{5} = 12x$$
$$3x^2 - 10 = 60x$$
$$3x^2 - 60x - 10 = 0$$
$$a = 3, \ b = -60, \ c = -10$$

13. Solve $x^2 - 2x - 8 = 0$ by factoring.

Solution:

$$x^2 - 2x - 8 = 0$$
$$(x+2)(x-4) = 0$$
$$x = -2 \quad \text{or} \quad x = 4$$

17. Solve $3 + 5x - 2x^2 = 0$ by factoring.

Solution:

$$3 + 5x - 2x^2 = 0$$
$$(3 - x)(1 + 2x) = 0$$
$$x = 3 \quad \text{or} \quad x = -\tfrac{1}{2}$$

21. Solve $x^2 = 16$ by taking the square root of both sides.

Solution:

$$x^2 = 16$$
$$x = \pm\sqrt{16}$$
$$x = \pm 4$$

25. Solve $3x^2 = 36$ by taking the square root of both sides.

Solution:

$$3x^2 = 36$$
$$x^2 = 12$$
$$x = \pm\sqrt{12}$$
$$x = \pm 2\sqrt{3}$$

29. Solve $(x - 7)^2 = (x + 3)^2$ by taking the square root of both sides.

Solution:

$$(x - 7)^2 = (x + 3)^2$$
$$x - 7 = \pm(x + 3)$$

For $x - 7 = +(x + 3)$
$$-7 = +3 \qquad \text{No solution}$$

For $x - 7 = -(x + 3)$
$$2x = 4$$
$$x = 2$$

33. Solve $x^2 + 4x - 32 = 0$ by completing the square.

Solution:

$$x^2 + 4x - 32 = 0$$
$$x^2 + 4x = 32$$
$$x^2 + 4x + 4 = 32 + 4$$
$$(x + 2)^2 = 36$$
$$x + 2 = \pm 6$$
$$x = -2 \pm 6$$
$$x = 4 \quad \text{or} \quad x = -8$$

37. Solve $9x^2 - 18x + 3 = 0$ by completing the square.

Solution:

$$9x^2 - 18x + 3 = 0$$
$$x^2 - 2x + \tfrac{1}{3} = 0$$
$$x^2 - 2x = -\tfrac{1}{3}$$
$$x^2 - 2x + 1 = -\tfrac{1}{3} + 1$$
$$(x - 1)^2 = \tfrac{2}{3}$$
$$x - 1 = \pm\sqrt{\tfrac{2}{3}}$$
$$x = 1 \pm \sqrt{\tfrac{2}{3}}$$
$$= 1 \pm \tfrac{\sqrt{6}}{3}$$

41. Solve $x^2 = 64$.

Solution:

$$x^2 = 64$$
$$x = \pm\sqrt{64}$$
$$x = \pm 8$$

45. Solve $16x^2 - 9 = 0$.

Solution:

$$16x^2 - 9 = 0$$
$$16x^2 = 9$$
$$4x = \pm 3$$
$$x = \pm\tfrac{3}{4}$$

49. Solve $(x + 3)^2 = 81$.

Solution:

$$(x + 3)^2 = 81$$
$$x + 3 = \pm 9$$
$$x = -3 \pm 9$$
$$x = 6 \quad \text{or} \quad x = -12$$

53. Solve $50 + 5x = 3x^2$.

Solution:

$$50 + 5x = 3x^2$$
$$0 = 3x^2 - 5x - 50$$
$$0 = (3x + 10)(x - 5)$$
$$x = -\tfrac{10}{3} \quad \text{or} \quad x = 5$$

57. Solve $x^2 - x - \frac{11}{4} = 0$.

Solution:

$$x^2 - x - \tfrac{11}{4} = 0$$
$$x^2 - x = \tfrac{11}{4}$$
$$x^2 - x + \tfrac{1}{4} = \tfrac{11}{4} + \tfrac{1}{4}$$
$$\left(x - \tfrac{1}{2}\right)^2 = \tfrac{12}{4}$$
$$x - \tfrac{1}{2} = \pm\sqrt{\tfrac{12}{4}}$$
$$x = \tfrac{1}{2} \pm \sqrt{3}$$

63. Solve $(x + 1)^2 = x^2$.

Solution:

$$(x + 1)^2 = x^2$$
$$x^2 = (x + 1)^2$$
$$x = \pm(x + 1)$$

For $x = +(x + 1)$
$$0 = 1 \quad \text{No solution}$$
For $x = -(x + 1)$
$$2x = -1$$
$$x = -\tfrac{1}{2}$$

67. Complete the square for the quadratic portion of

$$\frac{1}{x^2 - 4x - 12}.$$

Solution:

$$\frac{1}{x^2 - 4x - 12} = \frac{1}{x^2 - 4x + 4 - 4 - 12}$$

$$= \frac{1}{(x-2)^2 - 16}$$

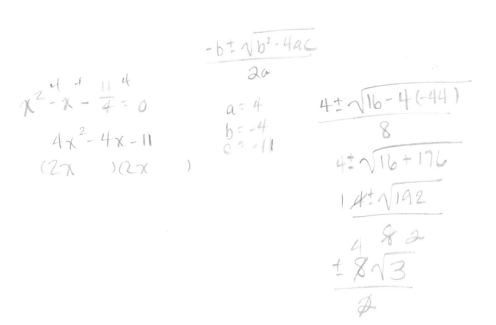

SECTION 2.4

The Quadratic Formula and Applications

- You should know the quadratic formula: For $ax^2 + bx + c = 0$, $a \neq 0$,

$$x = \frac{-b \pm \sqrt{b^2 - 4ac}}{2a}$$

- You should be able to determine the types of solutions of a quadratic equation by checking the discriminant $b^2 - 4ac$.

  (a) If $b^2 - 4ac > 0$, there are two distinct real solutions.
  (b) If $b^2 - 4ac = 0$, there is one repeating real solution.
  (c) If $b^2 - 4ac < 0$, there are no real solutions.

- You should be able to use your calculator to solve equations.

- You should be able to solve word problems involving quadratic equations. Study the examples in the text carefully.

Solutions to Selected Exercises

3. Use the discriminant to determine the number of real solutions of $3x^2 + 4x + 1 = 0$.

Solution:
$3x^2 + 4x + 1 = 0$; $a = 3$, $b = 4$, $c = 1$

$$b^2 - 4ac = (4)^2 - 4(3)(1) = 16 - 12 = 4 > 0$$

Two real solutions

7. Use the discriminant to determine the number of real solutions of

$$\tfrac{1}{5}x^2 + \tfrac{6}{5}x - 8 = 0.$$

Solution:

$$\tfrac{1}{5}x^2 + \tfrac{6}{5}x - 8 = 0$$
$$x^2 + 6x - 40 = 0; \quad a = 1, \ b = 6, \ c = -40$$
$$b^2 - 4ac = (6)^2 - 4(1)(-40) = 36 + 160 = 196 > 0$$

Two real solutions

11. Use the quadratic formula to solve $16x^2 + 8x - 3 = 0$.

Solution:

$16x^2 + 8x - 3 = 0$; $a = 16$, $b = 8$, $c = -3$

$$x = \frac{-8 \pm \sqrt{8^2 - 4(16)(-3)}}{2(16)} = \frac{-8 \pm \sqrt{256}}{32} = \frac{-8 \pm 16}{32}$$

$$x = \frac{-8 + 16}{32} = \frac{1}{4}$$

$$x = \frac{-8 - 16}{32} = -\frac{3}{4}$$

15. Use the quadratic formula to solve $x^2 + 14x + 44 = 0$.

Solution:

$x^2 + 14x + 44 = 0$; $a = 1$, $b = 14$, $c = 44$

$$x = \frac{-14 \pm \sqrt{14^2 - 4(1)(44)}}{2(1)} = \frac{-14 \pm \sqrt{20}}{2} = \frac{-14 \pm 2\sqrt{5}}{2}$$

$$x = -7 \pm \sqrt{5}$$

21. Use the quadratic formula to solve $36x^2 + 24x - 7 = 0$.

Solution:

$36x^2 + 24x - 7 = 0$; $a = 36$, $b = 24$, $c = -7$

$$x = \frac{-24 \pm \sqrt{24^2 - 4(36)(-7)}}{2(36)} = \frac{-24 \pm \sqrt{1584}}{72} = \frac{-24 \pm 12\sqrt{11}}{72}$$

$$x = \frac{-2 \pm \sqrt{11}}{6} = -\frac{1}{3} \pm \frac{\sqrt{11}}{6}$$

27. Use the quadratic formula to solve $25h^2 + 80h + 61 = 0$.

Solution:

$25h^2 + 80h + 61 = 0$; $a = 25$, $b = 80$, $c = 61$

$$x = \frac{-80 \pm \sqrt{(80)^2 - 4(25)(61)}}{2(25)}$$

$$= \frac{-80 \pm \sqrt{300}}{50} = \frac{-80 \pm 10\sqrt{3}}{50}$$

$$= \frac{-8 \pm \sqrt{3}}{5} = -\frac{8}{5} \pm \frac{\sqrt{3}}{5}$$

31. Use the quadratic formula to solve

$$\frac{1}{x} - \frac{1}{x+1} = 3.$$

Solution:

$$\frac{1}{x} - \frac{1}{x+1} = 3$$

$$\frac{(x+1) - x}{x(x+1)} = 3$$

$$\frac{1}{x^2 + x} = 3$$

$$1 = 3(x^2 + x)$$

$$0 = 3x^2 + 3x - 1; \quad a = 3, \ b = 3, \ c = -1$$

$$x = \frac{-3 \pm \sqrt{(3)^2 - 4(3)(-1)}}{2(3)} = \frac{-3 \pm \sqrt{21}}{6} = -\frac{1}{2} \pm \frac{\sqrt{21}}{6}$$

35. Use a calculator to solve $5.1x^2 - 1.7x - 3.2 = 0$. Round your answer to three decimal places.

Solution:

$$5.1x^2 - 1.7x - 3.2 = 0; \quad a = 5.1, \ b = -1.7, \ c = -3.2$$

$$x = \frac{-(-1.7) \pm \sqrt{(-1.7)^2 - 4(5.1)(-3.2)}}{2(5.1)}$$

$$x = \frac{1.7 \pm \sqrt{68.17}}{10.2} \approx \frac{1.7 \pm 8.2565}{10.2}$$

$$x \approx 0.976 \quad \text{or} \quad x \approx -0.643$$

41. Find two numbers whose sum is 100 and whose product is 2500.

Solution:

Let $x =$ one number and $100 - x =$ other number.

$$x(100 - x) = 2500$$

$$100x - x^2 = 2500$$

$$0 = x^2 - 100x + 2500$$

$$0 = (x - 50)^2$$

$$x = 50, \quad 100 - x = 50$$

43. Find two consecutive positive integers such that the sum of their squares is 113.

Solution:

Let n = first integer and $n + 1$ = next integer.

$$n^2 + (n + 1)^2 = 113$$
$$n^2 + n^2 + 2n + 1 = 113$$
$$2n^2 + 2n - 112 = 0$$
$$2(n^2 + n - 56) = 0$$
$$2(n + 8)(n - 7) = 0$$
$$n = -8 \quad \text{or} \quad n = 7$$

Since we want a positive integer, $n = 7$ and $n + 1 = 8$.

47. Use the cost equation $C = 800 + 0.04x + 0.0002x^2$ to find the number of units x that a manufacturer can produce for the given cost $C = \$1680$. (Round your answer to the nearest positive integer.)

Solution:

$$1680 = 800 + 0.04x + 0.0002x^2$$
$$0 = 0.0002x^2 + 0.04x - 880$$

Thus, $a = 0.0002$, $b = 0.04$, $c = -880$.

$$x = \frac{-0.04 \pm \sqrt{(0.04)^2 - 4(0.0002)(-880)}}{2(0.0002)} = \frac{-0.04 \pm 0.84}{0.0004}$$

$$x = \frac{-0.04 + 0.84}{0.0004} = 2000 \text{ units}$$

$$x = \frac{-0.04 - 0.84}{0.0004} = -2200 \qquad \text{Not a valid solution}$$

51. An object is dropped at a height of 64 feet from a balloon rising vertically at the rate of 16 feet per second. (The balloon's velocity becomes the object's initial velocity.) Find the time when the object hits the ground.

Solution:

$$s = -16t^2 + v_0 t + s_0$$
$$0 = -16t^2 + 16t + 64$$
$$0 = -16(t^2 - t - 4); \quad a = 1, \ b = -1, \ c = -4$$
$$t = \frac{-(-1) \pm \sqrt{(-1)^2 - 4(1)(-4)}}{2(1)}$$
$$t = \frac{1 \pm \sqrt{17}}{2}$$

Choosing the positive time value, we have

$$t = \frac{1 + \sqrt{17}}{2} \approx 2.56 \text{ seconds.}$$

55. Two brothers must mow a rectangular lawn 100 feet by 200 feet. Each wants to mow no more than half of the lawn. The first starts by mowing around the outside of the lawn. How wide a strip must he mow on each of the four sides? Approximately how many times must he go around the lawn if the mower has a 24-inch cut?

Solution:

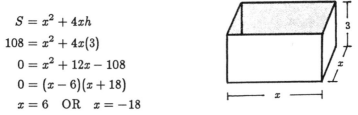

$$(200 - 2x)(100 - 2x) = \frac{1}{2}(100)(200)$$

$$20000 - 600x + 4x^2 = 10000$$

$$0 = 4x^2 - 600x + 10000$$

$$0 = 4(x^2 - 150x + 2500)$$

Thus, $a = 1$, $b = -150$, $c = 2500$.

$$x = \frac{150 \pm \sqrt{(-150)^2 - 4(1)(2500)}}{2(1)} \approx \frac{150 \pm 111.8034}{2}$$

$$x = \frac{150 + 111.8034}{2} \approx 130.902 \text{ ft} \qquad \text{Not possible since the lot is only 100 ft wide}$$

$$x = \frac{150 - 111.8034}{2} \approx 19.1 \text{ ft}$$

He must go around the lot

$$\frac{19.098 \text{ ft}}{24 \text{ in}} = \frac{19.098 \text{ ft}}{2 \text{ ft}} = 9.5 \text{ times.}$$

59. An open box with a square base is to be constructed from 108 square inches of material, as shown in the accompanying figure. What should be the dimensions of the base if the height of the box is to be 3 inches? [Hint: The surface area is given by $S = x^2 + 4xh$.]

Solution:

$$S = x^2 + 4xh$$

$$108 = x^2 + 4x(3)$$

$$0 = x^2 + 12x - 108$$

$$0 = (x - 6)(x + 18)$$

$$x = 6 \quad \text{OR} \quad x = -18$$

Choosing the positive value, we have $x = 6$. The dimensions of the base are 6 in. $\times$ 6 in.

61. Two planes leave simultaneously from the same airport, one flying due east and the other due south, as shown in the accompanying figure. The eastbound plane is flying 50 miles per hour faster than the southbound plane. After three hours the planes are 2440 miles apart. Find the speed of each plane.

Solution:

Let S = rate of the southbound plane and $E = S + 50$ = rate of the eastbound plane.

$$d_S = r_S t = 3S$$
$$d_E = r_E t = 3(S + 50)$$

By the Pythagorean Theorem,

$$d_S{}^2 + d_E{}^2 = (2440)^2$$
$$[3S]^2 + [3(S + 50)]^2 = (2440)^2$$
$$9S^2 + 9(S^2 + 100S + 2500) = 5,953,600$$
$$18S^2 + 900S - 5,931,100 = 0$$

$$S = \frac{-900 \pm \sqrt{(900)^2 - 4(18)(-5931100)}}{2(18)}$$

$$S \approx \frac{-900 \pm 20684.51595}{36}$$

Considering the positive solution,

$$S = 549.5699 \approx 550 \text{ mi/hr}$$
$$E = S + 50 \approx 600 \text{ mi/hr}$$

67. A lump sum of $10,000 is invested for 2 years at $r\%$, compounded annually. At the end of the two-year period, the investment has increased to $11,990.25. Find the annual percentage rate r.

Solution:

$A = P(1 + r)^t$ for annual compounding.

$$11,990.25 = 10,000(1 + r)^2$$
$$1.199025 = (1 + r)^2$$
$$+\sqrt{1.199025} = 1 + r \quad \text{Consider only the positive root}$$
$$1.095 = 1 + r$$
$$r = .095$$
$$r = 9.5\%$$

SECTION 2.5

Complex Numbers

- You should know how to work with complex numbers.

- Operations on Complex Numbers
  - (a) Addition: $(a + bi) + (c + di) = (a + c) + (b + d)i$
  - (b) Subtraction: $(a + bi) - (c + di) = (a - c) + (b - d)i$
  - (c) Multiplication: $(a + bi)(c + di) = (ac - bd) + (ad + bc)i$
  - (d) Division: $\dfrac{a + bi}{c + di} = \dfrac{a + bi}{c + di} \cdot \dfrac{c - di}{c - di} = \dfrac{ac + bd}{c^2 + d^2} + \dfrac{bc - ad}{c^2 + d^2}i$

- The complex conjugate of $a + bi$ is $a - bi$:

  $$(a + bi)(a - bi) = a^2 + b^2$$

- The additive inverse of $a + bi$ is $-a - bi$.

- The multiplicative inverse of $a + bi$ is

  $$\dfrac{a - bi}{a^2 + b^2}.$$

- $\sqrt{-a} = \sqrt{a}\,i$ for $a > 0$.

Solutions to Selected Exercises

1. Write out the first 16 positive powers of i and express each as i, $-i$, 1, or -1.

Solution:

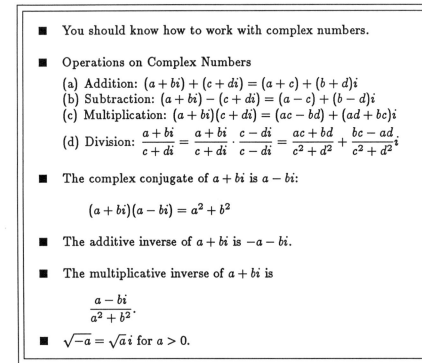

$$
\begin{array}{lllll}
i \;= i & i^5 = i & i^9 \;= i & i^{13} = i & i^{17} = i \\
i^2 = -1 & i^6 = -1 & i^{10} = -1 & i^{14} = -1 & i^{18} = -1 \\
i^3 = -i & i^7 = -i & i^{11} = -i & i^{15} = -i & i^{19} = -i \\
i^4 = 1 & i^8 = 1 & i^{12} = 1 & i^{16} = 1 & i^{20} = 1
\end{array}
$$

5. Find real numbers a and b so that the equation $(a - 1) + (b + 3)i = 5 + 8i$ is true.

Solution:
$(a - 1) + (b + 3)i = 5 + 8i$

$$a - 1 = 5 \quad \Rightarrow \quad a = 6$$
$$b + 3 = 8 \quad \Rightarrow \quad b = 5$$

9. Write $2 - \sqrt{-27}$ in standard form and find its complex conjugate.

Solution:

$$2 - \sqrt{-27} = 2 - \sqrt{27}\,i = 2 - 3\sqrt{3}\,i$$

Complex conjugate: $2 + 3\sqrt{3}\,i$

13. Write $-6i + i^2$ in standard form and find its complex conjugate.

Solution:

$$-6i + i^2 = -6i + (-1) = -1 - 6i$$

Complex conjugate: $-1 + 6i$

21. Perform the indicated operation and write the result in standard form.

$$(8 - i) - (4 - i)$$

Solution:

$$(8 - i) - (4 - i) = 8 - i - 4 + i = 4$$

23. Perform the indicated operation and write the result in standard form.

$$(-2 + \sqrt{-8}) + (5 - \sqrt{-50})$$

Solution:

$$(-2 + \sqrt{-8}) + (5 - \sqrt{-50}) = -2 + 2\sqrt{2}\,i + 5 - 5\sqrt{2}\,i = 3 - 3\sqrt{2}\,i$$

27. Perform the indicated operation and write the result in standard form.

$$\sqrt{-6}\sqrt{-2}$$

Solution:

$$\sqrt{-6}\sqrt{-2} = (\sqrt{6}\,i)(\sqrt{2}\,i) = \sqrt{12}\,i^2 = 2\sqrt{3}(-1) = -2\sqrt{3}$$

31. Perform the indicated operation and write the result in standard form.

$$(1+i)(3-2i)$$

Solution:

$$(1+i)(3-2i) = 3 - 2i + 3i - 2i^2 = 3 + i + 2 = 5 + i$$

35. Perform the indicated operation and write the result in standard form.

$$6i(5-2i)$$

Solution:

$$6i(5-2i) = 30i - 12i^2 = 12 + 30i$$

39. Perform the indicated operation and write the result in standard form.

$$(\sqrt{14} + \sqrt{10}\,i)(\sqrt{14} - \sqrt{10}\,i)$$

Solution:

$$(\sqrt{14} + \sqrt{10}\,i)(\sqrt{14} - \sqrt{10}\,i) = 14 - 10i^2 = 14 + 10 = 24$$

45. Perform the indicated operation and write the result in standard form.

$$\frac{2+i}{2-i}$$

Solution:

$$\frac{2+i}{2-i} = \frac{2+i}{2-i} \cdot \frac{2+i}{2+i} = \frac{4 + 4i + i^2}{4+1} = \frac{3+4i}{5} = \frac{3}{5} + \frac{4}{5}i$$

53. Perform the indicated operation and write the result in standard form.

$$\frac{(21-7i)(4+3i)}{2-5i}$$

Solution:

$$\frac{(21-7i)(4+3i)}{2-5i} = \frac{(84 + 63i - 28i - 21i^2)}{2-5i} \cdot \frac{2+5i}{2+5i}$$

$$= \frac{(105 + 35i)(2+5i)}{4+25}$$

$$= \frac{210 + 525i + 70i + 175i^2}{29}$$

$$= \frac{35 + 595i}{29} = \frac{35}{29} + \frac{595}{29}i$$

59. Use the quadratic formula to solve $4x^2 + 16x + 17 = 0$.

Solution:

$4x^2 + 16x + 17 = 0;\ a = 4,\ b = 16,\ c = 17$

$$x = \frac{-16 \pm \sqrt{(16)^2 - 4(4)(17)}}{2(4)}$$

$$= \frac{-16 \pm \sqrt{-16}}{8} = \frac{-16 \pm 4i}{8}$$

$$= -2 \pm \frac{1}{2}i$$

63. Use the quadratic formula to solve $16t^2 - 4t + 3 = 0$.

Solution:

$16t^2 - 4t + 3 = 0;\ a = 16,\ b = -4,\ c = 3$

$$x = \frac{-(-4) \pm \sqrt{(-4)^2 - 4(16)(3)}}{2(16)}$$

$$= \frac{4 \pm \sqrt{-176}}{32} = \frac{4 \pm 4\sqrt{11}i}{32}$$

$$= \frac{1}{8} \pm \frac{\sqrt{11}}{8}i$$

65. Prove that the sum of a complex number and its conjugate is a real number.

Solution:

$$(a + bi) + (a - bi) = (a + a) + (b - b)i$$
$$= 2a + 0i = 2a \qquad \text{which is a real number.}$$

69. Prove that the conjugate of the sum of two complex numbers is the sum of their conjugates.

Solution:

$$(a + bi) + (c + di) = (a + c) + (b + d)i$$

The complex conjugate of the sum is $(a + c) - (b + d)i$, and the sum of the conjugates is

$$(a - bi) + (c - di) = (a + c) + (-b - d)i$$
$$= (a + c) - (b + d)i$$

Thus, the conjugate of the sum is the sum of the conjugates.

SECTION 2.6

Other Types of Equations

- ■ You should be able to solve certain types of nonlinear or nonquadratic equations.

- ■ For equations involving radicals or fractional powers, raise both sides to the same power.

- ■ For equations that are of the quadratic type, $au^2 + bu + c = 0$, $a \neq 0$, use either factoring or the quadratic equation.

- ■ Always check for extraneous solutions.

Solutions to Selected Exercises

5. Find all solutions of $x^4 - 81 = 0$.

Solution:

$$x^4 - 81 = 0$$
$$(x^2 + 9)(x^2 - 9) = 0$$
$$(x^2 + 9)(x + 3)(x - 3) = 0$$
$$x = \pm 3 \quad \text{or} \quad x = \pm 3i$$

9. Find all solutions of $x^3 - 3x^2 - x + 3 = 0$.

Solution:

$$x^3 - 3x^2 - x + 3 = 0$$
$$x^2(x - 3) - (x - 3) = 0$$
$$(x - 3)(x^2 - 1) = 0$$
$$(x - 3)(x + 1)(x - 1) = 0$$
$$x = 3 \quad \text{or} \quad x = \pm 1$$

15. Find all solutions of $x^4 + 5x^2 - 36 = 0$.

Solution:

$$x^4 + 5x^2 - 36 = 0$$
$$(x^2 + 9)(x^2 - 4) = 0$$
$$(x^2 + 9)(x + 2)(x - 2) = 0$$
$$x = \pm 2 \quad \text{or} \quad x = \pm 3i$$

19. Find all solutions of $x^6 + 7x^3 - 8 = 0$.

Solution:

$$x^6 + 7x^3 - 8 = 0$$

$$(x^3 + 8)(x^3 - 1) = 0$$

$$(x + 2)(x^2 - 2x + 4)(x - 1)(x^2 + x + 1) = 0$$

$$x = -2, \quad x = \frac{2 \pm \sqrt{4 - 16}}{2}, \quad x = 1 \quad \text{or} \quad x = \frac{-1 \pm \sqrt{1 - 4}}{2}$$

$$x = -2, \quad x = 1 \pm 2\sqrt{3}\,i, \quad x = 1 \quad \text{or} \quad x = -\frac{1}{2} \pm \frac{\sqrt{3}}{2}i$$

21. Find all solutions of

$$\frac{1}{t^2} + \frac{8}{t} + 15 = 0.$$

Solution:

$$\frac{1}{t^2} + \frac{8}{t} + 15 = 0$$

$$1 + 8t + 15t^2 = 0$$

$$(1 + 3t)(1 + 5t) = 0$$

$$t = -\frac{1}{3} \quad \text{or} \quad t = -\frac{1}{5}$$

25. Find all solutions of $5 - 3x^{1/3} - 2x^{2/3} = 0$.

Solution:

$$5 - 3x^{1/3} - 2x^{2/3} = 0$$

$$(5 + 2x^{1/3})(1 - x^{1/3}) = 0$$

$$5 + 2x^{1/3} = 0 \quad \text{or} \quad 1 - x^{1/3} = 0$$

$$x^{1/3} = -\tfrac{5}{2} \quad \text{or} \quad x^{1/3} = 1$$

$$x = \left(-\tfrac{5}{2}\right)^3 \quad \text{or} \quad x = (1)^3$$

$$x = -\tfrac{125}{8} \quad \text{or} \quad x = 1$$

29. Find all solutions of $\sqrt{x-10}-4=0$.

Solution:

$$\sqrt{x-10}-4=0$$
$$\sqrt{x-10}=4$$
$$x-10=16$$
$$x=26$$

35. Find all solutions of $-\sqrt{26-11x}+4=x$.

Solution:

$$-\sqrt{26-11x}+4=x$$
$$4-x=\sqrt{26-11x}$$
$$(4-x)^2=26-11x$$
$$16-8x+x^2=26-11x$$
$$x^2+3x-10=0$$
$$(x+5)(x-2)=0$$
$$x=-5 \quad \text{or} \quad x=2$$

39. Find all solutions of $\sqrt{x}+\sqrt{x-20}=10$.

Solution:

$$\sqrt{x}+\sqrt{x-20}=10$$
$$\sqrt{x}=10-\sqrt{x-20}$$
$$(\sqrt{x})^2=(10-\sqrt{x-20})^2$$
$$x=100-20\sqrt{x-20}+x-20$$
$$x=x+80-20\sqrt{x-20}$$
$$-80=-20\sqrt{x-20}$$
$$4=\sqrt{x-20}$$
$$16=x-20$$
$$36=x$$

45. Find all solutions of $(x + 3)^{3/2} = 8$.

Solution:

$$(x + 3)^{3/2} = 8$$
$$\left[(x + 3)^{3/2}\right]^{2/3} = (8)^{2/3}$$
$$x + 3 = 4$$
$$x = 1$$

49. Find all solutions of $3x(x - 1)^{1/2} + 2(x - 1)^{3/2} = 0$.

Solution:

$$3x(x - 1)^{1/2} + 2(x - 1)^{3/2} = 0$$
$$(x - 1)^{1/2}\left[3x + 2(x - 1)\right] = 0$$
$$(x - 1)^{1/2}(5x - 2) = 0$$
$$x = 1 \quad \text{or} \quad x = \tfrac{2}{5}$$

Since $x = \tfrac{2}{5}$ is extraneous, the only real solution is $x = 1$.

53. Find all solutions of

$$x = \frac{3}{x} + \frac{1}{2} \ .$$

Solution:

$$x = \frac{3}{x} + \frac{1}{2}$$
$$2x^2 = 6 + x$$
$$2x^2 - x - 6 = 0$$
$$(2x + 3)(x - 2) = 0$$
$$x = -\frac{3}{2} \quad \text{or} \quad x = 2$$

57. Find all solutions of

$$\frac{4}{x + 1} - \frac{3}{x + 2} = 1.$$

Solution:

$$\frac{4}{x+1} - \frac{3}{x+2} = 1$$

$$4(x+2) - 3(x+1) = (x+1)(x+2)$$

$$4x + 8 - 3x - 3 = x^2 + 3x + 2$$

$$x + 5 = x^2 + 3x + 2$$

$$0 = x^2 + 2x - 3$$

$$0 = (x+3)(x-1)$$

$$x = -3 \quad \text{or} \quad x = 1$$

61. Find all solutions of $|2x - 1| = 5$.

Solution:

$$
\begin{array}{ccc}
2x - 1 = -5 & \text{or} & 2x - 1 = 5 \\
2x = -4 & & 2x = 6 \\
x = -2 & & x = 3
\end{array}
$$

65. Find all solutions of $|x - 10| = x^2 - 10x$.

Solution:

$$
\begin{array}{ccc}
x - 10 = x^2 - 10x & \text{or} & -(x-10) = x^2 - 10x \\
0 = x^2 - 11x + 10 & & 0 = x^2 - 9x - 10 \\
0 = (x-1)(x-10) & & 0 = (x+1)(x-10) \\
x = 1, \ x = 10 & & x = -1, \ x = 10
\end{array}
$$

By checking, we see that $x = 10$ and $x = -1$ are the only real solutions. $x = 1$ is an extraneous solution.

69. Use a calculator to find the real solutions of $1.8x - 6\sqrt{x} - 5.6 = 0$. Round your answer to three decimal places.

Solution:
$$1.8x - 6\sqrt{x} - 5.6 = 0, \quad u = \sqrt{x}$$

$$\sqrt{x} = \frac{6 \pm \sqrt{36 - 4(1.8)(-5.6)}}{2(1.8)} \approx \frac{6 \pm 8.7361}{3.6}$$

Considering only the positive value for $\sqrt{x}$, we have

$$\sqrt{x} \approx 4.0934$$
$$x \approx 16.756$$

73. A power station is on one side of a river that is 1/2–mile wide. A factory is 6 miles downstream on the other side of the river. It costs $18 per foot to run power lines overland and $24 per foot to run them underwater. The total cost of the project is $616,877.27. Find the length x as labeled in the figure.

Solution:

Distance underwater in feet $= 5280\sqrt{x^2 + (1/4)} = 2640\sqrt{4x^2 + 1}$

Distance overland in feet $= 5280(6 - x)$

Cost $=$ (cost underwater)(distance underwater) $+$ (cost overland)(distance overland)

$$616,877.27 = 24(2640)\sqrt{4x^2 + 1} + 18(5280)(6 - x)$$

$$616,877.27 = 12(2640)[2\sqrt{4x^2 + 1} + 3(6 - x)]$$

$$19.472136 = 2\sqrt{4x^2 + 1} + 18 - 3x$$

$$3x + 1.472136 = 2\sqrt{4x^2 + 1}$$

$$9x^2 + 8.8328163x + 2.16718455 = 4(4x^2 + 1)$$

$$7x^2 - 8.8328163x + 1.83281545 = 0$$

$$x = \frac{8.8328163 \pm \sqrt{26.69981119}}{14} \approx \frac{8.8328 \pm 5.1672}{14}$$

$$x = 1 \text{ mi} \quad \text{or} \quad x = 0.262 \text{ mi}$$

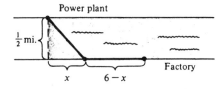

Power plant

$\frac{1}{2}$ mi.

Factory

x $6 - x$

77. The surface area of a cone is given by $S = \pi r \sqrt{r^2 + h^2}$. Solve this equation for h.

Solution:

$$S = \pi r \sqrt{r^2 + h^2}$$

$$S^2 = \pi^2 r^2 (r^2 + h^2)$$

$$S^2 = \pi^2 r^4 + \pi^2 r^2 h^2$$

$$\frac{S^2 - \pi^2 r^4}{\pi^2 r^2} = h^2$$

$$h = \frac{\sqrt{S^2 - \pi^2 r^4}}{\pi r}$$

SECTION 2.7

Linear Inequalities

■ You should know the properties of inequalities.

(a) Transitive: $a < b$ and $b < c$ implies $a < c$.

(b) Addition: $a < b$ and $c < d$ implies $a + c < b + d$.

(c) Adding or Subtracting a Constant: $a \pm c < b \pm c$ if $a < b$.

(d) Multiplying or Dividing a Constant: For $a < b$,

    1. If $c > 0$, then $ac < bc$ and $\dfrac{a}{c} < \dfrac{b}{c}$.

    2. If $c < 0$, then $ac > bc$ and $\dfrac{a}{c} > \dfrac{b}{c}$.

■ You should know that

$$|x| = \begin{cases} x & \text{if } x \geq 0 \\ -x & \text{if } x < 0 \end{cases}.$$

■ You should be able to solve absolute value inequalities.

(a) $|x| < a$ if and only if $-a < x < a$.

(b) $|x| > a$ if and only if $x < -a$ or $x > a$.

Solutions to Selected Exercises

3. Determine whether or not the given value of x satisfies the inequality.

$$0 < \frac{x-2}{4} < 2$$

Solution:

(a) $x = 4$

$$0 \overset{?}{<} \frac{4-2}{4} \overset{?}{<} 2$$

$$0 < \frac{1}{2} < 2, \quad x = 4 \text{ is a solution.}$$

(b) $x = 10$

$$0 \overset{?}{<} \frac{10-2}{4} \overset{?}{<} 2$$

$$0 < 2 \not< 2, \quad x = 10 \text{ is not a solution.}$$

(c) $x = 0$

$$0 \overset{?}{<} \frac{0-2}{4} \overset{?}{<} 2$$

$$0 \not< -\frac{1}{2} < 2, \quad x = 0 \text{ is not a solution.}$$

(d) $x = \dfrac{7}{2}$

$$0 \overset{?}{<} \frac{(7/2)-2}{4} \overset{?}{<} 2$$

$$0 < \frac{3}{8} < 2, \quad x = \frac{7}{2} \text{ is a solution.}$$

9. Match $|x| < 4$ with its graph.

Solution:

$$|x| < 4$$
$$-4 < x < 4 \qquad \text{Matches graph (g)}$$

13. Solve $4x < 12$ and sketch the solution on the real number line.

Solution:

$$4x < 12$$
$$x < 3$$

19. Solve $4(x + 1) < 2x + 3$ and sketch the solution on the real number line.

Solution:

$$4(x + 1) < 2x + 3$$
$$4x + 4 < 2x + 3$$
$$2x < -1$$
$$x < -\tfrac{1}{2}$$

23. Solve $4 - 2x < 3$ and sketch the solution on the real number line.

Solution:

$$4 - 2x < 3$$
$$-2x < -1$$
$$x > \tfrac{1}{2}$$

27. Solve

$$-4 < \frac{2x - 3}{3} < 4$$

and sketch the solution on the real number line.

Solution:

$$-4 < \frac{2x - 3}{3} < 4$$
$$-12 < 2x - 3 < 12$$
$$-9 < 2x < 15$$
$$-\frac{9}{2} < x < \frac{15}{2}$$

33. Solve $|x/2| > 3$ and sketch the solution on the real number line.

Solution:

$$\left|\frac{x}{2}\right| > 3$$

$$\frac{x}{2} < -3 \quad \text{or} \quad \frac{x}{2} > 3$$

$$x < -6 \quad \text{or} \quad x > 6$$

39. Solve

$$\left|\frac{x-3}{2}\right| \geq 5$$

and sketch the solution on the real number line.

Solution:

$$\left|\frac{x-3}{2}\right| \geq 5$$

$$\frac{x-3}{2} \leq -5 \quad \text{or} \quad \frac{x-3}{2} \geq 5$$

$$x - 3 \leq -10 \quad \text{or} \quad x - 3 \geq 10$$

$$x \leq -7 \quad \text{or} \quad x \geq 13$$

43. Solve $2|x + 10| \geq 9$ and sketch the solution on the real number line.

Solution:

$$2|x + 10| \geq 9$$

$$|x + 10| \geq \frac{9}{2}$$

$$x + 10 \leq -\frac{9}{2} \quad \text{or} \quad x + 10 \geq \frac{9}{2}$$

$$x \leq -\frac{29}{2} \quad \text{or} \quad x \geq -\frac{11}{2}$$

47. Find the interval on the real number line for which the radicand in $\sqrt{x - 5}$ is nonnegative.

Solution:
The radicand of $\sqrt{x - 5}$ is $x - 5$.

$$x - 5 \geq 0$$

$$x \geq 5$$

Therefore, the interval is $[5, \infty)$.

51. Find the interval on the real number line for which the radicand in $\sqrt[4]{7 - 2x}$ is nonnegative.

Solution:

The radicand in $\sqrt[4]{7 - 2x}$ is $7 - 2x$.

$$7 - 2x \geq 0$$
$$-2x \geq -7$$
$$x \leq \tfrac{7}{2}$$

Therefore, the interval is $\left(-\infty, \tfrac{7}{2}\right]$.

55. Use absolute value notation to define the pair of intervals on the real line.

Solution:

$$|x - 9| \geq 3$$

59. Use absolute value notation to define following the interval on the real line: All real numbers whose distances from -3 are more than 5.

Solution:

$$|x - (-3)| > 5$$
$$|x + 3| > 5$$

63. The revenue for selling x units of a product is $R = 115.95x$. The cost of producing x units is $C = 95x + 750$. In order to obtain a profit, the revenue must be greater than the cost. For what values of x will this product return a profit?

Solution:

$$R > C$$
$$115.95x > 95x + 750$$
$$20.95x > 750$$
$$x > 35.7995$$
$$x > 36 \text{ units}$$

67. Given two real numbers, a and b such that $a > b > 0$, prove that $1/a < 1/b$.

Solution:

$$a > b > 0$$
$$b < a \quad \text{where } a \text{ and } b \text{ are both positive}$$
$$1 < \frac{a}{b}$$
$$1 \cdot \frac{1}{a} < \frac{a}{b} \cdot \frac{1}{a}$$
$$\frac{1}{a} < \frac{1}{b}$$

SECTION 2.8

Other Types of Inequalities

- ■ You should be able to solve perfect square inequalities. For $a > 0$,
  - (a) $x^2 < a$ if and only if $-\sqrt{a} < x < \sqrt{a}$
  - (b) $x^2 > a$ if and only if $x < -\sqrt{a}$ or $x > \sqrt{a}$

- ■ You should be able to solve inequalities by factoring.
  - (a) Find the critical numbers.
    - 1. Values that make the expression zero
    - 2. Values that make the expression undefined
  - (b) Test one value in each interval on the real number line resulting from the critical numbers.
  - (c) Determine the solution intervals.

- ■ You should be able to solve inequalities by completing the square.

Solutions to Selected Exercises

3. Solve the inequality $x^2 > 4$ and graph the solution on the real number line.

Solution:

$$x^2 > 4$$

$\quad x < -\sqrt{4} \quad$ or $\quad x > \sqrt{4}$

$\quad x < -2 \quad$ or $\quad x > 2$

$(-\infty, -2) \quad$ or $\quad (2, \infty)$

7. Solve the inequality $x^2 + 4x + 4 \geq 9$ and graph the solution on the real number line.

Solution:

$$(x + 2)^2 \geq 9$$

$\quad x + 2 \leq -\sqrt{9} \quad$ or $\quad x + 2 \geq \sqrt{9}$

$\quad x + 2 \leq -3 \quad$ or $\quad x + 2 \geq 3$

$\quad\quad x \leq -5 \quad$ or $\quad\quad x \geq 1$

$(-\infty, -5] \quad$ or $\quad [1, \infty)$

11. Solve the inequality $3(x - 1)(x + 1) > 0$ and graph the solution on the real number line.

Solution:

$$3(x - 1)(x + 1) > 0$$

Critical numbers: $x = -1$, $x = 1$
Test intervals: $(-\infty, -1)$, $(-1, 1)$, $(1, \infty)$
Solution intervals: $(-\infty, -1)$, $(1, \infty)$ or $x < -1$, $x > 1$

15. Solve the inequality $4x^3 - 6x^2 < 0$ and graph the solution on the real number line.

Solution:

$$4x^3 - 6x^2 < 0$$
$$2x^2(2x - 3) < 0$$

Critical numbers: $x = 0$, $x = \frac{3}{2}$
Test intervals: $(-\infty, 0)$, $(0, \frac{3}{2})$, $(\frac{3}{2}, \infty)$
Solution intervals: $(-\infty, 0)$, $(0, \frac{3}{2})$ or $x < 0$, $0 < x < \frac{3}{2}$
Note: $x = 0$ is *not* a solution.

19. Solve the inequality $1/x > x$ and graph the solution on the real number line.

Solution:

$$\frac{1}{x} > x$$

$$\frac{1}{x} - x > 0$$

$$\frac{1 - x^2}{x} > 0$$

$$\frac{(1 + x)(1 - x)}{x} > 0$$

Critical numbers: $x = -1$, $x = 0$, $x = 1$
Test intervals: $(-\infty, -1)$, $(-1, 0)$, $(0, 1)$, $(1, \infty)$
Solution intervals: $(-\infty, -1)$, $(0, 1)$ or $x < -1$, $0 < x < 1$

23. Solve the following inequality and graph the solution on the real number line.

$$\frac{3x - 5}{x - 5} > 4$$

Solution:

$$\frac{3x - 5}{x - 5} > 4$$

$$\frac{3x - 5 - 4(x - 5)}{x - 5} > 0$$

$$\frac{15 - x}{x - 5} > 0$$

Critical numbers: $x = 5$, $x = 15$
Test intervals: $(-\infty, 5)$, $(5, 15)$, $(15, \infty)$
Solution interval: $(5, 15)$ or $5 < x < 15$

27. Solve the following inequality and graph the solution on the real number line.

$$\frac{1}{x - 3} \le \frac{9}{4x + 3}$$

Solution:

$$\frac{1}{x - 3} \le \frac{9}{4x + 3}$$

$$\frac{1}{x - 3} - \frac{9}{4x + 3} \le 0$$

$$\frac{4x + 3 - 9(x - 3)}{(x - 3)(4x + 3)} \le 0$$

$$\frac{30 - 5x}{(x - 3)(4x + 3)} \le 0$$

$$\frac{-5(x - 6)}{(x - 3)(4x + 3)} \le 0$$

Critical numbers: $x = -\frac{3}{4}$, $x = 3$, $x = 6$
Test intervals: $(-\infty, -\frac{3}{4})$, $(-\frac{3}{4}, 3)$, $(3, 6)$, $(6, \infty)$
Solution intervals: $(-\frac{3}{4}, 3)$, $[6, \infty)$ or $-\frac{3}{4} < x < 3$, $x \ge 6$

Note: We have $x = 6$ in the solution intervals, but not $x = -\frac{3}{4}$ and $x = 3$ since they yield a zero in the denominator.

31. Find the domain of x in the expression $\sqrt{x^2 - 7x + 12}$.

Solution:
The radicand is $x^2 - 7x + 12$.

$$x^2 - 7x + 12 \ge 0$$

$$(x - 3)(x - 4) \ge 0$$

Critical numbers: $x = 3$, $x = 4$
Test intervals: $(-\infty, 3)$, $(3, 4)$, $(4, \infty)$
Domain: $(-\infty, 3]$, $[4, \infty)$

35. Find the domain of x in the expression $\sqrt{x^2 - 3x + 3}$.

Solution:

$$x^2 - 3x + 3 \geq 0$$

Since the discriminant $b^2 - 4ac = 9 - 12 < 0$, there are no critical numbers. The inequality is true for all real numbers or has no real solutions. By testing (use $x = 0$), we find that it is true for all real numbers.
Domain: $(-\infty, \infty)$

39. A rectangle with a perimeter of 100 meters is to have an area of at least 500 square meters. Within what bounds must the length of the rectangle lie?

Solution:

$$2L + 2W = 100$$
$$W = \frac{100 - 2L}{2} = 50 - L$$
$$LW \geq 500$$
$$L(50 - L) \geq 500$$
$$50L - L^2 \geq 500$$
$$0 \geq L^2 - 50L + 500$$

By the quadratic formula the critical numbers are:

$$x = \frac{50 \pm \sqrt{(50)^2 - 4(500)}}{2}, \qquad x = \frac{50 \pm \sqrt{500}}{2} = \frac{50 \pm 10\sqrt{5}}{2} = 25 \pm 5\sqrt{5}$$

Solution interval: $[25 - 5\sqrt{5}, \ 25 + 5\sqrt{5}]$, or 13.8197 meters $\leq L \leq 36.1803$ meters

REVIEW EXERCISES FOR CHAPTER 2

Solutions to Selected Exercises

3. Solve the equation $5x^4 - 12x^3 = 0$.

Solution:

$$5x^4 - 12x^3 = 0$$
$$x^3(5x - 12) = 0$$
$$x^3 = 0 \quad \text{or} \quad 5x - 12 = 0$$
$$x = 0 \quad \text{or} \quad x = \frac{12}{5}$$

7. Solve the equation

$$3\left(1 - \frac{1}{5t}\right) = 0.$$

Solution:

$$3\left(1 - \frac{1}{5t}\right) = 0$$
$$1 - \frac{1}{5t} = 0$$
$$1 = \frac{1}{5t}$$
$$5t = 1$$
$$t = \frac{1}{5}$$

13. Solve the equation $4t^3 - 12t^2 + 8t = 0$.

Solution:

$$4t^3 - 12t^2 + 8t = 0$$
$$4t(t^2 - 3t + 2) = 0$$
$$4t(t - 1)(t - 2) = 0$$
$$t = 0, \ t = 1, \ t = 2$$

17. Solve the equation

$$\frac{(x - 1)(2x) - x^2}{(x - 1)^2} = 0.$$

Solution:

$$\frac{(x-1)(2x) - x^2}{(x-1)^2} = 0$$

$$(x-1)(2x) - x^2 = 0$$

$$2x^2 - 2x - x^2 = 0$$

$$x^2 - 2x = 0$$

$$x(x-2) = 0$$

$$x = 0 \quad \text{or} \quad x = 2$$

21. Solve the equation $|x - 5| = 10$.

Solution:

$$|x - 5| = 10$$

$$x - 5 = -10 \quad \text{or} \quad x - 5 = 10$$

$$x = -5 \qquad\qquad x = 15$$

25. Solve the equation $\sqrt{x + 4} = 3$.

Solution:

$$\sqrt{x + 4} = 3$$

$$(\sqrt{x + 4})^2 = (3)^2$$

$$x + 4 = 9$$

$$x = 5$$

29. Solve the equation $(x + 4)^{1/2} + 5x(x + 4)^{3/2} = 0$.

Solution:

$$(x + 4)^{1/2} + 5x(x + 4)^{3/2} = 0$$

$$(x + 4)^{1/2}[1 + 5x(x + 4)] = 0$$

$$(x + 4)^{1/2}(5x^2 + 20x + 1) = 0$$

$$(x + 4)^{1/2} = 0$$

$$x = -4$$

OR

$$5x^2 + 20x + 1 = 0$$

$$x = \frac{-20 \pm \sqrt{400 - 20}}{10}$$

$$x = \frac{-20 \pm 2\sqrt{95}}{10}$$

$$x = -2 \pm \frac{\sqrt{95}}{5}$$

33. Solve the equation $\sqrt{2x+3} + \sqrt{x-2} = 2$.

Solution:

$$\sqrt{2x+3} + \sqrt{x-2} = 2$$
$$\left(\sqrt{2x+3}\right)^2 = (2 - \sqrt{x-2})^2$$
$$2x + 3 = 4 - 4\sqrt{x-2} + x - 2$$
$$x + 1 = -4\sqrt{x-2}$$
$$(x+1)^2 = (-4\sqrt{x-2})^2$$
$$x^2 + 2x + 1 = 16(x-2)$$
$$x^2 - 14x + 33 = 0$$
$$(x-3)(x-11) = 0$$
$$x = 3, \text{ extraneous} \quad \text{OR} \quad x = 11, \text{ extraneous}$$

No solution

37. Solve the inequality $x^2 - 4 \leq 0$.

Solution:

$$x^2 - 4 \leq 0$$
$$(x+2)(x-2) \leq 0$$

Critical numbers: $x = 2,\ x = -2$
Test intervals: $x \leq -2,\ -2 \leq x \leq 2,\ x \geq 2$
Solution interval: $-2 \leq x \leq 2$

43. Solve the inequality.

$$\left| x - \tfrac{3}{2} \right| \geq \tfrac{3}{2}$$

Solution:

$$\left| x - \tfrac{3}{2} \right| \geq \tfrac{3}{2}$$
$$x - \tfrac{3}{2} \leq -\tfrac{3}{2} \quad \text{or} \quad x - \tfrac{3}{2} \geq \tfrac{3}{2}$$
$$x \leq 0 \quad \text{or} \quad x \geq 3$$

49. Solve $S = V_0 t - 16t^2$ for t.

Solution:

$$S = V_0 t - 16t^2$$
$$16t^2 - V_0 t + S = 0$$
$$t = \frac{V_0 \pm \sqrt{V_0{}^2 - 64S}}{32}$$

55. Perform the indicated operations and write the result in standard form.

$$\left(\frac{\sqrt{2}}{2} - \frac{\sqrt{2}}{2}i\right) - \left(\frac{\sqrt{2}}{2} + \frac{\sqrt{2}}{2}i\right)$$

Solution:

$$\left(\frac{\sqrt{2}}{2} - \frac{\sqrt{2}}{2}i\right) - \left(\frac{\sqrt{2}}{2} + \frac{\sqrt{2}}{2}i\right) = \left(\frac{\sqrt{2}}{2} - \frac{\sqrt{2}}{2}\right) + \left(-\frac{\sqrt{2}}{2} - \frac{\sqrt{2}}{2}\right)i$$
$$= 0 - \sqrt{2}\,i$$
$$= -\sqrt{2}\,i$$

59. Perform the indicated operations and write the result in standard form.

$$(10 - 8i)(2 - 3i)$$

Solution:

$$(10 - 8i)(2 - 3i) = 20 - 30i - 16i + 24i^2 = -4 - 46i$$

63. Perform the indicated operations and write the result in standard form.

$$\frac{4}{-3i}$$

Solution:

$$\frac{4}{-3i} = \frac{4}{-3i} \cdot \frac{3i}{3i} = \frac{12i}{9} = \frac{4i}{3} = 0 + \frac{4}{3}i$$

65. The distance from a spacecraft to the horizon is 1000 miles. Find x, the altitude of the craft, as shown in the figure. Assume that the radius of the earth is 4000 miles.

Solution:

$$1000^2 + 4000^2 = (4000 + x)^2 \qquad \text{Pythagorean Theorem}$$
$$1000^2 + 4000^2 = 4000^2 + 8000x + x^2$$
$$0 = x^2 + 8000x - 1000^2$$
$$x = \frac{-8000 \pm \sqrt{8000^2 - 4(-1000^2)}}{2}$$

Considering only the positive root,

$$x = \frac{-8000 + 2000\sqrt{17}}{2} = -4000 + 1000\sqrt{17}$$
$$x \approx 123.106 \text{ mi}$$

67. A group of farmers agree to share equally in the cost of a \$48,000 piece of machinery. If they could find two more farmers to join the group, each person's share of the cost would decrease by \$4000. How many farmers are presently in the group?

Solution:

Let x = number of farmers in the group

$$\text{Cost per farmer} = \frac{48,000}{x}$$

If two more farmers join the group, the cost per farmer will be $\dfrac{48,000}{x+2}$.

Since this new cost is \$4000 less than the original cost,

$$\frac{48,000}{x} - 4000 = \frac{48,000}{x+2}$$
$$48,000(x+2) - 4000x(x+2) = 48,000x$$
$$12(x+2) - x(x+2) = 12x$$
$$12x + 24 - x^2 - 2x = 12x$$
$$0 = x^2 + 2x - 24$$
$$0 = (x+6)(x-4)$$
$$x = -6, \text{ extraneous} \quad \text{OR} \quad x = 4$$
$$x = 4 \text{ farmers}$$

Practice Test for Chapter 2

1. Solve $5x + 4 = 7x - 8$.

2. Solve $\dfrac{x}{3} - 5 = \dfrac{x}{5} + 1$.

3. Solve $\dfrac{3x + 1}{6x - 7} = \dfrac{2}{5}$.

4. Solve $(x - 3)^2 + 4 = (x + 1)^2$.

5. Solve $A = \dfrac{1}{2}(a + b)h$ for a.

6. Find three consecutive natural numbers whose sum is 132.

7. 301 is what percent of 4300?

8. Cindy has \$6.05 in quarters and nickels. How many of each coin does she have if there are 53 coins in all?

9. Ed has \$15,000 invested in two funds paying $9\frac{1}{2}\%$ and 11% simple interest, respectively. How much is invested in each if the yearly interest is \$1582.50?

10. Solve $28 + 5x - 3x^2 = 0$ by factoring.

11. Solve $(x - 2)^2 = 24$ by taking the square root of both sides.

12. Solve $x^2 - 4x - 9 = 0$ by completing the square.

13. Complete the square on the denominator of $\dfrac{1}{x^2 - 6x + 1}$.

14. Solve $x^2 + 5x - 1 = 0$ by the quadratic formula.

15. Solve $3x^2 - 2x + 4 = 0$ by the quadratic formula.

16. The perimeter of a rectangle is 1100 feet. Find the dimensions so that the enclosed area will be 60,000 square feet.

17. Find two consecutive even positive integers whose product is 624.

18. Solve $x^3 - 10x^2 + 24x = 0$ by factoring.

19. Solve $\sqrt[3]{6 - x} = 4$.

20. Solve $(x^2 - 8)^{2/5} = 4$.

21. Solve $x^4 - x^2 - 12 = 0$.

22. Solve $4 - 3x > 16$.

23. Solve $\left| \dfrac{x - 3}{2} \right| < 5$.

24. Solve $\dfrac{x + 1}{x - 3} < 2$.

25. Solve $|3x - 4| \geq 9$.

CHAPTER 3
Functions and Graphs

SECTION 3.1

The Cartesian Plane

■ You should be able to plot points.

■ You should know that the distance between (x_1, y_1) and (x_2, y_2) in the plane is

$$d = \sqrt{(x_2 - x_1)^2 + (y_2 - y_1)^2}$$

■ You should know that the midpoint of the line segment joining (x_1, y_1) and (x_2, y_2) is

$$\left(\frac{x_1 + x_2}{2}, \frac{y_1 + y_2}{2} \right)$$

Solutions to Selected Exercises

3. Sketch the square with vertices $(2, 4)$, $(5, 1)$, $(2, -2)$, and $(-1, 1)$.

Solution:

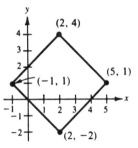

7. Find the distance between the points $(-3, -1)$ and $(2, -1)$.

Solution:
Since the points $(-3, -1)$ and $(2, -1)$ lie on a vertical line, the distance between the points is given by the absolute value of the difference of their x-coordinates.

$$d = | -3 - 2| = 5$$

11. For the indicated triangle (a) find the length of the two sides of the right triangle and use the Pythagorean Theorem to find the length of the hypotenuse, and (b) use the Distance Formula to find the length of the hypotenuse of the triangle.

Solution:

(a) $a = |-3 - 7| = 10$

$b = |4 - 1| = 3$

$c = \sqrt{10^2 + 3^2} = \sqrt{109}$

(b) $c = \sqrt{(7 - (-3))^2 + (4 - 1)^2}$

$= \sqrt{10^2 + 3^2}$

$= \sqrt{109}$

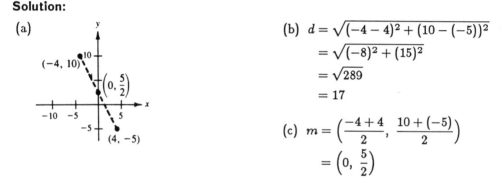

15. (a) Plot the points $(-4, \ 10)$ and $(4, \ -5)$, (b) find the distance between the points, and (c) find the midpoint of the line segment joining the points.

Solution:

(a)

(b) $d = \sqrt{(-4 - 4)^2 + (10 - (-5))^2}$

$= \sqrt{(-8)^2 + (15)^2}$

$= \sqrt{289}$

$= 17$

(c) $m = \left(\dfrac{-4 + 4}{2}, \ \dfrac{10 + (-5)}{2} \right)$

$= \left(0, \ \dfrac{5}{2} \right)$

21. (a) Plot the points $(6.2, \ 5.4)$, and $(-3.7, \ 1.8)$, (b) find the distance between the points, and (c) find the midpoint of the line segment joining the points.

Solution:

(a)

(b) $d = \sqrt{(6.2 - (-3.7))^2 + (5.4 - 1.8)^2}$

$= \sqrt{(9.9)^2 + (3.6)^2}$

$= \sqrt{110.97}$

≈ 10.5342

(c) $m = \left(\dfrac{6.2 + (-3.7)}{2}, \ \dfrac{5.4 + 1.8}{2} \right)$

$= (1.25, \ 3.6)$

25. Show that the points $(4, 0)$, $(2, 1)$, and $(-1, \ -5)$ form the vertices of a right triangle.

Solution:

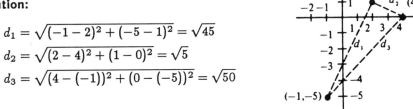

$$d_1 = \sqrt{(-1-2)^2 + (-5-1)^2} = \sqrt{45}$$
$$d_2 = \sqrt{(2-4)^2 + (1-0)^2} = \sqrt{5}$$
$$d_3 = \sqrt{(4-(-1))^2 + (0-(-5))^2} = \sqrt{50}$$

Since $d_1{}^2 + d_2{}^2 = d_3{}^2$, we can conclude by the Pythagorean Theorem that the triangle is a right triangle.

29. Find x so that the distance between $(1, 2)$ and $(x, -10)$ is 13.

Solution:

$$\sqrt{(x-1)^2 + (-10-2)^2} = 13$$
$$\sqrt{x^2 - 2x + 1 + 144} = 13$$
$$x^2 - 2x + 145 = 169$$
$$x^2 - 2x - 24 = 0$$
$$(x+4)(x-6) = 0$$
$$x = -4 \quad \text{or} \quad x = 6$$

33. Find a relationship between x and y so that (x, y) is equidistant from the points $(4, -1)$ and $(-2, 3)$.

Solution:
The distance between $(4, -1)$ and (x, y) is equal to the distance between $(-2, 3)$ and (x, y).

$$\sqrt{(x-4)^2 + (y+1)^2} = \sqrt{(x+2)^2 + (y-3)^2}$$
$$(x-4)^2 + (y+1)^2 = (x+2)^2 + (y-3)^2$$
$$x^2 - 8x + 16 + y^2 + 2y + 1 = x^2 + 4x + 4 + y^2 - 6y + 9$$
$$4 = 12x - 8y$$
$$1 = 3x - 2y$$
$$2y = 3x - 1$$

37. Determine the quadrant in which (x, y) is located so that the conditions $x > 0$ and $y > 0$ are satisfied.

Solution:

$x > 0 \rightarrow x$ lies in Quadrant I or in Quadrant IV

$y > 0 \rightarrow y$ lies in Quadrant I or in Quadrant II

$x > 0$ and $y > 0 \rightarrow (x, y)$ lies in Quadrant I

45. Use the Midpoint Formula twice to find the three points that divide the line segment joining (x_1, y_1) and (x_2, y_2) into four parts.

Solution:

The midpoint of the given line segment is

$$\left(\frac{x_1 + x_2}{2}, \frac{y_1 + y_2}{2}\right).$$

The midpoint between (x_1, y_1) and $\left(\frac{x_1 + x_2}{2}, \frac{y_1 + y_2}{2}\right)$ is

$$\left(\frac{x_1 + \dfrac{x_1 + x_2}{2}}{2}, \frac{y_1 + \dfrac{y_1 + y_2}{2}}{2}\right) = \left(\frac{3x_1 + x_2}{4}, \frac{3y_1 + y_2}{4}\right).$$

The midpoint between $\left(\frac{x_1 + x_2}{2}, \frac{y_1 + y_2}{2}\right)$ and (x_2, y_2) is

$$\left(\frac{\dfrac{x_1 + x_2}{2} + x_2}{2}, \frac{\dfrac{y_1 + y_2}{2} + y_2}{2}\right) = \left(\frac{x_1 + 3x_2}{4}, \frac{y_1 + 3y_2}{4}\right)$$

Thus, the three points are

$$\left(\frac{3x_1 + x_2}{4}, \frac{3y_1 + y_2}{4}\right), \quad \left(\frac{x_1 + x_2}{2}, \frac{y_1 + y_2}{2}\right), \quad \text{and} \quad \left(\frac{x_1 + 3x_2}{4}, \frac{y_1 + 3y_2}{4}\right).$$

47. Use the Midpoint Formula to estimate the sales of a company for 1983, given the sales in 1980 and 1986. Assume the annual sales followed a linear pattern.

Year	1980	1986
Sales	$520,000	$740,000

Solution:

$$\frac{520,000 + 740,000}{2} = 630,000$$

The estimated sales for 1983 is $630,000.

SECTION 3.2

Graphs of Equations

- ■ You should be able to use the point-plotting method of graphing.

- ■ You should be able to find x- and y-intercepts.

- ■ You should be able to test for symmetry.

- ■ You should know the standard equation of a circle with center (h, k) and radius r:

$$(x - h)^2 + (y - k)^2 = r^2$$

Solutions to Selected Exercises

5. Determine whether the points (a) $\left(1, \frac{1}{5}\right)$, and (b) $\left(2, \frac{1}{2}\right)$ lie on the graph of the equation $x^2y - x^2 + 4y = 0$.

Solution:

(a) $\left(1, \frac{1}{5}\right)$ lies on the graph since $(1)^2\left(\frac{1}{5}\right) - (1)^2 + 4\left(\frac{1}{5}\right) = \frac{1}{5} - 1 + \frac{4}{5} = 0$.

(b) $\left(2, \frac{1}{2}\right)$ lies on the graph since $(2)^2\left(\frac{1}{2}\right) - (2)^2 + 4\left(\frac{1}{2}\right) = 2 - 4 + 2 = 0$.

7. Find the constant C so that the ordered pair $(2, 6)$ is a solution point of the equation $y = x^2 + C$.

Solution:

$$y = x^2 + C$$
$$6 = (2)^2 + C$$
$$6 = 4 + C$$
$$C = 2$$

13. Find the x- and y-intercepts of the graph of the equation $y = x^2 + x - 2$.

Solution:

Let $y = 0$. Then $0 = x^2 + x - 2 = (x + 2)(x - 1)$ and $x = -2$ or $x = 1$.

x-intercepts: $(-2, 0)$ and $(1, 0)$

Let $x = 0$. Then $y = -2$.

y-intercept: $(0, -2)$

17. Find the x- and y-intercepts of the graph of the equation $xy - 2y - x + 1 = 0$.

Solution:
Let $y = 0$. Then $-x + 1 = 0$ and $x = 1$.

x-intercept: $(1, 0)$

Let $x = 0$. Then $-2y + 1 = 0$ and $y = \frac{1}{2}$.

y-intercept: $\left(0, \frac{1}{2}\right)$

21. Check for symmetry with respect to both axes and the origin for $x - y^2 = 0$.

Solution:
By replacing y with $-y$, we have

$$x - (-y)^2 = 0$$
$$x - y^2 = 0$$

which is the original equation. Replacing x with $-x$ or replacing both x and y with $-x$ and $-y$ does not yield equivalent equations. Thus, $x - y^2 = 0$ is symmetric with respect to the x-axis.

25. Check for symmetry with respect to both axes and the origin for

$$y = \frac{x}{x^2 + 1}.$$

Solution:
Replacing x with $-x$ or y with $-y$ does not yield equivalent equations. Replacing x with $-x$ and y with $-y$ yields

$$-y = \frac{-x}{(-x)^2 + 1}$$

$$-y = \frac{-x}{x^2 + 1} \qquad \text{Multiply both sides by } -1$$

$$y = \frac{x}{x^2 + 1}$$

Thus, $y = \frac{x}{x^2 + 1}$ is symmetric with respect to the origin.

Note: An equation is symmetric with respect to the origin if it is symmetric with respect to both the x-axis and the y-axis. Also, if an equation is symmetric with respect to the origin, then one of the following is true:

1. The equation has both x-axis and y-axis symmetry or
2. The equation has neither x-axis nor y-axis symmetry.

31. Match $y = x^3 - x$ with its graph.

Solution:

$y = x^3 - x$

x-intercepts: $(-1, 0)$, $(0, 0)$, $(1, 0)$

y-intercept: $(0, 0)$

Symmetry: Origin

Matches graph (e)

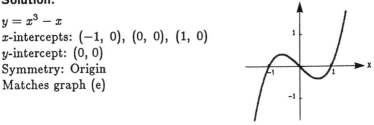

33. Sketch the graph of $y = -3x + 2$. Identify any intercepts and test for symmetry.

Solution:

$y = -3x + 2$

x-intercept: $\left(\frac{2}{3}, 0\right)$

y-intercept: $(0, 2)$

No symmetries

37. Sketch the graph of $y = x^2 - 4x + 3$. Identify any intercepts and test for symmetry.

Solution:

$y = x^2 - 4x + 3 = (x - 1)(x - 3)$

x-intercepts: $(1, 0)$, $(3, 0)$

y-intercept: $(0, 3)$

No symmetries

43. Sketch the graph of $y = \sqrt{x - 3}$. Identify any intercepts and test for symmetry.

Solution:

$y = \sqrt{x - 3}$

x-intercept: $(3, 0)$

No y-intercept

No symmetry

x	3	4	7	12
y	0	1	2	3

Note: The domain is $[3, \infty)$ and the range is $[0, \infty)$.

49. Sketch the graph of $x = y^2 - 1$. Identify any intercepts and test for symmetry.

Solution:

$x = y^2 - 1$
x-intercept: $(-1, 0)$
y-intercepts: $(0, -1)$, $(0, 1)$
x-axis symmetry

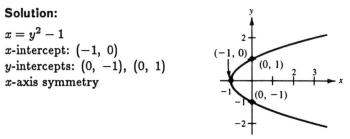

55. Find the standard form of the equation of the circle with center $(2, -1)$ and radius 4.

Solution:

$$(x - 2)^2 + (y + 1)^2 = 4^2$$
$$x^2 - 4x + 4 + y^2 + 2y + 1 = 16$$
$$x^2 + y^2 - 4x + 2y - 11 = 0$$

57. Find the standard form of the equation of the circle with center $(-1, 2)$ and solution point $(0, 0)$.

Solution:

$$(x + 1)^2 + (y - 2)^2 = r^2$$
$$(0 + 1)^2 + (0 - 2)^2 = r^2 \quad \rightarrow \quad r^2 = 5$$
$$(x + 1)^2 + (y - 2)^2 = 5$$
$$x^2 + y^2 + 2x - 4y = 0$$

61. Write the following equation of the circle in standard form and sketch its graph.

$$x^2 + y^2 - 2x + 6y + 6 = 0$$

Solution:

$$x^2 + y^2 - 2x + 6y + 6 = 0$$
$$(x^2 - 2x + 1) + (y^2 + 6y + 9) = -6 + 1 + 9$$
$$(x - 1)^2 + (y + 3)^2 = 4$$

Center: $(1, -3)$
Radius: 2

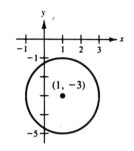

63. Write the following equation of the circle in standard form and sketch its graph.

$$x^2 + y^2 - 2x + 6y + 10 = 0$$

Solution:

$$x^2 + y^2 - 2x + 6y + 10 = 0$$
$$(x^2 - 2x + 1) + (y^2 + 6y + 9) = -10 + 1 + 9$$
$$(x - 1)^2 + (y + 3)^2 = 0$$

Graph is the point $(1, -3)$.

67. Write the following equation of the circle in standard form and sketch its graph.

$$16x^2 + 16y^2 + 16x + 40y - 7 = 0$$

Solution:

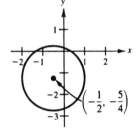

$$16x^2 + 16y^2 + 16x + 40y - 7 = 0$$
$$16\left(x^2 + x + \tfrac{1}{4}\right) + 16\left(y^2 + \tfrac{5}{2}y + \tfrac{25}{16}\right) = 7 + 4 + 25$$
$$16\left(x + \tfrac{1}{2}\right)^2 + 16\left(y + \tfrac{5}{4}\right)^2 = 36$$
$$\left(x + \tfrac{1}{2}\right)^2 + \left(y + \tfrac{5}{4}\right)^2 = \tfrac{9}{4}$$

Center: $\left(-\tfrac{1}{2}, -\tfrac{5}{4}\right)$
Radius: $\tfrac{3}{2}$

SECTION 3.3

Lines in the Plane

You should know the following important facts about lines.

- The slope of the line through (x_1, y_1) and (x_2, y_2) is

$$m = \frac{y_2 - y_1}{x_2 - x_1}.$$

- (a) If $m > 0$, the line rises from left to right.
  (b) If $m = 0$, the line is horizontal.
  (c) If $m < 0$, the line falls from left to right.
  (d) If m is undefined, the line is vertical.

- Equations of Lines
  (a) Point-Slope: $y - y_1 = m(x - x_1)$
  (b) Two-Point: $y - y_1 = \dfrac{y_2 - y_1}{x_2 - x_1}(x - x_1)$
  (c) Slope-Intercept: $y = mx + b$
  (d) General: $Ax + By + C = 0$
  (d) Vertical: $x = a$
  (e) Horizontal: $y = b$

- Given two distinct nonvertical lines

$$L_1 : y = m_1 x + b_1 \quad \text{and} \quad L_2 : y = m_2 x + b_2$$

  (a) L_1 is parallel to L_2 if and only if $m_1 = m_2$.
  (b) L_1 is perpendicular to L_2 if and only if $m_1 = -1/m_2$.

Solutions to Selected Exercises

9. Plot the points $(-3, -2)$ and $(1, 6)$ and find the slope of the line passing through the points.

Solution:

$$m = \frac{6 - (-2)}{1 - (-3)} = \frac{8}{4} = 2$$

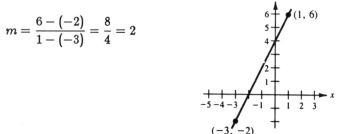

11. Plot the points $(-6, -1)$ and $(-6, 4)$ and find the slope of the line passing through the points.

Solution:

$$m = \frac{4 - (-1)}{-6 - (-6)} = \frac{5}{0}$$

The slope is undefined.

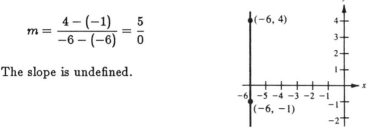

15. Determine if the lines L_1 and L_2 passing through the given pairs of points are parallel, perpendicular, or neither.

$$L_1 : (0, -1), \ (5, 9)$$
$$L_2 : (0, 3), \ (4, 1)$$

Solution:

The slope of L_1 is $m_1 = \dfrac{9 - (-1)}{5 - 0} = \dfrac{10}{5} = 2.$

The slope of L_2 is $m_2 = \dfrac{1 - 3}{4 - 0} = -\dfrac{2}{4} = -\dfrac{1}{2}.$

Since $m_1 \cdot m_2 = 2\left(-\frac{1}{2}\right) = -1$, the lines are perpendicular.

19. Use the point $(2, 1)$ on the line and the slope $m = 0$ of the line to find three additional points that the line passes through. (The solution is not unique.)

Solution:

Since $m = 0$, the line is horizontal, and since the line passes through $(2, 1)$, all other points on the line will be of the form $(x, 1)$. Three additional points are: $(0, 1)$, $(1, 1)$, $(3, 1)$.

25. Find the slope and y-intercept, if possible, of the line specified by $5x - y + 3 = 0$.

Solution:

$$5x - y + 3 = 0$$
$$-y = -5x - 3$$
$$y = 5x + 3$$

Slope: $m = 5$
y-intercept: $(0, 3)$

27. Find the slope and y-intercept, if possible, of the line specified by $5x - 2 = 0$.

Solution:

$$5x - 2 = 0$$
$$5x = 2$$
$$x = \tfrac{2}{5} \qquad \text{Vertical line}$$

Slope: Undefined
y-intercept: None

33. Find an equation for the line passing through the points $\left(2, \tfrac{1}{2}\right)$, $\left(\tfrac{1}{2}, \tfrac{5}{4}\right)$ and sketch a graph of the line.

Solution:

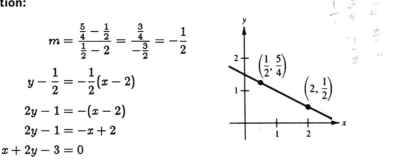

$$m = \frac{\tfrac{5}{4} - \tfrac{1}{2}}{\tfrac{1}{2} - 2} = \frac{\tfrac{3}{4}}{-\tfrac{3}{2}} = -\frac{1}{2}$$

$$y - \frac{1}{2} = -\frac{1}{2}(x - 2)$$

$$2y - 1 = -(x - 2)$$

$$2y - 1 = -x + 2$$

$$x + 2y - 3 = 0$$

37. Find an equation for the line passing through the points $(1, \ 0.6)$, and $(-2, \ -0.6)$ and sketch a graph of the line.

Solution:

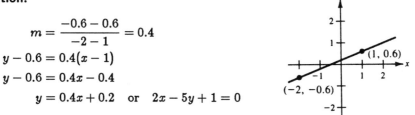

$$m = \frac{-0.6 - 0.6}{-2 - 1} = 0.4$$

$$y - 0.6 = 0.4(x - 1)$$

$$y - 0.6 = 0.4x - 0.4$$

$$y = 0.4x + 0.2 \quad \text{or} \quad 2x - 5y + 1 = 0$$

41. Find an equation of the line that passes through the point $(-3, \ 6)$ and has a slope of $m = -2$. Sketch a graph of the line.

Solution:

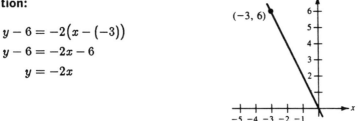

$$y - 6 = -2\big(x - (-3)\big)$$

$$y - 6 = -2x - 6$$

$$y = -2x$$

45. Find an equation of the line that passes through the point $(6, -1)$ and has an undefined slope. Sketch a graph of the line.

Solution:
Since the slope is undefined, the line is vertical and since the line passes through $(6, -1)$, its equation is $x = 6$.

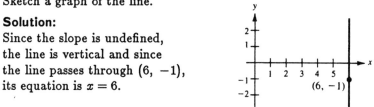

49. Prove that the line with intercepts $(a, 0)$ and $(0, b)$ has the following equation.

$$\frac{x}{a} + \frac{y}{b} = 1, \quad a \neq 0, \ b \neq 0$$

Solution:
Using the points $(a, 0)$ and $(0, b)$ we have

$$m = \frac{b - 0}{0 - a} = -\frac{b}{a}$$

$$y - 0 = -\frac{b}{a}(x - a)$$

$$y = -\frac{b}{a}x + b$$

$$ay = -bx + ab$$

$$bx + ay = ab$$

$$\frac{bx + ay}{ab} = \frac{ab}{ab}$$

$$\frac{x}{a} + \frac{y}{b} = 1.$$

53. Use the result of Exercise 49 to write an equation of the line with x-intercept $\left(-\frac{1}{6}, 0\right)$ and y-intercept $\left(0, -\frac{2}{3}\right)$.

Solution:

x-intercept: $\left(-\frac{1}{6}, 0\right)$

y-intercept: $\left(0, -\frac{2}{3}\right)$

$$\frac{x}{-1/6} + \frac{y}{-2/3} = 1$$

$$-6x - \frac{3}{2}y = 1$$

$$-12x - 3y = 2$$

$$12x + 3y = -2$$

59. Write the equation of the line through the point $(-6, 4)$ (a) parallel to the line $3x + 4y = 7$ and (b) perpendicular to the line $3x + 4y = 7$.

Solution:

$$3x + 4y = 7$$
$$4y = -3x + 7$$
$$y = -\frac{3}{4}x + \frac{7}{4}$$

The slope of the given line is $m_1 = -3/4$.

(a) The slope of the parallel line is $m_2 = m_1 = -3/4$.

$$y - 4 = -\frac{3}{4}(x - (-6))$$
$$y - 4 = -\frac{3}{4}x - \frac{9}{2}$$
$$y = -\frac{3}{4}x - \frac{1}{2}$$
$$4y = -3x - 2$$
$$3x + 4y = -2$$

(b) The slope of the perpendicular line is $m_2 = -1/m_1 = 4/3$.

$$y - 4 = \frac{4}{3}(x - (-6))$$
$$y - 4 = \frac{4}{3}x + 8$$
$$y = \frac{4}{3}x + 12$$
$$3y = 4x + 36$$
$$4x - 3y = -36$$

63. Find the equation of the line giving the relationship between the temperature in degrees Celsius, C, and degrees Fahrenheit, F. Use the fact that water freezes at $0°$ Celsius ($32°$ Fahrenheit) and boils at $100°$ Celsius ($212°$ Fahrenheit).

Solution:

Using the points $(0, 32)$ and $(100, 212)$, we have

$$m = \frac{212 - 32}{100 - 0} = \frac{180}{100} = \frac{9}{5}$$

$$F - 32 = \frac{9}{5}(C - 0)$$

$$F = \frac{9}{5}C + 32$$

67. A store is offering a 15% discount on all items in its inventory. Write a linear equation giving the sale price S, for an item with a list price, L.

Solution:

$$S = L - 0.15L$$
$$S = 0.85L$$

73. Prove that if two distinct lines have equal slope, they must be parallel.

Solution:
In slope-intercept form,

$$L_1 : y = mx + b_1 \quad \text{and} \quad L_2 : y = mx + b_2, \quad b_1 \neq b_2$$

If $m = 0$, then L_1 is a horizontal line through $(0, b_1)$ and L_2 is a horizontal line through $(0, b_2)$. Thus, the lines are parallel. If $m \neq 0$, assume that L_1 and L_2 are not parallel. Then L_1 and L_2 must intersect at some point (a, b). To find this point, set $L_1 = L_2$.

$$mx + b_1 = mx + b_2$$
$$b_1 - b_2 = 0$$

Since $b_1 \neq b_2$, this is not possible. The lines do not intersect; therefore, they must be parallel. If m is undefined, then L_1 and L_2 are vertical lines and since they are distinct, they are parallel.

SECTION 3.4

Functions

■ Given an equation, you should be able to determine if it represents a function.

■ Given a function, you should be able to do the following.

(a) Find the domain.
(b) Find the range.
(c) Determine if it is one-to-one.
(d) Evaluate it at specific values.

Solutions to Selected Exercises

5. Evaluate the function at the specified value of the independent variable and simplify the results.

$$f(x) = 2x - 3$$

(a) $f(1)$ (b) $f(-3)$
(c) $f(x-1)$ (d) $f(1/4)$

Solution:

(a) $f(1) = 2(1) - 3 = -1$ (b) $f(-3) = 2(-3) - 3 = -9$
(c) $f(x-1) = 2(x-1) - 3 = 2x - 5$ (d) $f(1/4) = 2(1/4) - 3 = -5/2$

9. Evaluate the function at the specified value of the independent variable and simplify the results.

$$f(y) = 3 - \sqrt{y}$$

(a) $f(4)$ (b) $f(100)$
(c) $f(4x^2)$ (d) $f(0.25)$

Solution:

(a) $f(4) = 3 - \sqrt{4} = 1$ (b) $f(100) = 3 - \sqrt{100} = -7$
(c) $f(4x^2) = 3 - \sqrt{4x^2} = 3 - 2|x|$ (d) $f(0.25) = 3 - \sqrt{0.25} = 2.5$

13. Evaluate the function at the specified value of the independent variable and simplify the results.

$$f(x) = \frac{|x|}{x}$$

(a) $f(2)$

(b) $f(-2)$

(c) $f(x^2)$

(d) $f(x-1)$

Solution:

(a) $f(2) = \frac{|2|}{2} = 1$

(b) $f(-2) = \frac{|-2|}{-2} = -1$

(c) $f(x^2) = \frac{|x^2|}{x^2} = 1$

(d) $f(x-1) = \frac{|x-1|}{x-1}$

15. Evaluate the function at the specified value of the independent variable and simplify the results.

$$f(x) = \begin{cases} 2x+1, & x < 0 \\ 2x+2, & x \geq 0 \end{cases}$$

(a) $f(-1)$

(b) $f(0)$

(c) $f(1)$

(d) $f(2)$

Solution:

(a) $f(-1) = 2(-1) + 1 = -1$

(b) $f(0) = 2(0) + 2 = 2$

(c) $f(1) = 2(1) + 2 = 4$

(d) $f(2) = 2(2) + 2 = 6$

17. For $f(x) = x^2 - x + 1$, find

$$\frac{f(2+h) - f(2)}{h}$$

and simplify your answer.

Solution:

$$f(x) = x^2 - x + 1$$
$$f(2+h) = (2+h)^2 - (2+h) + 1$$
$$= 4 + 4h + h^2 - 2 - h + 1$$
$$= h^2 + 3h + 3$$
$$f(2) = (2)^2 - 2 + 1 = 3$$
$$f(2+h) - f(2) = h^2 + 3h$$
$$\frac{f(2+h) - f(2)}{h} = h + 3$$

25. Find all real values x such that $f(x) = 0$ for $f(x) = x^2 - 9$.

Solution:

$$x^2 - 9 = 0$$
$$x^2 = 9$$
$$x = \pm 3$$

27. Find all real values x such that $f(x) = 0$ for

$$f(x) = \frac{3}{x-1} + \frac{4}{x-2}.$$

Solution:

$$\frac{3}{x-1} + \frac{4}{x-2} = 0$$
$$3(x-2) + 4(x-1) = 0$$
$$7x - 10 = 0$$
$$x = \frac{10}{7}$$

31. Find the domain of $h(t) = 4/t$.

Solution:

The domain includes all real numbers except 0, i.e. $t \neq 0$.

35. Find the domain of $f(x) = \sqrt[4]{1 - x^2}$.

Solution:

Choose x-values for which $1 - x^2 \geq 0$. Using methods of Section 2.8, we find that the domain is $-1 \leq x \leq 1$.

39. Determine if y is a function of x for $x^2 + y^2 = 4$.

Solution:

y is not a function of x since some values of x give two values for y. For example, if $x = 0$, then $y = \pm 2$.

43. Determine if y is a function of x for $2x + 3y = 4$.

Solution:

$$2x + 3y = 4$$
$$y = \tfrac{1}{3}(4 - 2x)$$

y is a function of x.

47. Determine if y is a function of x for $x^2y - x^2 + 4y = 0$.

Solution:

$$x^2y - x^2 + 4y = 0$$
$$y(x^2 + 4) = x^2$$
$$y = \frac{x^2}{x^2 + 4}$$

y is a function of x.

51. Assume that the domain of $f(x) = x^2$ is the set $A = \{-2, -1, 0, 1, 2\}$. Determine the set of ordered pairs representing the function f.

Solution:

$$\{(-2, \ f(-2)), \ (-1, \ f(-1)), \ (0, \ f(0)), \ (1, \ f(1)), \ 2, \ f(2))\}$$
$$\{(-2, \ 4), \ (-1, \ 1), \ (0, \ 0), \ (1, \ 1), \ (2, \ 4)\}$$

57. Find the value(s) of x for which $f(x) = g(x)$ where $f(x) = \sqrt{3x} + 1$ and $g(x) = x + 1$.

Solution:

$$f(x) = g(x)$$
$$\sqrt{3x} + 1 = x + 1$$
$$\sqrt{3x} = x$$
$$3x = x^2$$
$$0 = x^2 - 3x$$
$$0 = x(x - 3)$$
$$x = 0 \quad \text{or} \quad x = 3$$

61. Express the area A of a circle as a function of its circumference C.

Solution:

$$A = \pi r^2, \quad C = 2\pi r$$
$$r = \frac{C}{2\pi}$$
$$A = \pi \left(\frac{C}{2\pi}\right)^2$$
$$A = \frac{C^2}{4\pi}$$

65. A right triangle is formed in the first quadrant by the x- and y-axes and a line through the point $(1, 2)$, as shown in the figure. Write the area of the triangle as a function of x, and determine the domain of the function.

Solution:

$$A = \frac{1}{2}bh = \frac{1}{2}xy$$

Since $(0, y)$, $(1, 2)$ and $(x, 0)$ all lie on the same line, the slopes between any pair are equal.

$$\frac{2-y}{1-0} = \frac{0-2}{x-1}$$

$$2 - y = -\frac{2}{x-1}$$

$$y = \frac{2}{x-1} + 2$$

$$y = \frac{2x}{x-1}$$

Therefore,

$$A = \frac{1}{2}x\left(\frac{2x}{x-1}\right)$$

$$A = \frac{x^2}{x-1}$$

The domain of A includes x-values such that $x^2/(x-1) > 0$. This results in a domain of $x > 1$.

69. A company produces a product for which the variable cost is $\$12.30$ per unit and the fixed costs are $\$98,000$. The product sells for $\$17.98$. Let x be the number of units produced.

   (a) Write the total cost C as a function of the number of units produced.
   (b) Write the revenue R as a function of the number of units produced.
   (c) Write the profit P as a function of the number of units produced.

     (Note: $P = R - C$.)

Solution:

   (a) Cost = variable costs + fixed costs
      $C = 12.30x + 98,000$

   (b) Revenue = price per unit $\times$ number of units
      $R = 17.98x$

   (c) Profit = Revenue $-$ Cost
      $P = 17.98x - (12.30x + 98,000)$
      $P = 5.68x - 98,000$

SECTION 3.5

Graphs of Functions

- ■ You should be able to determine the domain and range of a function from its graph.

- ■ You should be able to use the vertical line test for functions.

- ■ You should know that the graph of $f(x) = c$ is a horizontal line through $(0, c)$.

- ■ You should be able to determine when a function is constant, increasing, or decreasing.

- ■ You should know that f is
  - (a) Odd if $f(-x) = -f(x)$.
  - (b) Even if $f(-x) = f(x)$.

- ■ You should know the basic types of transformations.

Solutions to Selected Exercises

5. Determine the domain and range of the function $f(x) = \sqrt{25 - x^2}$.

Solution:
From the graph we see that the x-values do not extend beyond $x = -5$ (on the left) and $x = 5$ (on the right). The domain is $[-5, 5]$. Similarly, the y-values do not extend beyond $y = 0$ and $y = 5$. The range is $[0, 5]$.

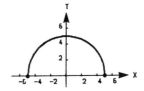

7. Use the vertical line test to determine if y is a function of x where $y = x^2$.

Solution:
Since no vertical line would ever cross the graph more than one time, y *is* a function of x.

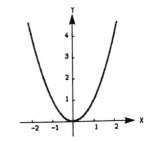

11. Use the vertical line test to determine if y is a function of x where $x^2 = xy - 1$.

Solution:
Since no vertical line would ever
cross the graph more than one time,
y *is* a function of x.

$$y = \frac{x^2 + 1}{x}$$

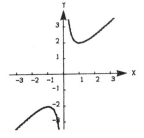

15. (a) Determine the intervals over which the function is increasing, decreasing, or constant, and
(b) determine if the function is even, odd, or neither for $f(x) = x^3 - 3x^2$.

Solution:
(a) By its graph we see that f
     is increasing on $(-\infty, 0)$ and
     $(2, \infty)$ and is decreasing on $(0, 2)$.

(b) $f(-x) = (-x)^3 - 3(-x)^2$
$$= -x^3 - 3x^2$$
$f(-x) \neq f(x)$ and $f(x) \neq -f(x)$, so
the function is neither odd nor even.

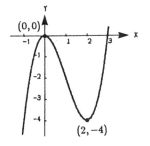

19. (a) Determine the intervals over which the function is increasing, decreasing, or constant, and
(b) determine if the function is even, odd, or neither for $f(x) = x\sqrt{x + 3}$.

Solution:
(a) By its graph we see that f
     is increasing on $(-2, \infty)$ and
     decreasing on $(-3, -2)$.

(b) $f(-x) = -x\sqrt{-x + 3}$
     $f(-x) \neq f(x)$ and $f(-x) \neq -f(x)$, so
     the function is neither odd nor even.

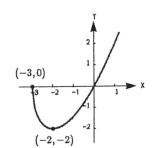

23. Determine whether $g(x) = x^3 - 5x$ is even, odd, or neither.

Solution:

$$g(x) = x^3 - 5x$$
$$g(-x) = (-x)^3 - 5(-x)$$
$$= -x^3 + 5x$$
$$= -(x^3 - 5x)$$
$$= -g(x)$$

Therefore, g is odd.

27. Sketch the graph of $f(x) = 3$ and determine whether the function is odd, even, or neither.

Solution:
$f(x) = 3$
Domain: $(-\infty, \infty)$
Range: $\{3\}$
y-intercept: $(0, 3)$
y-axis symmetry
$f(-x) = 3 = f(x)$
Therefore, f is even.

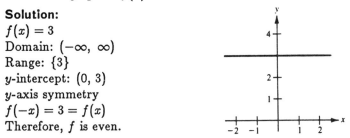

31. Sketch the graph of $g(s) = s^3/4$ and determine whether the function is odd, even, or neither.

Solution:
$g(s) = s^3/4$
Intercept: $(0, 0)$
Origin symmetry
Domain: $(-\infty, \infty)$
Range: $(-\infty, \infty)$
$g(-s) = -g(s)$
Therefore, g is odd.

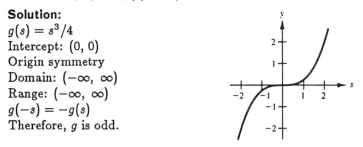

35. Sketch the graph of $g(t) = \sqrt[3]{t-1}$ and determine whether the function is odd, even, or neither.

Solution:
$g(t) = \sqrt[3]{t-1}$
x-intercept: $(1, 0)$
y-intercept: $(0, -1)$
Domain: $(-\infty, \infty)$
Range: $(-\infty, \infty)$

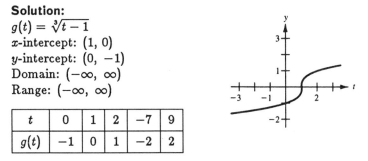

t	0	1	2	-7	9
$g(t)$	-1	0	1	-2	2

$g(-t) = \sqrt[3]{-t-1} \neq g(t)$ and $\neq -g(t)$. Therefore, g is neither odd nor even.

37. Sketch the graph of

$$f(x) = \begin{cases} x + 3, & \text{if } x \leq 0 \\ 3, & \text{if } 0 < x \leq 2 \\ 2x - 1, & \text{if } x > 2 \end{cases}$$

and determine whether the function is odd, even, or neither.

Solution:

For $x \leq 0$, $f(x) = x + 3$. For $0 < x \leq 2$, $f(x) = 3$. For $x > 2$, $f(x) = 2x - 1$. Thus, the graph of f is as shown.

$$f(-x) = \begin{cases} -x + 3, & \text{if } x \leq 0 \\ 3, & \text{if } 0 < x \leq 2 \\ -2x - 1, & \text{if } x > 2 \end{cases}$$

So, f is neither odd nor even.

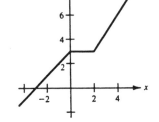

41. Sketch the graph of $f(x) = x^2 - 9$ and determine the interval(s), if any, on the real axis for which $f(x) \geq 0$.

Solution:

$f(x) = x^2 - 9$

x-intercepts: $(-3, 0)$, $(0, 3)$

y-intercept: $(0, -9)$

y-axis symmetry

Domain: $(-\infty, \infty)$

Range: $[-9, \infty)$

$f(x) \geq 0$ on the intervals $(-\infty, -3]$ and $[3, \infty)$.

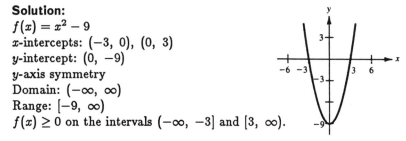

45. Sketch the graph of $f(x) = x^2 + 1$ and determine the interval(s), if any, on the real axis for which $f(x) \geq 0$.

Solution:

$f(x) = x^2 + 1$

x-intercept: None

y-intercept: $(0, 1)$

y-axis symmetry

Domain: $(-\infty, \infty)$

Range: $[1, \infty)$

$f(x) \geq 0$ for all real numbers.

51. Use the graph of $f(x) = \sqrt{x}$ to sketch the graph of each of the following.

(a) $y = \sqrt{x} + 2$

(b) $y = -\sqrt{x}$

(c) $y = \sqrt{x - 2}$

(d) $y = \sqrt{x + 3}$

(e) $y = 2 - \sqrt{x - 4}$

(f) $y = \sqrt{2x}$

Solution:

(a) $y = \sqrt{x} + 2$
   Vertical shift 2 units upward

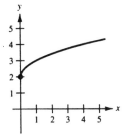

(b) $y = -\sqrt{x}$
   Reflection about the x-axis

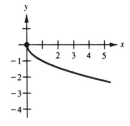

(c) $y = \sqrt{x - 2}$
   Horizontal shift 2 units to the right

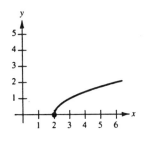

(d) $y = \sqrt{x + 3}$
   Horizontal shift 3 units to the left

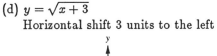
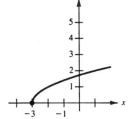

(e) $y = 2 - \sqrt{x - 4}$
   Reflection about the x-axis,
   horizontal shift of 4 units to
   the right and a vertical shift
   2 units upward

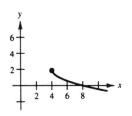

(f) $y = \sqrt{2x}$

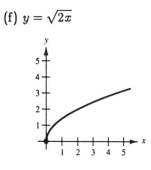

57. Write the height h of the given rectangle as a function of x.

Solution:

$$h = \text{top} - \text{bottom}$$
$$= \left(4x - x^2\right) - x^2$$
$$= 4x - 2x^2$$

61. Prove that a function of the following form is odd.

$$f(x) = a_{2n+1}x^{2n+1} + a_{2n-1}x^{2n-1} + \ldots + a_3 x^3 + a_1 x$$

Solution:

$$f(x) = a_{2n+1}x^{2n+1} + a_{2n-1}x^{2n-1} + \ldots + a_3 x^3 + a_1 x$$
$$f(-x) = a_{2n+1}(-x)^{2n+1} + a_{2n-1}(-x)^{2n-1} + \ldots + a_3(-x)^3 + a_1(-x)$$
$$= -a_{2n+1}x^{2n+1} - a_{2n-1}x^{2n-1} - \ldots - a_3 x^3 - a_1 x$$
$$= -f(x)$$

Therefore, $f(x)$ is odd.

SECTION 3.6

Combinations of Functions

■ Given two functions, f and g, you should be able to form the following functions (if defined):

1. Sum: $(f+g)(x) = f(x) + g(x)$
2. Difference: $(f-g)(x) = f(x) - g(x)$
3. Product: $(fg)(x) = f(x)g(x)$
4. Quotient: $(f/g)(x) = f(x)/g(x), \ g(x) \neq 0$
5. Composition of f with g: $(f \circ g)(x) = f\big(g(x)\big)$
6. Composition of g with f: $(g \circ f)(x) = g\big(f(x)\big)$

Solutions to Selected Exercises

5. Find (a) $(f+g)(x)$, (b) $(f-g)(x)$, (c) $(fg)(x)$, and (d) $(f/g)(x)$. What is the domain of f/g?

Solution:

$$f(x) = x^2 + 5, \quad g(x) = \sqrt{1-x}$$

(a) $(f+g)(x) = f(x) + g(x) = x^2 + 5 + \sqrt{1-x}$
(b) $(f-g)(x) = f(x) - g(x) = x^2 + 5 - \sqrt{1-x}$
(c) $(fg)(x) = f(x)g(x) = (x^2+5)\sqrt{1-x}$
(d) $\left(\dfrac{f}{g}\right)(x) = \dfrac{f(x)}{g(x)} = \dfrac{x^2+5}{\sqrt{1-x}}, \ x < 1$

The domain of f/g is $(-\infty, \ 1)$.

11. Evaluate $(f-g)(2t)$ for $f(x) = x^2 + 1$ and $g(x) = x - 4$.

Solution:

$$
\begin{aligned}
(f-g)(2t) &= f(2t) - g(2t) \\
&= [(2t)^2 + 1] - [(2t) - 4] \\
&= 4t^2 + 1 - 2t + 4 \\
&= 4t^2 - 2t + 5
\end{aligned}
$$

15. Evaluate $(f/g)(5)$ for $f(x) = x^2 + 1$ and $g(x) = x - 4$.

Solution:

$$\left(\frac{f}{g}\right)(5) = \frac{f(5)}{g(5)} = \frac{(5)^2 + 1}{5-4} = 26$$

19. Evaluate $(f/g)(-1) - g(3)$ for $f(x) = x^2 + 1$ and $g(x) = x - 4$.

Solution:

$$\left(\frac{f}{g}\right)(-1) - g(3) = \frac{f(-1)}{g(-1)} - g(3) = \frac{(-1)^2 + 1}{-1 - 4} - (3 - 4) = -\frac{2}{5} + 1 = \frac{3}{5}$$

23. Find (a) $f \circ g$, (b) $g \circ f$, and (c) $f \circ f$ for $f(x) = 3x + 5$ and $g(x) = 5 - x$.

Solution:

(a) $f \circ g = f(g(x))$

$\quad\quad = f(5 - x)$

$\quad\quad = 3(5 - x) + 5$

$\quad\quad = 20 - 3x$

(b) $g \circ f = g(f(x))$

$\quad\quad = g(3x + 5)$

$\quad\quad = 5 - (3x + 5)$

$\quad\quad = -3x$

(c) $f \circ f = f(f(x))$

$\quad\quad = f(3x + 5)$

$\quad\quad = 3(3x + 5) + 5$

$\quad\quad = 9x + 20$

25. Find (a) $f \circ g$ and (b) $g \circ f$ for $f(x) = \sqrt{x + 4}$ and $g(x) = x^2$.

Solution:

(a) $f \circ g = f(g(x))$

$\quad\quad = f(x^2)$

$\quad\quad = \sqrt{x^2 + 4}$

(b) $g \circ f = g(f(x))$

$\quad\quad = g(\sqrt{x + 4})$

$\quad\quad = (\sqrt{x + 4})^2$

$\quad\quad = x + 4$

29. Find (a) $f \circ g$ and (b) $g \circ f$ for $f(x) = \sqrt{x}$ and $g(x) = \sqrt{x}$.

Solution:

(a) $f \circ g = f(g(x)) = f(\sqrt{x}) = \sqrt{\sqrt{x}} = \sqrt[4]{x}$

(b) Same as (a)

31. Find (a) $f \circ g$ and (b) $g \circ f$ for $f(x) = |x|$ and $g(x) = x + 6$.

Solution:

(a) $f \circ g = f(g(x)) = f(x + 6) = |x + 6|$

(b) $g \circ f = g(f(x)) = g(|x|) = |x| + 6$

37. Find functions f and g such that $(f \circ g)(x) = h(x)$ for $h(x) = (2x + 1)^2$.

Solution:

Let $f(x) = x^2$ and $g(x) = 2x + 1$, then $(f \circ g)(x) = h(x)$.

Note: This is not a unique solution. For example, if $f(x) = (x + 1)^2$ and $g(x) = 2x$, then $(f \circ g)(x) = h(x)$ as well.

41. Find functions f and g such that $(f \circ g)(x) = h(x)$ for $h(x) = 1/(x + 2)$.

Solution:

Let $f(x) = 1/x$ and $g(x) = x + 2$, then $(f \circ g)(x) = h(x)$. Again, this is not a unique solution. Other possibilities are:

$$f(x) = \frac{1}{x + 2} \quad \text{and} \quad g(x) = x$$

OR

$$f(x) = \frac{1}{x + 1} \quad \text{and} \quad g(x) = x + 1$$

OR

$$f(x) = \frac{1}{x^2 + 2} \quad \text{and} \quad g(x) = \sqrt{x}$$

47. Determine the domain of (a) f, (b) g, and (c) $f \circ g$ for $f(x) = 3/(x^2 - 1)$ and $g(x) = x + 1$.

Solution:

(a) The domain of $f(x) = 3/(x^2 - 1)$ includes all real numbers except $x = \pm 1$.

(b) The domain of $g(x) = x + 1$ includes all real numbers.

(c) $f \circ g = f(g(x)) = f(x + 1) = \dfrac{3}{(x + 1)^2 - 1} = \dfrac{3}{x^2 + 2x} = \dfrac{3}{x(x + 2)}$

The domain of $f \circ g$ includes all real numbers except $x = 0$ and $x = -2$.

53. Prove that the product of two odd functions is an even function.

Solution:

Let $f(x)$ and $g(x)$ be two odd functions and define $h(x) = f(x)g(x)$. Then

$$
\begin{aligned}
h(-x) &= f(-x)g(-x) \\
&= [-f(x)][-g(x)] \quad \text{Since } f(x) \text{ and } g(x) \text{ are odd} \\
&= f(x)g(x) \\
&= h(x)
\end{aligned}
$$

Thus, h is even.

SECTION 3.7

Inverse Functions

- Two functions f and g are inverses of each other if $f(g(x)) = x$ for every x in the domain of g and $g(f(x)) = x$ for every x in the domain of f.

- A function f has an inverse if and only if f is one-to-one.

- Be able to find the inverse of a function, if it exists.

Solutions to Selected Exercises

5. (a) Show that $f(x) = x^3$ and $g(x) = \sqrt[3]{x}$ are inverse functions by showing that $f(g(x)) = x$ and $g(f(x)) = x$, and (b) graph f and g on the same set of coordinate axes.

Solution:

$$f(x) = x^3, \quad g(x) = \sqrt[3]{x}$$

(a) $f(g(x)) = f(\sqrt[3]{x}) = (\sqrt[3]{x})^3 = x$ (b)
$g(f(x)) = g(x^3) = \sqrt[3]{x^3} = x$

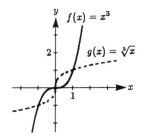

7. (a) Show that $f(x) = \sqrt{x-4}$ and $g(x) = x^2 + 4$, $x \geq 0$ are inverse functions by showing that $f(g(x)) = x$ and $g(f(x)) = x$, and (b) graph f and g on the same set of coordinate axes.

Solution:

$$f(x) = \sqrt{x-4}, \quad g(x) = x^2 + 4, \quad x \geq 0$$

(a) $f\big(g(x)\big) = f\big(x^2 + 4\big) = \sqrt{(x^2 + 4) - 4} = \sqrt{x^2} = |x| = x, \quad x \geq 0$

$g\big(f(x)\big) = g\big(\sqrt{x - 4}\big) = \big(\sqrt{x - 4}\big)^2 + 4 = (x - 4) + 4 = x$

(b)

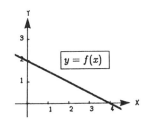

$g(x) = x^2 + 4$

$f(x) = \sqrt{x - 4}$

11. Determine whether the function shown is one-to-one.

Solution:

Since the function is decreasing on its entire domain, it is one-to-one.

$y = f(x)$

15. Determine whether the function $g(x) = (4 - x)/6$ is one-to-one.

Solution:

Let a and b be real numbers with $g(a) = g(b)$. Then we have

$$\frac{4 - a}{6} = \frac{4 - b}{6}$$

$$4 - a = 4 - b$$

$$-a = -b$$

$$a = b$$

Therefore, $g(x)$ is one-to-one.

19. Determine whether the function $f(x) = -\sqrt{16 - x^2}$ is one-to-one.

Solution:

Since $f(4) = 0$ and $f(-4) = 0$, the function is not one-to-one.

23. Find the inverse of the one-to-one function $f(x) = x^5$. Then graph both f and f^{-1} on the same coordinate plane.

Solution:

$$f(x) = x^5$$
$$y = x^5$$
$$x = \sqrt[5]{y}$$
$$f^{-1}(x) = \sqrt[5]{x}$$

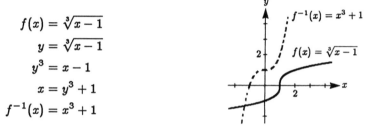

29. Find the inverse of the one-to-one function $f(x) = \sqrt[3]{x-1}$. Then graph both f and f^{-1} on the same coordinate plane.

Solution:

$$f(x) = \sqrt[3]{x-1}$$
$$y = \sqrt[3]{x-1}$$
$$y^3 = x - 1$$
$$x = y^3 + 1$$
$$f^{-1}(x) = x^3 + 1$$

33. Determine whether the function $g(x) = x/8$ is one-to-one. If it is, find its inverse.

Solution:

$$g(a) = g(b)$$
$$\frac{a}{8} = \frac{b}{8}$$
$$a = b \qquad \text{Therefore, } g \text{ is one-to-one.}$$
$$g(x) = \frac{x}{8}$$
$$y = \frac{x}{8}$$
$$x = 8y$$
$$g^{-1}(x) = 8x$$

35. Determine whether the function $p(x) = -4$ is one-to-one. If it is, find its inverse.

Solution:

$p(x) = -4$ for all real numbers x. Therefore, $p(x)$ is not one-to-one.

39. Determine whether the function $h(x) = 1/x$ is one-to-one. If it is, find its inverse.

Solution:

$$h(a) = h(b)$$
$$\frac{1}{a} = \frac{1}{b}$$
$$a = b \qquad \text{Therefore, } h \text{ is one-to-one.}$$
$$h(x) = \frac{1}{x}$$
$$y = \frac{1}{x}$$
$$xy = 1$$
$$x = \frac{1}{y}$$
$$h^{-1}(x) = \frac{1}{x}$$

43. Determine whether the function $g(x) = x^2 - x^4$ is one-to-one. If it is, find its inverse.

Solution:

Since $g(0) = 0$ and $g(1) = 0$, g is not one-to-one.

45. Determine whether the function $f(x) = 25 - x^2$, $x \leq 0$ is one-to-one. If it is, find its inverse.

Solution:

$$f(a) = f(b)$$
$$25 - a^2 = 25 - b^2$$
$$a^2 = b^2 \qquad \text{Since } a, \ b \leq 0, \text{ we have } a = b \text{ and } f \text{ is one-to-one.}$$
$$f(x) = 25 - x^2, \quad x \leq 0$$
$$y = 25 - x^2$$
$$x^2 = 25 - y$$
$$x = -\sqrt{25 - y} \quad \text{Since } x \leq 0$$
$$f^{-1}(x) = -\sqrt{25 - x}$$

49. Use the functions $f(x) = (1/8)x - 3$ and $g(x) = x^3$ to find $(f^{-1} \circ g^{-1})(1)$.

Solution:

$$f(x) = (1/8)x - 3 \quad \Longrightarrow \quad f^{-1}(x) = 8(x + 3)$$
$$g(x) = x^3 \quad \Longrightarrow \quad g^{-1}(x) = \sqrt[3]{x}$$

$$(f^{-1} \circ g^{-1})(1) = f^{-1}(g^{-1}(1))$$
$$= f^{-1}(\sqrt[3]{1}) = f^{-1}(1) = 8(1 + 3) = 32$$

53. Use the functions $f(x) = x + 4$ and $g(x) = 2x - 5$ to find $g^{-1} \circ f^{-1}$.

Solution:

$$f(x) = x + 4 \quad \implies \quad f^{-1}(x) = x - 4$$

$$g(x) = 2x - 5 \quad \implies \quad g^{-1}(x) = \frac{x + 5}{2}$$

$$\begin{aligned} g^{-1} \circ f^{-1} &= g^{-1}(f^{-1}(x)) \\ &= g^{-1}(x - 4) \\ &= \frac{(x - 4) + 5}{2} \\ &= \frac{x + 1}{2} \end{aligned}$$

57. Prove that if f is a one-to-one odd function, then f^{-1} is an odd function.

Solution:

Suppose f^{-1} is not an odd function. Then there exists a value $x = a$ such that

$$f^{-1}(-a) \neq -f^{-1}(a).$$

Since f is one-to-one, we have $f(f^{-1}(-a)) \neq f(-f^{-1}(a))$, but $f(f^{-1}(-a)) = -a$ since f and f^{-1} are inverses and

$$f(-f^{-1}(a)) = -f(f^{-1}(a)) = -a$$

since f is odd. Therefore,

$$f(f^{-1}(-a)) = f(-f^{-1}(a)),$$

which is a contradiction. Therefore, f^{-1} must be an odd function.

SECTION 3.8

Variation and Mathematical Models

You should know the following terms and formulas for variation.

- ■ Direct Variation

    (a) $y = kx$
    (b) $y = kx^n$ (as nth power)

- ■ Inverse Variation

    (a) $y = k/x$
    (b) $y = k/(x^n)$ (as nth power)

- ■ Joint Variation

    (a) $z = kxy$
    (b) $z = kx^n y^m$ (as nth power of x and mth power of y)

- ■ k is called the constant of proportionality.

Solutions to Selected Exercises

5. Find a mathematical model for the statement "z is proportional to the cube root of u".

    Solution:

    $$z = k\sqrt[3]{u}$$

9. Find a mathematical model for the statement "F varies directly as g and inversely as the square of r".

    Solution:

    $$F = \frac{kg}{r^2}$$

13. Find a mathematical model for **Newton's Law of Universal Gravitation**: The gravitational attraction F between two objects of masses m_1 and m_2 is proportional to the product of the masses and inversely proportional to the square of the distance r between the objects.

Solution:

$$F = \frac{km_1m_2}{r^2}$$

17. Find a mathematical model for the statement "A varies directly as the square of r". Determine the constant of proportionality given $A = 9\pi$ when $r = 3$.

Solution:

$$A = kr^2$$
$$9\pi = k(3)^2$$
$$\pi = k$$
$$A = \pi r^2$$

21. Find a mathematical model for the statement "h is inversely proportional to the third power of t". Determine the constant of proportionality given $h = 3/16$ when $t = 4$.

Solution:

$$h = \frac{k}{t^3}$$
$$\frac{3}{16} = \frac{k}{(4)^3}$$
$$\frac{3}{16} = \frac{k}{64}$$
$$k = 12$$
$$h = \frac{12}{t^3}$$

25. Find a mathematical model for the statement "F is jointly proportional to r and the third power of s". Determine the constant of proportionality given $F = 4158$ when $r = 11$ and $s = 3$.

Solution:

$$F = krs^3$$
$$4158 = k(11)(3)^3$$
$$k = 14$$
$$F = 14rs^3$$

29. Find a mathematical model for the statement "S varies directly as L and inversely as $L - S$". Determine the constant of proportionality given $S = 4$ when $L = 6$.

Solution:

$$S = \frac{kL}{L - S}$$

$$4 = \frac{k(6)}{6 - 4}$$

$$4 = 3k$$

$$k = \frac{4}{3}$$

$$S = \frac{4/3L}{L - S} = \frac{4L}{3(L - S)}$$

33. The coiled spring of a toy supports the weight of a child. The spring compresses a distance of 1.9 inches under the weight of a 25-pound child. The toy will not work properly if its spring is compressed more than 3 inches. What is the weight of the heaviest child who should be allowed to use the toy?

Solution:
From Example 1, we have

$$d = kF$$

$$1.9 = k(25) \quad \Longrightarrow \quad k = 0.076$$

$$d = 0.076F$$

When the distance compressed is 3 inches, we have

$$3 = 0.076F$$

$$F \approx 39.4737$$

No child over 39 pounds should use the toy.

35. A stream with a velocity of 1/4 mile per hour can move coarse sand particles of about 0.02 inch diameter. What must the velocity be to carry particles with a diameter of 0.12 inch? Use the fact that the diameter of a particle moved by a stream varies approximately as the square of the velocity of the stream.

Solution:

$$d = kv^2$$

$$0.02 = k(1/4)^2$$

$$k = 0.32$$

$$d = 0.32v^2$$

$$0.12 = 0.32v^2$$

$$v^2 = 0.12/0.32 = 3/8$$

$$v = \sqrt{3}/(2\sqrt{2}) = \sqrt{6}/4 \approx 0.612 \text{ mi/hr}$$

39. The illumination from a light source varies inversely as the square of the distance from the light source. When the distance from a light source is doubled, how does the illumination change?

Solution:

$$l = \frac{k}{d^2}$$

When the distance is doubled:

$$l = \frac{k}{(2d)^2}$$

$$l = \frac{1}{4}\left(\frac{k}{d^2}\right)$$

The amount of illumination is 1/4 as bright.

41. The resistance of a wire carrying electrical current is directly proportional to its length and inversely proportional to its cross-sectional area. #28 copper wire (which has a diameter of 0.0126 inch) has a resistance of 66.17 ohms per thousand feet. A 14-foot piece of copper wire produces a resistance of 0.05 ohms. Find the diameter of the wire.

Solution:

$$r = \frac{kl}{A}, \quad A = \pi r^2 = \frac{\pi d^2}{4}$$

$$r = \frac{4kl}{\pi d^2}$$

$$66.17 = \frac{4(1000)k}{\pi(0.0126/12)^2}$$

$$k = 5.7 \times 10^{-8}$$

$$r = \frac{4(5.7 \times 10^{-8})l}{\pi d^2}$$

$$r = 7.3 \times 10^{-8}\frac{l}{d^2} \qquad \text{From Exercise 40}$$

$$0.05 = (7.3 \times 10^{-8})\frac{14}{d^2}$$

$$d^2 = (7.3 \times 10^{-8})\frac{14}{0.05}$$

$$d^2 = 2.044 \times 10^{-5}$$

$$d = 0.00452 \text{ ft}$$

$$d = 0.05425 \text{ in}$$

REVIEW EXERCISES FOR CHAPTER 3

Solutions to Selected Exercises

3. For the points $(2, 1)$ and $(14, 6)$, find (a) the distance between the two points, (b) the coordinates of the midpoint of the line segment between the two points, (c) an equation of the line through the two points, and (d) an equation of the circle whose diameter is the line segment between the two points.

Solution:

(a) $d = \sqrt{(14 - 2)^2 + (6 - 1)^2}$

$\quad = \sqrt{144 + 25}$

$\quad = \sqrt{169}$

$\quad = 13$

(b) $m = \left(\dfrac{2 + 14}{2},\ \dfrac{1 + 6}{2} \right)$

$\quad = \left(8,\ \dfrac{7}{2} \right)$

(c) $\qquad y - 1 = \dfrac{6 - 1}{14 - 2}(x - 2)$

$\qquad\qquad = \dfrac{5}{12}(x - 2)$

$\qquad 12y - 12 = 5x - 10$

$\qquad 5x - 12y + 2 = 0$

(d) The length of the diameter is 13, so the length of the radius is $\frac{13}{2}$. The midpoint of the line segment is the center of the circle. Center: $(8, \frac{7}{2})$ Radius: $\frac{13}{2}$

$$(x - 8)^2 + \left(y - \frac{7}{2} \right)^2 = \left(\frac{13}{2} \right)^2$$

$$x^2 - 16x + 64 + y^2 - 7y + \frac{49}{4} = \frac{169}{4}$$

$$x^2 + y^2 - 16x - 7y + 34 = 0$$

7. Find t so that the points $(-2, 5)$, $(0, t)$ and $(1, 1)$ are collinear.

Solution:
The line through $(-2, 5)$ and $(1, 1)$ is

$$y - 5 = \frac{1 - 5}{1 + 2}(x + 2)$$

$$y - 5 = -\frac{4}{3}(x + 2)$$

$$3y - 15 = -4x - 8$$

$$4x + 3y = 7$$

For $(0,\ t)$ to be on this line also, it must satisfy the equation $4x + 3y = 7$.

$$4(0) + 3(t) = 7$$

Thus, $t = \frac{7}{3}$.

11. Show that the points $(1,\ 1)$, $(8,\ 2)$, $(9,\ 5)$, and $(2,\ 4)$ form the vertices of a parallelogram.

Solution:

$$d_1 = \sqrt{(2-1)^2 + (4-1)^2} = \sqrt{10}$$
$$d_2 = \sqrt{(9-2)^2 + (5-4)^2} = \sqrt{50} = 5\sqrt{2}$$
$$d_3 = \sqrt{(8-9)^2 + (2-5)^2} = \sqrt{10}$$
$$d_4 = \sqrt{(1-8)^2 + (1-2)^2} = \sqrt{50} = 5\sqrt{2}$$

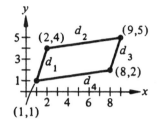

Since $d_1 = d_3$ and $d_2 = d_4$, these points are the vertices of a parallelogram.

15. Find the intercepts of the graph of $2y^2 = x^3$ and check for symmetry with respect to each of the coordinate axes and the origin.

Solution:

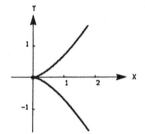

The only intercept is the origin, $(0,\ 0)$.
The graph is symmetric with respect to the x-axis since $2(-y)^2 = x^3$ results in the original equation. Replacing x with $-x$ or replacing both x and y with $-x$ and $-y$ does not yield equivalent equations. Thus, the graph is not symmetric with respect to either the y-axis or the origin.

19. Find the intercepts of the graph of $y = x\sqrt{4 - x^2}$ and check for symmetry with respect to each of the coordinate axes and the origin.

Solution:

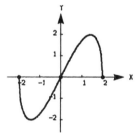

Let $y = 0$, then $0 = x\sqrt{4 - x^2}$ and $x = 0, \pm 2$.
x-intercepts: $(0,\ 0)$, $(2,\ 0)$, $(-2,\ 0)$
Let $x = 0$, then $y = 0\sqrt{4 - 0^2}$ and $y = 0$.
y-intercept: $(0,\ 0)$
The graph is symmetric with respect to the origin since

$$-y = -x\sqrt{4 - (-x)^2}$$
$$-y = -x\sqrt{4 - x^2}$$
$$y = x\sqrt{4 - x^2}$$

The graph is not symmetric with respect to either axis.

27. Determine the center and radius of the circle. Then, sketch the graph of $4x^2 + 4y^2 - 4x - 40y + 92 = 0$.

Solution:

$$4x^2 + 4y^2 - 4x - 40y + 92 = 0$$
$$x^2 + y^2 - x - 10y + 23 = 0$$
$$\left(x^2 - x + \tfrac{1}{4}\right) + \left(y^2 - 10y + 25\right) = -23 + \tfrac{1}{4} + 25$$
$$\left(x - \tfrac{1}{2}\right)^2 + (y - 5)^2 = \tfrac{9}{4}.$$

Center: $\left(\tfrac{1}{2},\ 5\right)$ Radius: $\tfrac{3}{2}$

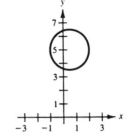

29. Sketch a graph of the equation $y - 2x - 3 = 0$.

Solution:
$y - 2x - 3 = 0$
x-intercept: $\left(-\tfrac{3}{2},\ 0\right)$
y-intercept: $(0,\ 3)$

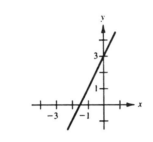

33. Sketch a graph of the equation $y = \sqrt{5 - x}$.

Solution:
$y = \sqrt{5 - x}$
x-intercept: $(5,\ 0)$
Domain: $(-\infty,\ 5]$
Range: $[0,\ \infty)$

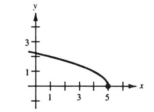

37. Sketch a graph of the equation $y = \sqrt{25 - x^2}$.

Solution:
$y = \sqrt{25 - x^2}$
x-intercepts: $(5,\ 0),\ (-5,\ 0)$
y-intercept: $(0,\ 5)$
y-axis symmetry
Domain: $[-5,\ 5]$
Range: $[0,\ 5]$

41. Sketch a graph of the equation $y = \frac{1}{4}(x+1)^3$.

Solution:
$y = \frac{1}{4}(x+1)^3$
x-intercept: $(-1,\ 0)$
y-intercept: $(0,\ \frac{1}{4})$
Domain: $(-\infty,\ \infty)$
Range: $(-\infty,\ \infty)$

45. Evaluate the function $h(x) = 6 - 5x^2$ at the specified values of the independent variable and simplify your answers.

(a) $h(2)$

(b) $h(x+3)$

(c) $\dfrac{h(4) - h(2)}{4 - 2}$

(d) $\dfrac{h(x + \Delta x) - h(x)}{\Delta x}$

Solution:

(a) $h(2) = 6 - 5(2)^2 = -14$

(b) $h(x+3) = 6 - 5(x+3)^2$
$\qquad\qquad = 6 - 5(x^2 + 6x + 9)$
$\qquad\qquad = -5x^2 - 30x - 39$

(c) $\qquad h(4) = 6 - 5(4)^2 = -74$
$\qquad h(2) = -14 \quad$ from part (a)

$\dfrac{h(4) - h(2)}{4 - 2} = \dfrac{-74 - (-14)}{4 - 2} = \dfrac{-60}{2} = -30$

(d) $\qquad h(x + \Delta x) = 6 - 5(x + \Delta x)^2$
$\qquad\qquad\qquad = 6 - 5(x^2 + 2x\Delta x + (\Delta x)^2)$
$\qquad\qquad\qquad = 6 - 5x^2 - 10x\Delta x - 5(\Delta x)^2$
$h(x + \Delta x) - h(x) = -10x\Delta x - 5(\Delta x)^2$
$\dfrac{h(x + \Delta x) - h(x)}{\Delta x} = \dfrac{-10x\Delta x - 5(\Delta x)^2}{\Delta x} = -10x - 5\Delta x$

49. Determine the domain of the function

$$g(s) = \frac{5}{3s - 9}.$$

Solution:
The domain of $g(s) = 5/(3s - 9)$ includes all real numbers except $s = 3$, since this value would yield a zero in the denominator.

55. For $f(x) = \sqrt{x+1}$ (a) find f^{-1}, (b) sketch the graphs of f and f^{-1} on the same coordinate plane, and (c) verify that $f^{-1}(f(x)) = x = f(f^{-1}(x))$.

Solution:

(a)
$$y = \sqrt{x+1}, \quad y \geq 0$$
$$y^2 = x+1$$
$$x = y^2 - 1$$
$$f^{-1}(x) = x^2 - 1, \quad x \geq 0$$

(c) $f^{-1}[f(x)] = f^{-1}(\sqrt{x+1})$
$$= (\sqrt{x+1})^2 - 1 = (x+1) - 1 = x$$
$$f[f^{-1}(x)] = f(x^2 - 1)$$
$$= \sqrt{(x^2 - 1) + 1}$$
$$= \sqrt{x^2} = x, \quad x \geq 0$$

(b)

59. Restrict the domain of the function $f(x) = 2(x-4)^2$ to an interval where the function is increasing and determine f^{-1} over that interval.

Solution:

$f(x) = 2(x-4)^2$ is increasing on the interval $[4, \infty)$. It is decreasing on the interval $(-\infty, 4)$.

$$f(x) = 2(x-4)^2, \quad x \geq 4$$
$$y = 2(x-4)^2, \quad x \geq 4$$
$$\sqrt{y} = \sqrt{2}(x-4)$$
$$\sqrt{y/2} = x - 4$$
$$x = \sqrt{y/2} + 4$$
$$f^{-1}(x) = \sqrt{x/2} + 4$$

63. Let $f(x) = 3 - 2x$, $g(x) = \sqrt{x}$, and $h(x) = 3x^2 + 2$. Find $(f - g)(4)$.

Solution:

$$(f - g)(4) = f(4) - g(4)$$
$$= [3 - 2(4)] - \sqrt{4}$$
$$= -7$$

67. Let $f(x) = 3 - 2x$, $g(x) = \sqrt{x}$, and $h(x) = 3x^2 + 2$. Find $(h \circ g)(7)$.

Solution:

$$(h \circ g)(7) = h(g(7))$$
$$= h(\sqrt{7})$$
$$= 3(\sqrt{7})^2 + 2$$
$$= 23$$

73. Find a mathematical model representing the statement "z varies directly as the square of x and inversely as y". Determine the constant of proportionality if $z = 16$ when $x = 5$ and $y = 2$.

Solution:

$$z = \frac{kx^2}{y}$$

$$16 = \frac{k(5)^2}{2}$$

$$32 = 25k$$

$$k = \frac{32}{25}, \quad \text{therefore, } z = \frac{32x^2}{25y}.$$

77. A wire 24 inches long is to be cut into four pieces to form a rectangle whose shortest side has a length of x. Express the area A of the rectangle as a function of x. Determine the domain of the function and sketch its graph over that domain.

Solution:
Let y be the longer side of the rectangle. Then we have $A = xy$. Since the perimeter is 24 inches, we have $2x + 2y = 24$ or $y = (24 - 2x)/2 = 12 - x$. The area equation now becomes: $A = xy = x(12 - x)$. To find the domain of A, we realize that area is a nonnegative quantity. Thus, $x(12 - x) \geq 0$. This gives us the interval $[0, 12]$. We also have the further restriction that x is the shortest side. This occurs on the interval $[0, 6]$.

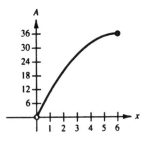

Practice Test for Chapter 3

1. Find the distance between $(4, -1)$ and $(0, 3)$.

2. Find the midpoint of the line segment joining $(4, -1)$ and $(0, 3)$.

3. Find x so that the distance from the origin to $(x, -2)$ is 6.

4. Given $y = \dfrac{x-2}{x+3}$, find the intercepts.

5. Given $xy^2 = 6$, list all symmetries.

6. Graph $y = x^3 - 4x$.

7. Find the center and radius of the circle $x^2 + y^2 - 6x + 2y + 6 = 0$.

8. Given $f(x) = x^2 - 2x + 1$, find $f(x - 3)$.

9. Given $f(x) = 4x - 11$, find $\dfrac{f(x) - f(3)}{x - 3}$.

10. Find the domain and range of $f(x) = \sqrt{36 - x^2}$.

11. Which equations determine y as a function of x?
    (a) $6x - 5y + 4 = 0$
    (b) $x^2 + y^2 = 9$
    (c) $y^3 = x^2 + 6$

12. Sketch the graph of $f(x) = x^2 - 5$.

13. Sketch the graph of $f(x) = |x + 3|$.

14. Sketch the graph of $f(x) = \begin{cases} 2x + 1 & \text{if } x \geq 0, \\ x^2 - x & \text{if } x < 0. \end{cases}$

15. Find the equation of the line through $(2, 4)$ and $(3, -1)$.

16. Find the equation of the line with slope $m = 4/3$ and y-intercept $b = -3$.

17. Find the equation of the line through $(4, 1)$ and perpendicular to the line $2x + 3y = 0$.

18. If it costs a company \$32 to produce 5 units of a product and \$44 to produce 9 units, how much does it cost to produce 20 units? (Assume that the cost function is linear.)

19. Given $f(x) = x^2 - 2x + 16$ and $g(x) = 2x + 3$, find $f(g(x))$.

20. Given $f(x) = x^3 + 7$, find $f^{-1}(x)$.

21. Which of the following functions are one-to-one?
(a) $f(x) = |x - 6|$
(b) $f(x) = ax + b$, $a \neq 0$
(c) $f(x) = x^3 - 19$

22. Given $f(x) = \sqrt{\dfrac{3 - x}{x}}$, $0 < x \leq 3$, find $f^{-1}(x)$.

23. Find the equation: y varies directly as x and $y = 30$ when $x = 5$.

24. Find the equation: y varies inversely as x and $y = 0.5$ when $x = 14$.

25. z varies directly as the square of x and inversely as y, and $z = 3$ when $x = 3$ and $y = -6$. Find the equation relating z to x and y.

CHAPTER 4

Polynomial Functions: Graphs and Zeros

SECTION 4.1

Quadratic Functions

You should know the following facts about parabolas.

- $f(x) = ax^2 + bx + c$, $a \neq 0$, is a quadratic function, and its graph is a parabola.

- If $a > 0$, the parabola opens upward. If $a < 0$, the parabola opens downward.

- The vertex is $(-b/2a, \; f(-b/2a))$.

- To find the x-intercepts (if any), solve

$$ax^2 + bx + c = 0$$

- The standard form of the equation of a parabola is

$$f(x) = a(x - h)^2 + k$$

where $a \neq 0$.
(a) The vertex is $(h, \; k)$.
(b) The axis is the vertical line $x = h$.

Solutions to Selected Exercises

7. Find an equation for the given parabola.

Solution:
The vertex is $(2, 0)$ and the parabola passes through the point $(0, 4)$.

$$f(x) = a(x - 2)^2 + 0$$
$$f(x) = a(x - 2)^2$$
$$4 = a(0 - 2)^2 \quad \Longrightarrow \quad a = 1$$
$$f(x) = (x - 2)^2$$

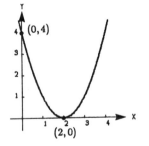

11. Find an equation for the given parabola.

Solution:
The vertex is $(-3,\ 3)$ and the parabola passes through $(-2,\ 1)$.

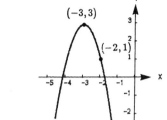

$$f(x) = a(x - (-3))^2 + 3$$
$$f(x) = a(x + 3)^2 + 3$$
$$1 = a(-2 + 3)^2 + 3 \implies a = -2$$
$$f(x) = -2(x + 3)^2 + 3$$

17. Sketch the graph of $f(x) = (x + 5)^2 - 6$. Identify the vertex and x- and y-intercepts.

Solution:
Vertex: $(-5,\ -6)$
x-intercepts:

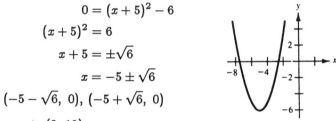

$$0 = (x + 5)^2 - 6$$
$$(x + 5)^2 = 6$$
$$x + 5 = \pm\sqrt{6}$$
$$x = -5 \pm \sqrt{6}$$
$$(-5 - \sqrt{6},\ 0),\ (-5 + \sqrt{6},\ 0)$$

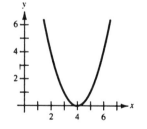

y-intercept: $(0,\ 19)$

19. Sketch the graph of $h(x) = x^2 - 8x + 16$. Identify the vertex and x- and y-intercepts.

Solution:

$$h(x) = x^2 - 8x + 16$$
$$h(x) = (x - 4)^2$$

Vertex: $(4,\ 0)$
x-intercept: $(4,\ 0)$
y-intercept: $(0,\ 16)$

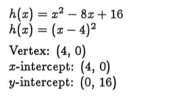

23. Sketch the graph of $f(x) = x^2 - x + \frac{5}{4}$. Identify the vertex and x- and y-intercepts.

Solution:

$$f(x) = x^2 - x + \frac{5}{4}$$
$$f(x) = x^2 - x + \frac{1}{4} - \frac{1}{4} + \frac{5}{4}$$
$$f(x) = (x - \tfrac{1}{2})^2 + 1$$

Vertex: $(\frac{1}{2}, 1)$

x-intercept: None since

$$0 = (x - \tfrac{1}{2})^2 + 1$$
$$-1 = (x - \tfrac{1}{2})^2$$
$$\pm\sqrt{-1} = x - \tfrac{1}{2} \quad \text{has no real solutions.}$$

y-intercept: $(0, \frac{5}{4})$

27. Sketch the graph of $h(x) = 4x^2 - 4x + 21$. Identify the vertex and x- and y-intercepts.

Solution:

$$h(x) = 4x^2 - 4x + 21$$
$$h(x) = 4(x^2 - x + \tfrac{1}{4} - \tfrac{1}{4}) + 21$$
$$h(x) = 4(x^2 - x + \tfrac{1}{4}) - 1 + 21$$
$$h(x) = 4(x - \tfrac{1}{2})^2 + 20$$

Vertex: $(\frac{1}{2}, 20)$

x-intercept: None since

$$0 = 4(x - \tfrac{1}{2})^2 + 20$$
$$-20 = 4(x - \tfrac{1}{2})^2$$
$$-5 = (x - \tfrac{1}{2})^2$$
$$\pm\sqrt{-5} = x - \tfrac{1}{2} \quad \text{has no real solutions.}$$

y-intercept: $(0, 21)$

33. Find the quadratic function with a vertex of $(5, 12)$ and whose graph passes through the point $(7, 15)$.

Solution:

$(5, 12)$ is the vertex.

$$f(x) = a(x - 5)^2 + 12$$

Since the graph passes through the point $(7, 15)$, we have

$$15 = a(7 - 5)^2 + 12$$
$$3 = 4a \quad \Longrightarrow \quad a = \tfrac{3}{4}$$
$$f(x) = \tfrac{3}{4}(x - 5)^2 + 12.$$

37. Find two quadratic functions whose graphs have the x-intercepts $(0, 0)$ and $(10, 0)$. (One function has a graph that opens upward and the other has a graph that opens downward.)

Solution:

$$f(x) = (x - 0)(x - 10) \qquad \text{opens upward}$$
$$= x^2 - 10x$$
$$g(x) = -(x - 0)(x - 10) \qquad \text{opens downward}$$
$$= -x^2 + 10x$$

43. Find two positive real numbers satisfying the requirements "the sum of the first and twice the second is 24 and the product is a maximum".

Solution:

Let $x =$ the first number and $y =$ the second number. Then

$$x + 2y = 24 \quad \Longrightarrow \quad y = \frac{24 - x}{2}.$$

The product is $P(x) = xy = x\left(\dfrac{24 - x}{2}\right)$.

$$P(x) = \frac{1}{2}(-x^2 + 24x)$$
$$= -\frac{1}{2}(x^2 - 24x + 144 - 144)$$
$$= -\frac{1}{2}[(x - 12)^2 - 144]$$
$$= -\frac{1}{2}(x - 12)^2 + 72$$

The maximum value of the product occurs at the vertex of $P(x)$ and is 72. This happens when $x = 12$ and $y = (24 - 12)/2 = 6$. Thus, the numbers are 12 and 6.

47. A rancher has 200 feet of fencing to enclose two adjacent rectangular corrals, as shown in the figure. What dimensions will produce a maximum enclosed area?

Solution:

Since the rancher has 200 feet of fencing, we have the equation $4x + 3y = 200$ or $y = (200 - 4x)/3$. The area is

$$A = 2xy = 2x\left(\frac{200 - 4x}{3}\right).$$

$$A = \frac{2}{3}(-4x^2 + 200x)$$

$$= -\frac{8}{3}(x^2 - 50x)$$

$$= -\frac{8}{3}(x^2 - 50x + 625 - 625)$$

$$= -\frac{8}{3}[(x - 25)^2 - 625]$$

$$= -\frac{8}{3}(x - 25)^2 + \frac{5000}{3}$$

The maximum area occurs at the vertex and is $5000/3$ square feet. This happens when $x = 25$ feet and $y = (200 - 4(25))/3 = 100/3$ feet. The dimensions are $2x = 50$ feet by $33\frac{1}{3}$ feet.

51. Let x be the amount (in hundreds of dollars) a company spends on advertising, and let P be the profit, where $P = 230 + 20x - 0.5x^2$. What expenditure for advertising gives a maximum profit?

Solution:

$$P = 230 + 20x - 0.5x^2$$

$$= -0.5(x^2 - 40x - 460)$$

$$= -0.5(x^2 - 40x + 400 - 400 - 460)$$

$$= -0.5[(x - 20)^2 - 860]$$

$$= -0.5(x - 20)^2 + 430$$

The profit is maximized when $x = 20$, or when \$2000 is spent on advertising.

55. Assume that the function $f(x) = ax^2 + bx + c$ $(a \neq 0)$ has two real zeros. Show that the x-coordinate of the vertex of the graph is the average of the zeros of f. [*Hint:* Use the Quadratic Formula.]

Solution:

If $f(x) = ax^2 + bx + c$ has two real zeros, then by the Quadratic Formula they are

$$x = \frac{-b \pm \sqrt{b^2 - 4ac}}{2a}.$$

The average of the zeros of f is

$$\frac{\dfrac{-b - \sqrt{b^2 - 4ac}}{2a} + \dfrac{-b + \sqrt{b^2 - 4ac}}{2a}}{2} = \frac{\dfrac{-2b}{2a}}{2} = -\frac{b}{2a}.$$

This is the x-coordinate of the vertex of the graph.

SECTION 4.2

Polynomial Functions of Higher Degree

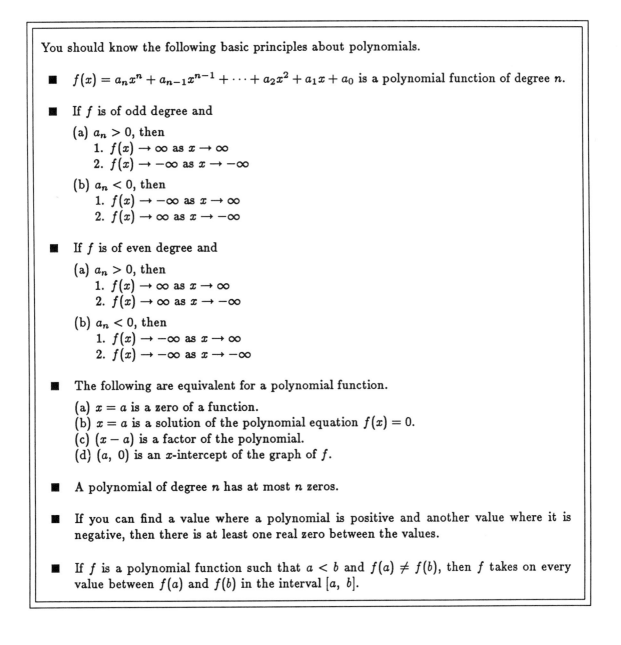

You should know the following basic principles about polynomials.

- $f(x) = a_n x^n + a_{n-1}x^{n-1} + \cdots + a_2 x^2 + a_1 x + a_0$ is a polynomial function of degree n.

- If f is of odd degree and

   (a) $a_n > 0$, then
   1. $f(x) \to \infty$ as $x \to \infty$
   2. $f(x) \to -\infty$ as $x \to -\infty$

   (b) $a_n < 0$, then
   1. $f(x) \to -\infty$ as $x \to \infty$
   2. $f(x) \to \infty$ as $x \to -\infty$

- If f is of even degree and

   (a) $a_n > 0$, then
   1. $f(x) \to \infty$ as $x \to \infty$
   2. $f(x) \to \infty$ as $x \to -\infty$

   (b) $a_n < 0$, then
   1. $f(x) \to -\infty$ as $x \to \infty$
   2. $f(x) \to -\infty$ as $x \to -\infty$

- The following are equivalent for a polynomial function.

   (a) $x = a$ is a zero of a function.
   (b) $x = a$ is a solution of the polynomial equation $f(x) = 0$.
   (c) $(x - a)$ is a factor of the polynomial.
   (d) $(a,\ 0)$ is an x-intercept of the graph of f.

- A polynomial of degree n has at most n zeros.

- If you can find a value where a polynomial is positive and another value where it is negative, then there is at least one real zero between the values.

- If f is a polynomial function such that $a < b$ and $f(a) \neq f(b)$, then f takes on every value between $f(a)$ and $f(b)$ in the interval $[a,\ b]$.

Solutions to Selected Exercises

7. Match the polynomial function $f(x) = 3x^4 + 4x^3$ with the correct graph.

Solution:

$$f(x) = 3x^4 + 4x^3 = x^3(3x + 4)$$

Zeros: 0, $-\frac{4}{3}$
$f(x) \to \infty$ as $x \to \infty$
$f(x) \to \infty$ as $x \to -\infty$
Matches (d)

11. Determine the right-hand and left-hand behavior of the graph of $g(x) = 5 - \frac{7}{2}x - 3x^2$.

Solution:

$$g(x) = 5 - \frac{7}{2}x - 3x^2$$

Even degree with leading coefficient of -3
Left: $g(x) \to -\infty$ as $x \to -\infty$, so the graph moves down to the left.
Right: $g(x) \to -\infty$ as $x \to +\infty$, so the graph moves down to the right.

15. Determine the right-hand and left-hand behavior of the graph of $f(x) = 6 - 2x + 4x^2 - 5x^3$.

Solution:

$$f(x) = 6 - 2x + 4x^2 - 5x^3$$

Odd degree with a negative leading coefficient of -5
Left: $f(x) \to \infty$ as $x \to -\infty$, so the graph moves up to the left.
Right: $f(x) \to -\infty$ as $x \to \infty$, so the graph moves down to the right.

21. Find all the real zeros of $h(t) = t^2 - 6t + 9$.

Solution:

$$h(t) = t^2 - 6t + 9$$
$$0 = t^2 - 6t + 9$$
$$0 = (t - 3)^2$$
$$t = 3$$

25. Find all the real zeros of $f(x) = 3x^2 - 12x + 3$.

Solution:

$$f(x) = 3x^2 - 12x + 3$$
$$0 = 3(x^2 - 4x + 1)$$
$$x = \frac{4 \pm \sqrt{12}}{2} \qquad \text{by the Quadratic Formula}$$
$$x = 2 \pm \sqrt{3}$$

29. Find all the real zeros of $g(t) = \frac{1}{2}t^4 - \frac{1}{2}$.

Solution:

$$g(t) = \frac{1}{2}t^4 - \frac{1}{2}$$
$$0 = \frac{1}{2}(t^4 - 1)$$
$$0 = \frac{1}{2}(t^2 + 1)(t^2 - 1)$$
$$0 = \frac{1}{2}(t^2 + 1)(t + 1)(t - 1)$$
$$t = \pm 1$$

33. Find all the real zeros of $f(x) = 5x^4 + 15x^2 + 10$.

Solution:

$$f(x) = 5x^4 + 15x^2 + 10$$
$$0 = 5(x^4 + 3x^2 + 2)$$
$$0 = 5(x^2 + 1)(x^2 + 2)$$

No real zeros

35. Find a polynomial function that has the zeros 0 and 10.

Solution:

$$f(x) = (x - 0)(x - 10)$$
$$f(x) = x^2 - 10x$$

41. Find a polynomial function that has the zeros 4, -3, 3 and 0.

Solution:

$$f(x) = (x - 4)(x + 3)(x - 3)(x - 0)$$
$$= (x - 4)(x^2 - 9)x$$
$$= x^4 - 4x^3 - 9x^2 + 36x$$

47. Sketch the graph of $f(x) = -\frac{3}{2}$.

Solution:

$f(x) = -\frac{3}{2}$ is a horizontal line.

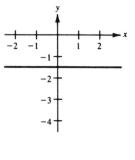

51. Sketch the graph of $f(x) = x^3 - 3x^2$.

Solution:

$$f(x) = x^3 - 3x^2 = x^2(x-3)$$

Zeros: 0 and 3
Right: Moves up
Left: Moves down

x	0	1	2	3	-1
$f(x)$	0	-2	-4	0	-4

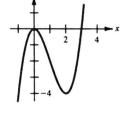

55. Sketch the graph of $g(t) = -\frac{1}{4}(t-2)^2(t+2)^2$.

Solution:

$$g(t) = -\frac{1}{4}(t-2)^2(t+2)^2$$

Zeros: 2 and -2
Right: Moves down
Left: Moves down

t	-3	-2	-1	0	1	2	3
$g(t)$	$-\frac{25}{4}$	0	$-\frac{9}{4}$	-4	$-\frac{9}{4}$	0	$-\frac{25}{4}$

61. Follow the procedure given in Example 8 to estimate the zero of $f(x) = x^4 - 10x^2 - 11$ in the interval [3, 4]. (Give your approximation to the nearest tenth.)

Solution:

$$f(x) = x^4 - 10x^2 - 11, \quad [3, \, 4]$$

x	3	3.1	3.2	3.3	3.4	3.5	3.6	3.7	3.8	3.9	4
$f(x)$	-20	-14.748	-8.542	-1.308	7.034	16.563	27.362	39.516	53.114	68.244	85

The zero lies between 3.3 and 3.4. It is closer to 3.3.

SECTION 4.3

Polynomial Division and Synthetic Division

You should know the following basic techniques and principles of polynomial division.

■ The Division Algorithm (Long Division of Polynomials)

■ Synthetic Division

■ $f(k)$ is equal to the remainder of $f(x)$ divided by $(x - k)$.

■ $f(k) = 0$ if and only if $(x - k)$ is a factor of $f(x)$.

■ Horner's Method

Solutions to Selected Exercises

5. Divide $x^4 + 5x^3 + 6x^2 - x - 2$ by $x + 2$ using long division.

Solution:

$$
\begin{array}{r}
x^3 + 3x^2 \phantom{{}+6x^2} - 1 \phantom{{}-x-2} \\
x+2{\overline{\smash{\big)}\,x^4 + 5x^3 + 6x^2 - x - 2}} \\
\underline{-(x^4 + 2x^3)\phantom{{}+6x^2-x-2)}} \\
3x^3 + 6x^2 \phantom{{}-x-2} \\
\underline{-(3x^3 + 6x^2)\phantom{{}-x-2)}} \\
-x - 2 \\
\underline{-(-x - 2)} \\
0
\end{array}
$$

Thus, $\dfrac{x^4 + 5x^3 + 6x^2 - x - 2}{x + 2} = x^3 + 3x^2 - 1.$

7. Divide $7x + 3$ by $x + 2$ using long division.

Solution:

$$
\begin{array}{r}
7 \\
x+2{\overline{\smash{\big)}\,7x + 3}} \\
\underline{-(7x + 14)} \\
-11
\end{array}
$$

Thus, $\dfrac{7x + 3}{x + 2} = 7 - \dfrac{11}{x + 2}.$

11. Divide $x^4 + 3x^2 + 1$ by $x^2 - 2x + 3$ using long division.

Solution:

$$
\begin{array}{r}
x^2 + 2x + 4 \\
x^2 - 2x + 3 \overline{\smash{)}\ x^4 + 0x^3 + 3x^2 + 0x + 1} \\
\underline{-\left(x^4 - 2x^3 + 3x^2\right)} \\
2x^3 + 0x^2 + 0x \\
\underline{-\left(2x^3 - 4x^2 + 6x\right)} \\
4x^2 - 6x + 1 \\
\underline{-\left(4x^2 - 8x + 12\right)} \\
2x - 11
\end{array}
$$

Thus, $\dfrac{x^4 + 3x^2 + 1}{x^2 - 2x + 3} = x^2 + 2x + 4 + \dfrac{2x - 11}{x^2 - 2x + 3}$.

15. Divide $3x^3 - 17x^2 + 15x - 25$ by $x - 5$ using synthetic division.

Solution:

$$
\begin{array}{r|rrrr}
5 & 3 & -17 & 15 & -25 \\
  &   & 15 & -10 & 25 \\
\hline
  & 3 & -2 & 5 & 0
\end{array}
$$

Thus, $\dfrac{3x^3 - 17x^2 + 15x - 25}{x - 5} = 3x^2 - 2x + 5$.

19. Divide $-x^3 + 75x - 250$ by $x + 10$ using synthetic division.

Solution:

$$
\begin{array}{r|rrrr}
-10 & -1 & 0 & 75 & -250 \\
    &   & 10 & -100 & 250 \\
\hline
    & -1 & 10 & -25 & 0
\end{array}
$$

Thus, $\dfrac{-x^3 + 75x - 250}{x + 10} = -x^2 + 10x - 25$.

23. Divide $10x^4 - 50x^3 - 800$ by $x - 6$ using synthetic division.

Solution:

$$
\begin{array}{r|rrrrr}
6 & 10 & -50 & 0 & 0 & -800 \\
  &   & 60 & 60 & 360 & 2160 \\
\hline
  & 10 & 10 & 60 & 360 & 1360
\end{array}
$$

Thus, $\dfrac{10x^4 - 50x^3 - 800}{x - 6} = 10x^3 + 10x^2 + 60x + 360 + \dfrac{1360}{x - 6}$.

27. Divide $-3x^4$ by $x - 2$ using synthetic division.

Solution:

$$
\begin{array}{r|rrrrr}
2 & -3 & 0 & 0 & 0 & 0 \\
  &   & -6 & -12 & -24 & -48 \\
\hline
  & -3 & -6 & -12 & -24 & -48
\end{array}
$$

Thus, $\dfrac{-3x^4}{x-2} = -3x^3 - 6x^2 - 12x - 24 - \dfrac{48}{x-2}$.

31. Divide $4x^3 + 16x^2 - 23x - 15$ by $x + \frac{1}{2}$ using synthetic division.

Solution:

$$
\begin{array}{r|rrrr}
-\dfrac{1}{2} & 4 & 16 & -23 & -15 \\
  &   & -2 & -7 & 15 \\
\hline
  & 4 & 14 & -30 & 0
\end{array}
$$

Thus, $\dfrac{4x^3 + 16x^2 - 23x - 15}{x + \frac{1}{2}} = 4x^2 + 14x - 30$.

35. Use synthetic division to show that $x = \frac{1}{2}$ is a solution of $2x^3 - 15x^2 + 27x - 10 = 0$, and use the result to factor the polynomial completely.

Solution:

$$
\begin{array}{r|rrrr}
\dfrac{1}{2} & 2 & -15 & 27 & -10 \\
  &   & 1 & -7 & 10 \\
\hline
  & 2 & -14 & 20 & 0
\end{array}
$$

$$
\begin{aligned}
2x^3 - 15x^2 + 27x - 10 &= \left(x - \frac{1}{2}\right)\left(2x^2 - 14x + 20\right) \\
&= \left(x - \frac{1}{2}\right)2(x^2 - 7x + 10) \\
&= (2x - 1)(x - 2)(x - 5)
\end{aligned}
$$

37. Use synthetic division to show that $x = 1 + \sqrt{3}$ is a solution of $x^3 - 3x^2 + 2 = 0$, and use the result to factor the polynomial completely.

Solution:

$$
\begin{array}{r|rrrr}
1+\sqrt{3} & 1 & -3 & 0 & 2 \\
& & 1+\sqrt{3} & 1-\sqrt{3} & -2 \\
\hline
& 1 & -2+\sqrt{3} & 1-\sqrt{3} & 0
\end{array}
$$

$$
\begin{aligned}
x^3 - 3x^2 + 2 &= \left[x - (1+\sqrt{3})\right]\left[x^2 + (-2+\sqrt{3})x + 1 - \sqrt{3}\right] \\
&= \left[x - (1+\sqrt{3})\right]\left[x - (1-\sqrt{3})\right](x-1)
\end{aligned}
$$

41. Express the function $f(x) = x^3 - x^2 - 14x + 11$ in the form $f(x) = (x-k)q(x) + r$ for $k = 4$, and demonstrate that $f(k) = r$.

Solution:

$$
\begin{array}{r|rrrr}
4 & 1 & -1 & -14 & 11 \\
& & 4 & 12 & -8 \\
\hline
& 1 & 3 & -2 & 3
\end{array}
$$

$$
\begin{aligned}
f(x) &= (x-4)(x^2 + 3x - 2) + 3 \\
r &= 3 \\
f(4) &= 4^3 - 4^2 - 14(4) + 11 \\
&= 64 - 16 - 56 + 11 \\
&= 3
\end{aligned}
$$

45. Use synthetic division to find the required function values of $f(x) = 4x^3 - 13x + 10$.

(a) $f(1)$ (b) $f(-2)$ (c) $f(1/2)$ (d) $f(8)$

Solution:

(a)
$$
\begin{array}{r|rrrr}
1 & 4 & 0 & -13 & 10 \\
& & 4 & 4 & -9 \\
\hline
& 4 & 4 & -9 & 1
\end{array}
$$
Thus, $f(1) = 1$.

(b)
$$
\begin{array}{r|rrrr}
-2 & 4 & 0 & -13 & 10 \\
& & -8 & 16 & -6 \\
\hline
& 4 & -8 & 3 & 4
\end{array}
$$
Thus, $f(-2) = 4$.

(c)
$$
\begin{array}{r|rrrr}
\frac{1}{2} & 4 & 0 & -13 & 10 \\
& & 2 & 1 & -6 \\
\hline
& 4 & 2 & -12 & 4
\end{array}
$$
Thus, $f(1/2) = 4$.

(d)
$$
\begin{array}{r|rrrr}
8 & 4 & 0 & -13 & 10 \\
& & 32 & 256 & 1944 \\
\hline
& 4 & 32 & 243 & 1954
\end{array}
$$
Thus, $f(8) = 1954$.

49. Use synthetic division to find the required function values of $f(x) = x^3 - 2x^2 - 11x + 52$.

    (a) $f(5)$ (b) $f(-4)$ (c) $f(1.2)$ (d) $f(2)$

Solution:

(a) 5 | 1   −2   −11   52
             5   15   20
           1   3   4   72

Thus, $f(5) = 72$.

(b) −4 | 1   −2   −11   52
            −4   24   −52
          1   −6   13   0

Thus, $f(-4) = 0$.

(c) 1.2 | 1   −2   −11   52
             1.2   −0.96   −14.352
          1   −0.8   −11.96   37.648

Thus, $f(1.2) = 37.648$.

(d) 2 | 1   −2   −11   52
           2   0   −22
         1   0   −11   30

Thus, $f(2) = 30$.

53. Use Horner's Method to find the required function values of $f(x) = -5x^4 + 8.5x^3 + 10x - 3$.

    (a) $f(1.08)$ (b) $f(-5.4)$

Solution:

$$
\begin{aligned}
f(x) &= -5x^4 + 8.5x^3 + 10x - 3 \\
&= (-5x^3 + 8.5x^2 + 10)x - 3 \\
&= ([-5x^2 + 8.5x]x + 10)x - 3 \\
&= ([-5x + 8.5]x^2 + 10)x - 3
\end{aligned}
$$

    (a) $f(1.08) \approx 11.705$

    (b) $f(-5.4) \approx -5646.972$

SECTION 4.4

Real Zeros of Polynomial Functions

- You should know Descartes's Rule of Signs.

  (a) The number of positive real zeros of f is either equal to the number of variations of sign of f or is less than that number by an even integer.

  (b) The number of negative real zeros of f is either equal to the number of variations in sign of $f(-x)$ or is less than that number by an even integer.

  (c) When there is only one variation in sign, there is exactly one positive (or negative) real zero.

- You should know the Rational Zero Test.

- You should know shortcuts for the Rational Zero Test.

  (a) Use a programmable calculator.

  (b) Sketch a graph.

  (c) After finding a root, use synthetic division to reduce the degree of the polynomial.

- You should be able to observe the last row obtained from synthetic division in order to determine upper or lower bounds.

  (a) If the test value is positive and all of the entries in the last row are positive, then the test value is an upper bound.

  (b) If the test value is negative and the entries in the last row alternate from positive to negative, then the test value is a lower bound.

Solutions to Selected Exercises

5. Use Descartes's Rule of Signs to determine the possible number of positive and negative zeros of $g(x) = 2x^3 - 3x^2 - 3$.

   Solution:

   $$g(x) = 2x^3 - 3x^2 - 3$$
   $$g(-x) = -2x^3 - 3x^2 - 3$$

   Since $g(x)$ has one variation in sign, g has exactly one positive real zero. Since $g(-x)$ has no variations in sign, there are no negative real zeros.

9. Use Descartes's Rule of Signs to determine the possible number of positive and negative real zeros of $h(x) = 4x^2 - 8x + 3$.

   Solution:

   $$h(x) = 4x^2 - 8x + 3$$
   $$h(-x) = 4x^2 + 8x + 3$$

   Since $h(x)$ has two variations in sign, h has either two or zero positive real zeros. Since $h(-x)$ has no variations in sign, there are no negative real zeros.

13. Use the Rational Zero Test to list all the possible rational zeros of $f(x) = -4x^3 + 15x^2 - 8x - 3$ and verify that the zeros of f shown on the graph are contained in the list.

    Solution:

    Since the leading coefficient is -4 and the constant term is -3, the possible rational zeros of f are

    $$\frac{\text{factors of } -3}{\text{factors of } -4} = \frac{\pm 1, \pm 3}{\pm 1, \pm 2, \pm 4} = \pm 1, \pm 3, \pm \frac{1}{2}, \pm \frac{3}{2}, \pm \frac{1}{4}, \pm \frac{3}{4}$$

    The zeros shown on the graph are $-\frac{1}{4}$, 1 and 3 and are contained in the list.

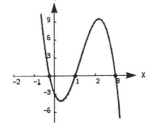

17. Use synthetic division to determine if the given x-value is an upper bound or lower bound of the zeros of $f(x) = x^4 - 4x^3 + 15$.

    (a) $x = 4$ (b) $x = -1$ (c) $x = 3$

    Solution:

    (a)
    $$\begin{array}{r|rrrrr} 4 & 1 & -4 & 0 & 0 & 15 \\ & & 4 & 0 & 0 & 0 \\ \hline & 1 & 0 & 0 & 0 & 15 \end{array}$$

    Since the test value is positive and all the entries in the last row are positive, $x = 4$ is an upper bound.

    (b)
    $$\begin{array}{r|rrrrr} -1 & 1 & -4 & 0 & 0 & 15 \\ & & -1 & 5 & -5 & 5 \\ \hline & 1 & -5 & 5 & -5 & 20 \end{array}$$

    Since the test value is negative and the entries in the last row alternate in sign, $x = -1$ is a lower bound.

(c) 3 | 1 −4   0   0   15
      | 3 −3 −9 −27
      ——————————————————————
        1 −1 −3 −9 −12

$x = 3$ is neither an upper nor a lower bound.

21. Find the real zeros of $f(x) = x^3 - 6x^2 + 11x - 6$.

Solution:

Possible rational zeros: $\pm 1, \pm 2, \pm 3, \pm 6$

1 | 1 −6   11 −6
  | 1   −5   6
  ——————————————————
    1 −5   6   0

$$x^3 - 6x^2 + 11x - 6 = (x - 1)(x^2 - 5x + 6) = (x - 1)(x - 2)(x - 3)$$

The zeros are 1, 2, and 3.

25. Find the real zeros of $h(t) = t^3 + 12t^2 + 21t + 10$.

Solution:

Possible rational zeros: $\pm 1, \pm 2, \pm 5, \pm 10$

−1 | 1   12   21   10
   | −1 −11 −10
   ————————————————————
     1   11   10   0

$$t^3 + 12t^2 + 21t + 10 = (t + 1)(t^2 + 11t + 10) = (t + 1)(t + 1)(t + 10)$$

Thus, the zeros are −1 and −10.

27. Find the real zeros of $f(x) = x^3 - 4x^2 + 5x - 2$.

Solution:

Possible rational zeros: $\pm 1, \pm 2$

1 | 1 −4   5 −2
  | 1   −3   2
  ——————————————————
    1 −3   2   0

$$x^3 - 4x^2 + 5x - 2 = (x - 1)(x^2 - 3x + 2) = (x - 1)(x - 1)(x - 2)$$

Thus, the zeros are 1 and 2.

31. Find the real zeros of $f(x) = 4x^3 - 3x - 1$.

Solution:

Possible rational zeros: $\pm 1,\ \pm\frac{1}{2},\ \pm\frac{1}{4}$

$$
\begin{array}{r|rrrr}
1 & 4 & 0 & -3 & -1 \\
  &   & 4 & 4 & 1 \\
\hline
  & 4 & 4 & 1 & 0
\end{array}
$$

$4x^3 - 3x - 1 = (x - 1)(4x^2 + 4x + 1) = (x - 1)(2x + 1)^2$

Thus, the zeros are 1 and $-\frac{1}{2}$.

33. Find the real zeros of $f(y) = 4y^3 + 3y^2 + 8y + 6$.

Solution:

Possible rational zeros: $\pm 1,\ \pm 2,\ \pm 3,\ \pm 6,\ \pm\frac{1}{2},\ \pm\frac{3}{2},\ \pm\frac{1}{4},\ \pm\frac{3}{4}$

$$
\begin{array}{r|rrrr}
-\frac{3}{4} & 4 & 3 & 8 & 6 \\
  &   & -3 & 0 & -6 \\
\hline
  & 4 & 0 & 8 & 0
\end{array}
$$

$4y^3 + 3y^2 + 8y + 6 = (y + \frac{3}{4})(4y^2 + 8) = (y + \frac{3}{4})4(y^2 + 2) = (4y + 3)(y^2 + 2)$

Thus, the only zero is $-\frac{3}{4}$.

35. Find the real zeros of $f(x) = x^4 - 3x^2 + 2$.

Solution:

$$
\begin{aligned}
f(x) &= x^4 - 3x^2 + 2 \\
&= (x^2 - 1)(x^2 - 2) \\
&= (x + 1)(x - 1)(x + \sqrt{2})(x - \sqrt{2})
\end{aligned}
$$

Thus, the zeros are ± 1 and $\pm\sqrt{2}$.

39. Find all the real solutions of $x^4 - 13x^2 - 12x = 0$.

Solution:

$$
f(x) = x^4 - 13x^2 - 12x = x(x^3 - 13x - 12)
$$

0 is a zero.

Possible rational zeros: $\pm 1,\ \pm 2,\ \pm 3,\ \pm 4,\ \pm 6,\ \pm 12$

$$
\begin{array}{r|rrrr}
-1 & 1 & 0 & -13 & -12 \\
   &   & -1 & 1 & 12 \\
\hline
   & 1 & -1 & -12 & 0
\end{array}
$$

$x^4 - 13x^2 - 12x = x(x^3 - 13x - 12) = x(x + 1)(x^2 - x - 12) = x(x + 1)(x + 3)(x - 4)$

Thus, the zeros are $0,\ -1,\ -3,$ and 4.

43. Find all the real solutions of $x^5 - 7x^4 + 10x^3 + 14x^2 - 24x = 0$.

Solution:

$$f(x) = x^5 - 7x^4 + 10x^3 + 14x^2 - 24x = x(x^4 - 7x^3 + 10x^2 + 14x - 24)$$

0 is a zero.

Possible rational zeros: ± 1, ± 2, ± 3, ± 4, ± 6, ± 8, ± 12, ± 24

$$
\begin{array}{r|rrrrr}
4 & 1 & -7 & 10 & 14 & -24 \\
  &   & 4 & -12 & -8 & 24 \\
\hline
3 & 1 & -3 & -2 & 6 & 0 \\
  &   & 3 & 0 & 0 & \\
\hline
  & 1 & 0 & -2 & 0 &
\end{array}
$$

$$
\begin{aligned}
x^5 - 7x^4 + 10x^3 + 14x^2 - 24x &= x(x^4 - 7x^3 + 10x^2 + 14x - 24) \\
&= x(x - 4)(x - 3)(x^2 - 2) \\
&= x(x - 4)(x - 3)(x + \sqrt{2})(x - \sqrt{2})
\end{aligned}
$$

Thus, the zeros are 0, 4, 3, and $\pm\sqrt{2}$.

47. For $f(x) = 4x^3 + 7x^2 - 11x - 18$

   (a) list all the possible rational zeros of f,

   (b) sketch the graph of f so that some of the possible zeros in part (a) can be disregarded, and

   (c) then determine all the real zeros of f.

Solution:

(a) Possible rational roots: ± 1, ± 2, ± 3, ± 6, ± 9, ± 18, $\pm\frac{1}{2}$, $\pm\frac{3}{2}$, $\pm\frac{9}{2}$, $\pm\frac{1}{4}$, $\pm\frac{3}{4}$, $\pm\frac{9}{4}$

(b)

x	0	1	-1	$\frac{1}{2}$	-2	-3	$-\frac{3}{2}$
$f(x)$	-18	-18	-4	-21.25	0	-30	0.75

By testing values using synthetic division, we find that 2 is an upper bound and -3 is a lower bound. This eliminates 3, ± 6, ± 9, ± 18, $\pm\frac{9}{2}$, and $\frac{9}{4}$ as possible zeros.

(c) -2 is a zero.

$4x^3 + 7x^2 - 11x - 18 = (x + 2)(4x^2 - x - 9) = 0$

$4x^2 - x - 9$ does not factor, so by the Quadratic Formula

$$x = \frac{1 \pm \sqrt{145}}{8} \text{ are also zeros.}$$

51. Find all the rational zeros of $f(x) = x^3 - \frac{1}{4}x^2 - x + \frac{1}{4}$.

Solution:

$$f(x) = x^3 - \frac{1}{4}x^2 - x + \frac{1}{4} = \frac{1}{4}(4x^3 - x^2 - 4x + 1)$$

Possible rational zeros: ± 1, $\pm\frac{1}{4}$, $\pm\frac{1}{2}$

By testing these values, we see that $x = \pm 1$ and $x = \frac{1}{4}$ work.

SECTION 4.5

Complex Zeros and the Fundamental Theorem of Algebra

- ■ You should know that if f is a polynomial of degree $n > 0$, then f has exactly n zeros (roots) in the complex number system.

- ■ You should know that if $a + bi$ is a complex zero of a polynomial f, with real coefficients, then $a - bi$ is also a complex zero of f.

- ■ You should know the difference between a factor that is irreducible over the rationals (such as $x^2 - 7$) and a factor that is irreducible over the reals (such as $x^2 + 9$).

Solutions to Selected Exercises

3. Find all the zeros of $h(x) = x^2 - 4x + 1$ and write the polynomial as a product of linear factors.

Solution:

f has no rational zeros.

By the Quadratic Formula, the zeros are $x = \dfrac{4 \pm \sqrt{16 - 4}}{2} = 2 \pm \sqrt{3}.$

$$f(x) = [x - (2 + \sqrt{3})][x - (2 - \sqrt{3})] = (x - 2 - \sqrt{3})(x - 2 + \sqrt{3})$$

7. Find all the zeros of $f(z) = z^2 - 2z + 2$ and write the polynomial as a product of linear factors.

Solution:

f has no rational zeros.

By the Quadratic Formula, the zeros are $z = \dfrac{2 \pm \sqrt{4 - 8}}{2} = 1 \pm i.$

$$f(z) = [z - (1 + i)][z - (1 - i)] = (z - 1 - i)(z - 1 + i)$$

9. Find all the zeros of $g(x) = x^3 - 6x^2 + 13x - 10$ and write the polynomial as a product of linear factors.

Solution:

Possible rational zeros: $\pm 1,\ \pm 2,\ \pm 5,\ \pm 10$

$$
\begin{array}{r|rrrr}
2 & 1 & -6 & 13 & -10 \\
  &   & 2 & -8 & 10 \\
\hline
  & 1 & -4 & 5 & 10
\end{array}
$$

$g(x) = (x - 2)(x^2 - 4x + 5)$

$x = 2$ is a zero, and by the Quadratic Formula $x = \dfrac{4 \pm \sqrt{16 - 20}}{2} = 2 \pm i$ are also zeros.

$$g(x) = (x - 2)[x - (2 + i)][x - (2 - i)] = (x - 2)(x - 2 - i)(x - 2 + i)$$

15. Find all the zeros of $f(x) = 16x^3 - 20x^2 - 4x + 15$ and write the polynomial as a product of linear factors.

Solution:

Possible rational zeros: ± 1, ± 3, ± 5, ± 15, $\pm\dfrac{1}{2}$, $\pm\dfrac{3}{2}$, $\pm\dfrac{5}{2}$, $\pm\dfrac{15}{2}$, $\pm\dfrac{1}{4}$, $\pm\dfrac{3}{4}$, $\pm\dfrac{5}{4}$, $\pm\dfrac{15}{4}$, $\pm\dfrac{1}{8}$, $\pm\dfrac{3}{8}$,

$$\pm\dfrac{5}{8},\ \pm\dfrac{15}{8},\ \pm\dfrac{1}{16},\ \pm\dfrac{3}{16},\ \pm\dfrac{5}{16},\ \pm\dfrac{15}{16}$$

$$
\begin{array}{r|rrrr}
-\dfrac{3}{4} & 16 & -20 & -4 & 15 \\
 & & -12 & 24 & -15 \\
\hline
 & 16 & -32 & 20 & 0
\end{array}
$$

$$f(x) = \left(x + \frac{3}{4}\right)(16x^2 - 32x + 20) = 4\left(x + \frac{3}{4}\right)(4x^2 - 8x + 5) = (4x + 3)(4x^2 - 8x + 5)$$

$x = -\dfrac{3}{4}$ is a zero, and by the Quadratic Formula $x = \dfrac{8 \pm \sqrt{64 - 80}}{8} = 1 \pm \dfrac{1}{2}i$ are also zeros.

$$f(x) = 4\left(x + \frac{3}{4}\right)\left[x - \left(1 + \frac{1}{2}i\right)\right]\left[x - \left(1 - \frac{1}{2}i\right)\right] = (4x + 3)(2x - 2 - i)(2x - 2 + i)$$

21. Find all the zeros of $g(x) = x^4 - 4x^3 + 8x^2 - 16x + 16$ and write the polynomial as a product of linear factors.

Solution:

Possible rational zeros: ± 1, ± 2, ± 4, ± 8, ± 16

$$
\begin{array}{r|rrrrr}
2 & 1 & -4 & 8 & -16 & 16 \\
 & & 2 & -4 & 8 & -16 \\
\hline
2 & 1 & -2 & 4 & -8 & 0 \\
 & & 2 & 0 & 8 & \\
\hline
 & 1 & 0 & 4 & 0 &
\end{array}
$$

$$g(x) = (x - 2)(x - 2)(x^2 + 4) = (x - 2)^2(x + 2i)(x - 2i)$$

The zeros of g are 2 and $\pm 2i$.

27. Find a polynomial with integer coefficients that has the zeros 1, $5i$, and $-5i$.

Solution:

$$
\begin{aligned}
f(x) &= (x - 1)(x - 5i)(x + 5i) \\
&= (x - 1)(x^2 + 25) \\
&= x^3 - x^2 + 25x - 25
\end{aligned}
$$

31. Find a polynomial with integer coefficients that has the zeros i, $-i$, $6i$, and $-6i$.

Solution:

$$f(x) = (x - i)(x + i)(x - 6i)(x + 6i)$$
$$= (x^2 + 1)(x^2 + 36)$$
$$= x^4 + 37x^2 + 36$$

35. Find a polynomial with integer coefficients that has the zeros $\frac{3}{4}$, -2, and $-\frac{1}{2} + i$.

Solution:
Since $-\frac{1}{2} + i$ is a zero, so is $-\frac{1}{2} - i$.

$$f(x) = 16\left(x - \tfrac{3}{4}\right)(x + 2)\left[x - \left(-\tfrac{1}{2} + i\right)\right]\left[x - \left(-\tfrac{1}{2} - i\right)\right]$$
$$= 4(4x - 3)(x + 2)\left[x^2 + x + \left(\tfrac{1}{4} + 1\right)\right]$$
$$= (4x^2 + 5x - 6)(4x^2 + 4x + 5)$$
$$= 16x^4 + 36x^3 + 16x^2 + x - 30$$

39. Write $f(x) = x^4 - 4x^3 + 5x^2 - 2x - 6$
 (a) as the product of factors that are irreducible over the rationals,
 (b) as the product of linear and quadratic factors that are irreducible over the reals, and
 (c) in completely factored form. [*Hint:* One factor is $x^2 - 2x - 2$.]

Solution:

$$
\require{enclose}
\begin{array}{r}
x^2 - 2x + 3 \\
x^2 - 2x - 2 \enclose{longdiv}{x^4 - 4x^3 + 5x^2 - 2x - 6} \\
\end{array}
$$

$$
\begin{array}{r}
 x^2\ -\ 2x\ +\ 3 \\[2pt]
x^2 - 2x - 2\ \overline{)\ x^4\ -\ 4x^3 +\ 5x^2\ -\ 2x\ -\ 6} \\[2pt]
-(x^4\ -\ 2x^3 -\ 2x^2) \\[2pt]
\hline
-\ 2x^3 +\ 7x^2\ -\ 2x \\[2pt]
-(-\ 2x^3 +\ 4x^2\ +\ 4x) \\[2pt]
\hline
3x^2\ -\ 6x\ -\ 6 \\[2pt]
-(3x^2\ -\ 6x\ -\ 6) \\[2pt]
\hline
0
\end{array}
$$

$$f(x) = (x^2 - 2x + 3)(x^2 - 2x - 2)$$

 (a) $f(x) = (x^2 - 2x + 3)(x^2 - 2x - 2)$
 (b) $f(x) = (x^2 - 2x + 3)(x - 1 + \sqrt{3})(x - 1 - \sqrt{3})$
 (c) $f(x) = (x - 1 + \sqrt{2}\,i)(x - 1 - \sqrt{2}\,i)(x - 1 + \sqrt{3})(x - 1 - \sqrt{3})$

Note: Use the Quadratic Formula for (b) and (c).

43. Use the zero, $r = 2i$, to find all the zeros of $f(x) = 2x^4 - x^3 + 7x^2 - 4x - 4$.

Solution:

Since $2i$ is a zero of f, so is $-2i$.

$$
\begin{array}{r|rrrrr}
2i & 2 & -1 & 7 & -4 & -4 \\
 & & 0+4i & -8-2i & 4-2i & 4 \\
\hline
-2i & 2 & -1+4i & -1-2i & -2i & 0 \\
 & & 0-4i & 0+2i & 2i & \\
\hline
 & 2 & -1 & -1 & 0 &
\end{array}
$$

$$f(x) = (x - 2i)(x + 2i)(2x^2 - x - 1) = (x - 2i)(x + 2i)(2x + 1)(x - 1)$$

The zeros of f are $\pm 2i$, $-\frac{1}{2}$, and 1.

47. Use the zero, $r = -3 + \sqrt{2}\,i$, to find all the zeros of $f(x) = x^4 + 3x^3 - 5x^2 - 21x + 22$.

Solution:

Since $-3 + \sqrt{2}\,i$ is a zero of f, so is $-3 - \sqrt{2}\,i$.

$$
\begin{array}{r|rrrrr}
-3+\sqrt{2}\,i & 1 & 3 & -5 & -21 & 22 \\
 & & -3+\sqrt{2}\,i & -2-3\sqrt{2}\,i & 27+2\sqrt{2}\,i & 22 \\
\hline
-3-\sqrt{2}\,i & 1 & \sqrt{2}\,i & -7-3\sqrt{2}\,i & 6+2\sqrt{2}\,i & 0 \\
 & & -3-\sqrt{2}\,i & 9+3\sqrt{2}\,i & -6-2\sqrt{2}\,i & \\
\hline
 & 1 & -3 & 2 & 0 &
\end{array}
$$

$$
\begin{aligned}
f(x) &= [x - (-3 + \sqrt{2}\,i)][x - (-3 - \sqrt{2}\,i)](x^2 - 3x + 2) \\
&= [x - (-3 + \sqrt{2}\,i)][x - (-3 - \sqrt{2}\,i)](x - 1)(x - 2)
\end{aligned}
$$

The zeros of f are $-3 + \sqrt{2}\,i$, $-3 - \sqrt{2}\,i$, 1, and 2.

51. Find a quadratic function f (with integer coefficients) that has $\pm\sqrt{b}\,i$ as zeros. Assume that b is a positive integer.

Solution:

$$f(x) = (x - \sqrt{b}\,i)(x + \sqrt{b}\,i) = x^2 + b$$

SECTION 4.6

Approximation Techniques for Zeros of Polynomials

- You should be able to use the Bisection Method to approximate the zeros of a polynomial f.
  - (a) Sketch f and roughly approximate x_0, a point where the graph crosses the x-axis.
  - (b) Find an x-value a such that $f(a) < 0$.
  - (c) Find an x-value b such that $f(b) > 0$.
  - (d) Find the midpoint $c = (a+b)/2 = x_1$.
  - (e) Approximate the zero.
    1. If $f(c) = 0$, c is a zero of f.
    2. If $f(c) > 0$, the zero is between a and c.
    3. If $f(c) < 0$, the zero is between b and c.
  - (f) The maximum error is $|b - a|/2$.
  - (g) Continue this process until the error falls below the desired bound.

- You should know that the smaller the initial interval about the zero is, the fewer the number of iterations you will have.

Solutions to Selected Exercises

3. Use the Bisection Method to approximate the indicated real zero of $f(x) = 2x^3 - 6x^2 + 6x - 1$ to within 0.01 unit.

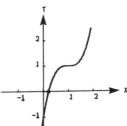

Solution:

Iteration	a	c	b	$f(a)$	$f(c)$	$f(b)$	Error
1	0.2	0.25	0.3	−0.0240	0.1562	0.3140	0.05
2	0.2	0.225	0.25	−0.0240	0.0690	0.1562	0.025
3	0.2	0.2125	0.225	−0.0240	0.0232	0.0690	0.0125
4	0.2	0.2062	0.2125	−0.0240	−0.0004	0.0232	0.0062

Within 0.01 units the zero of f is approximately 0.21.

7. Approximate the indicated real zeros of $f(x) = x^4 - x - 3$ to within 0.01 unit.

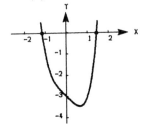

Solution:

Iteration	a	c	b	$f(a)$	$f(c)$	$f(b)$	Error
1	-1	-1.25	-1.5	-1.000	0.691	3.562	0.25
2	-1	-1.125	-1.25	-1.000	-0.273	0.691	0.125
3	-1.125	-1.188	-1.25	-0.273	0.180	0.691	0.063
4	-1.125	-1.156	-1.188	-0.273	-0.058	0.180	0.032
5	-1.156	-1.172	-1.188	-0.058	0.059	0.180	0.016
6	-1.156	-1.164	-1.172	-0.058	-0.000	0.059	0.008

Within 0.01 unit one zero of f is approximately -1.16.

Iteration	a	c	b	$f(a)$	$f(c)$	$f(b)$	Error
1	1.3	1.4	1.5	-1.444	-0.558	0.562	0.10
2	1.4	1.45	1.5	-0.558	-0.029	0.562	0.05
3	1.45	1.475	1.5	-0.029	0.258	0.562	0.025
4	1.45	1.462	1.475	-0.029	0.107	0.258	0.013
5	1.45	1.456	1.462	-0.029	0.038	0.107	0.006
6	1.45	1.453	1.456	-0.029	0.004	0.038	0.003

Within 0.01 unit, the other zero of f is approximately 1.45.

11. Find the zero of $f(x) = 7x^4 - 42x^3 + 43x^2 + 216x - 324$ in $[1, 2]$ to the nearest hundredth.

Solution:

Iteration	a	c	b	$f(a)$	$f(c)$	$f(b)$	Error
1	1	1.5	2	-100	-9.5625	56	0.5
2	1.5	1.75	2	-9.5625	26.2461	56	0.25
3	1.5	1.625	1.75	-9.5625	9.1345	26.2461	0.125
4	1.5	1.5625	1.625	-9.5625	-0.0136	9.1345	0.0625
5	1.5625	1.5938	1.625	-0.0136	4.6104	9.1345	0.0312
6	1.5625	1.5782	1.5938	-0.0136	2.3146	4.6104	0.0156
7	1.5625	1.5704	1.5782	-0.0136	1.1574	2.3146	0.0078
8	1.5625	1.5665	1.5704	-0.0136	0.5839	1.1574	0.004
9	1.5625	1.5645	1.5665	-0.0136	0.2853	0.5839	0.002

The zero of f is approximately 1.56.

REVIEW EXERCISES FOR CHAPTER 4

Solutions to Selected Exercises

5. Sketch the graph of $g(x) = x^4 - x^3 - 2x^2$.

   Solution:

   $$g(x) = x^4 - x^3 - 2x^2$$
   $$= x^2(x^2 - x - 2)$$
   $$= x^2(x + 1)(x - 2)$$

   The zeros of g are 0, -1, and 2, so the graph of g crosses the x-axis at these points. Since the degree of g is even and the leading coefficient is positive, the graph moves up to the right and left.

x	0	-1	2	1	$-\frac{1}{2}$	$\frac{1}{2}$
$g(x)$	0	0	0	-2	$-\frac{5}{16}$	$-\frac{9}{16}$

11. Find the maximum or minimum value of $g(x) = x^2 - 2x$.

    Solution:

    $$g(x) = x^2 - 2x \qquad \text{has a minimum since } a > 0$$
    $$= x^2 - 2x + 1 - 1$$
    $$= (x - 1)^2 - 1$$

    Minimum value is $g(1) = -1$.

17. Find the maximum or minimum value of $f(t) = -2t^2 + 4t + 1$.

    Solution:

    $$f(t) = -2t^2 + 4t + 1 \qquad \text{has a maximum since } a < 0$$
    $$= -2(t^2 - 2t - \tfrac{1}{2})$$
    $$= -2(t^2 - 2t + 1 - 1 - \tfrac{1}{2})$$
    $$= -2[(t - 1)^2 - \tfrac{3}{2}]$$
    $$= -2(t - 1)^2 + 3$$

    Maximum value is $f(1) = 3$.

23. Perform the indicated division.

$$\frac{x^4 + x^3 - x^2 + 2x}{x^2 + 2x}$$

Solution:

$$
\begin{array}{r}
x^2 - x + 1 \\
x^2 + 2x\ \overline{\smash{\big)}\ x^4 + x^3 - x^2 + 2x} \\
\underline{-\,(x^4 + 2x^3)} \\
-\,x^3 - x^2 \\
\underline{-\,(-x^3 - 2x^2)} \\
x^2 + 2x \\
\underline{-\,(x^2 + 2x)} \\
0
\end{array}
$$

Thus, $\dfrac{x^4 + x^3 - x^2 + 2x}{x^2 + 2x} = x^2 - x + 1.$

27. Perform the indicated division.

$$\frac{x^4 - 3x^3 + 4x^2 - 6x + 3}{x^2 + 2}$$

Solution:

$$
\begin{array}{r}
x^2 - 3x + 2 \\
x^2 + 2\ \overline{\smash{\big)}\ x^4 - 3x^3 + 4x^2 - 6x + 3} \\
\underline{-\,(x^4 + 2x^2)} \\
-\,3x^3 + 2x^2 - 6x \\
\underline{-\,(-3x^3 - 6x)} \\
2x^2 + 3 \\
\underline{-\,(2x^2 + 4)} \\
-\,1
\end{array}
$$

Thus, $\dfrac{x^4 - 3x^3 + 4x^2 - 6x + 3}{x^2 + 2} = x^2 - 3x + 2 - \dfrac{1}{x^2 + 2}.$

31. Use synthetic division to perform the indicated division.

$$\frac{6x^4 - 4x^3 - 27x^2 + 18x}{x - (2/3)}$$

Solution:

$$
\begin{array}{r|rrrrr}
\dfrac{2}{3} & 6 & -4 & -27 & 18 & 0 \\
 & & 4 & 0 & -18 & 0 \\
\hline
 & 6 & 0 & -27 & 0 & 0
\end{array}
$$

Thus, $\dfrac{6x^4 - 4x^3 - 27x^2 + 18x}{x - (2/3)} = 6x^3 - 27x.$

37. Use synthetic division to determine whether the given values of x are zeros of

$$f(x) = 2x^3 + 7x^2 - 18x - 30.$$

(a) $x = 1$ (b) $x = \frac{5}{2}$ (c) $x = -3 + \sqrt{3}$ (d) $x = 0$

Solution:

(a) $\begin{array}{r|rrrr} 1 & 2 & 7 & -18 & -30 \\ & & 2 & 9 & -9 \\ \hline & 2 & 9 & -9 & -39 \end{array}$

$x = 1$ is *not* a zero of f.

(b) $\begin{array}{r|rrrr} \frac{5}{2} & 2 & 7 & -18 & -30 \\ & & 5 & 30 & 30 \\ \hline & 2 & 12 & 12 & 0 \end{array}$

$x = \frac{5}{2}$ *is* a zero of f.

(c) $\begin{array}{r|rrrr} -3 + \sqrt{3} & 2 & 7 & -18 & -30 \\ & & -6 + 2\sqrt{3} & 3 - 5\sqrt{3} & 30 \\ \hline & 2 & 1 + 2\sqrt{3} & -15 - 5\sqrt{3} & 0 \end{array}$

$x = -3 + \sqrt{3}$ *is* a zero of f.

(d) $\begin{array}{r|rrrr} 0 & 2 & 7 & -18 & -30 \\ & & 0 & 0 & 0 \\ \hline & 2 & 7 & -18 & -30 \end{array}$

$x = 0$ is *not* a zero of f.

41. Use synthetic division to find the specified value of $f(x) = x^4 + 10x^3 - 24x^2 + 20x + 44$.

(a) $f(-3)$ (b) $f(\sqrt{2}\,i)$

Solution:

(a) $\begin{array}{r|rrrrr} -3 & 1 & 10 & -24 & 20 & 44 \\ & & -3 & -21 & 135 & -465 \\ \hline & 1 & 7 & -45 & 155 & -421 \end{array}$

Thus, $f(-3) = -421$.

(b) $\begin{array}{r|rrrrr} \sqrt{2}\,i & 1 & 10 & -24 & 20 & 44 \\ & & 0 + \sqrt{2}\,i & -2 + 10\sqrt{2}\,i & -20 - 26\sqrt{2}\,i & 52 \\ \hline & 1 & 10 + \sqrt{2}\,i & -26 + 10\sqrt{2}\,i & -26\sqrt{2}\,i & 96 \end{array}$

Thus, $f(\sqrt{2}\,i) = 96$.

43. Find a fourth degree polynomial with the zeros -1, -1, $\frac{1}{3}$, and $-\frac{1}{2}$.

Solution:

$$f(x) = 6(x+1)^2\left(x - \tfrac{1}{3}\right)\left(x + \tfrac{1}{2}\right) \qquad \text{Multiply by 6 to clear the fractions.}$$
$$= (x+1)^2 3\left(x - \tfrac{1}{3}\right)2\left(x + \tfrac{1}{2}\right)$$
$$= (x^2 + 2x + 1)(3x - 1)(2x + 1)$$
$$= (x^2 + 2x + 1)(6x^2 + x - 1)$$
$$= 6x^4 + 13x^3 + 7x^2 - x - 1$$

47. Find all the zeros of $f(x) = 6x^3 - 5x^2 + 24x - 20$.

Solution:
Possible rational zeros: $\pm 1,\ \pm 2,\ \pm 4,\ \pm 5,\ \pm 10,\ \pm 20,\ \pm\frac{1}{2},\ \pm\frac{5}{2},\ \pm\frac{1}{3},\ \pm\frac{2}{3},\ \pm\frac{4}{3},\ \pm\frac{5}{3},\ \pm\frac{10}{3},\ \pm\frac{20}{3},$
$\pm\frac{1}{6},\ \pm\frac{5}{6}$

$$\begin{array}{r|rrrr}
\frac{5}{6} & 6 & -5 & 24 & -20 \\
 &   & 5 & 0 & 20 \\
\hline
 & 6 & 0 & 24 & 0
\end{array}$$

$$f(x) = \left(x - \tfrac{5}{6}\right)(6x^2 + 24) = 6\left(x - \tfrac{5}{6}\right)(x^2 + 4) = 6\left(x - \tfrac{5}{6}\right)(x + 2i)(x - 2i)$$

The zeros of f are $\frac{5}{6}$ and $\pm 2i$.

This problem can also be solved by factoring by grouping.

$$f(x) = 6x^3 - 5x^2 + 24x - 20 = x^2(6x - 5) + 4(6x - 5)$$
$$= (6x - 5)(x^2 + 4) = (6x - 5)(x + 2i)(x - 2i)$$

The zeros of f are $\frac{5}{6}$ and $\pm 2i$.

51. Use the Bisection Method to find the zero of $f(x) = x^4 + 2x - 1$ in the interval $[0,\ 1]$ to the nearest hundredth.

Solution:

Iteration	a	c	b	$f(a)$	$f(c)$	$f(b)$	Error
1	0	0.5000	1	-1	0.0625	2	0.5
2	0	0.2500	0.5000	-1	-0.4961	0.0625	0.25
3	0.2500	0.3750	0.5000	-0.4961	-0.2302	0.0625	0.125
4	0.3750	0.4375	0.5000	-0.2302	-0.0884	0.0625	0.0625
5	0.4375	0.4688	0.5000	-0.0884	-0.0141	0.0625	0.0312
6	0.4688	0.4844	0.5000	-0.0141	0.0238	0.0625	0.0156
7	0.4688	0.4766	0.4844	-0.0141	0.0048	0.0238	0.0078

The zero of f is approximately 0.48.

55. Find the number of units x that produce a maximum revenue R for $R = 900x - 0.1x^2$.

Solution:

$$R = 900x - 0.1x^2 = -0.1(x^2 - 9000x + 4500^2) + 2{,}025{,}000$$
$$= 2{,}025{,}000 - 0.1(x - 4500)^2$$
$$x = 4500 \text{ units}$$

59. A rectangle is inscribed in the region bounded by the x-axis, the y-axis, and the graph of $x + 2y - 6 = 0$, as shown in the figure. Find the coordinates (x, y) that yield a maximum area for the rectangle.

Solution:

$$x + 2y - 6 = 0 \quad \Longrightarrow \quad y = \frac{6 - x}{2}$$

The area of the rectangle is

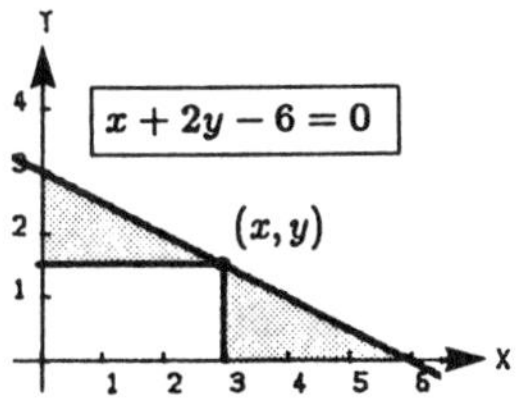

$$A = xy = x\left(\frac{6 - x}{2}\right) = -\frac{1}{2}x^2 + 3x$$
$$= -\frac{1}{2}(x^2 - 6x + 9 - 9)$$
$$= -\frac{1}{2}[(x - 3)^2 - 9]$$
$$= -\frac{1}{2}(x - 3)^2 + \frac{9}{2}$$

The maximum value of the area is $9/2$ square units and this occurs when $x = 3$ and $y = (6 - 3)/2 = 3/2$.

Practice Test for Chapter 4

1. Sketch the graph of $f(x) = x^2 - 6x + 5$ and identify the vertex and the intercepts.

2. Find the number of units x that produce a minimum cost C if $C = 0.01x^2 - 90x + 15{,}000$.

3. Find the quadratic function that has a maximum at $(1, 7)$ and passes through the point $(2, 5)$.

4. Find two quadratic functions that have x-intercepts $(2, 0)$ and $\left(\frac{4}{3}, 0\right)$.

5. Use the Leading Coefficient Test to determine the right-hand and left-hand behavior of the graph of the polynomial function $f(x) = -3x^5 + 2x^3 - 17$.

6. Find all the real zeros of $f(x) = x^5 - 5x^3 + 4x$.

7. Find a polynomial function with 0, 3, and -2 as zeros.

8. Sketch $f(x) = x^3 - 12x$.

9. Divide $3x^4 - 7x^2 + 2x - 10$ by $x - 3$ using long division.

10. Divide $x^3 - 11$ by $x^2 + 2x - 1$.

11. Use synthetic division to divide $3x^5 + 13x^4 + 12x - 1$ by $x + 5$.

12. Use synthetic division to find $f(-6)$ when $f(x) = 7x^3 + 40x^2 - 12x + 15$.

13. Find the real zeros of $f(x) = x^3 - 19x - 30$.

14. Find the real zeros of $f(x) = x^4 + x^3 - 8x^2 - 9x - 9$.

15. List all the possible rational zeros of the function $f(x) = 6x^3 - 5x^2 + 4x - 15$.

16. Find the rational zeros of the polynomial $f(x) = x^3 - \dfrac{20}{3}x^2 + 9x - \dfrac{10}{3}$.

17. Write $f(x) = x^4 + x^3 + 3x^2 + 5x - 10$ as a product of linear factors.

18. Find a polynomial with real coefficients that has 2, $3 + i$, and $3 - i$ as zeros.

19. Use synthetic division to show that $3i$ is a zero of $f(x) = x^3 + 4x^2 + 9x + 36$.

20. Find the zero of the function $f(x) = x^3 + 2x - 1$ in the interval $[0, 1]$, accurate to within 0.001 unit.

CHAPTER 5

Rational Functions and Conic Sections

SECTION 5.1

Rational Functions and Their Graphs

■ You should know the following basic facts about rational functions.

(a) A function of the form $f(x) = P(x)/Q(x)$, $Q(x) \neq 0$, where $P(x)$ and $Q(x)$ are polynomials, is called a rational function.

(b) The domain of a rational function is the set of all real numbers except those which make the denominator zero.

(c) If $f(x) = P(x)/Q(x)$ is in reduced form, and a is a value such that $Q(a) = 0$, then the line $x = a$ is a vertical asymptote of the graph of f.

(d) The line $y = b$ is a horizontal asymptote of the graph of f if $f(x) \to b$ as $x \to \infty$ or $x \to -\infty$.

(e) If $f(x) = P(x)/Q(x) = mx + b + R(x)/Q(x)$, then the line $y = mx + b$ is a slant asymptote of the graph of f.

■ Be able to graph rational functions.

Solutions to Selected Exercises

3. Match $f(x) = (x+1)/x$ with its graph.

Solution:

$$f(x) = \frac{x+1}{x} = 1 + \frac{1}{x}$$

Vertical asymptote: $x = 0$
Horizontal asymptote: $y = 1$
x-intercept: $(-1, 0)$
Matches graph (a)

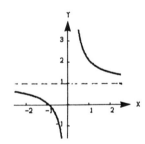

7. Match $f(x) = (x^2 + 1)/x$ with its graph.

Solution:

$$f(x) = \frac{x^2 + 1}{x} = x + \frac{1}{x}$$

Vertical asymptote: $x = 0$
Slant asymptote: $y = x$
No intercepts
Matches graph (h)

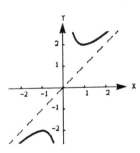

11. Find the domain of the following function and identify any horizontal, vertical, or slant asymptotes.

$$f(x) = \frac{2 + x}{2 - x}$$

Solution:

$$f(x) = \frac{2 + x}{2 - x} = -1 + \frac{4}{2 - x}$$

Domain: all real numbers except 2
Vertical asymptote: $x = 2$
Horizontal asymptote: $y = -1$

15. Find the domain of the following function and identify any horizontal, vertical, or slant asymptotes.

$$f(x) = \frac{3x^2 + 1}{x^2 + 9}$$

Solution:

$$f(x) = \frac{3x^2 + 1}{x^2 + 9} = 3 - \frac{26}{x^2 + 9}$$

Domain: all real numbers
Horizontal asymptotes: $y = 3$

23. Sketch the graph of the following rational function. As sketching aids, check for intercepts, symmetry, vertical asymptotes, and horizontal asymptotes.

$$h(x) = \frac{-1}{x + 2}$$

Solution:
Vertical asymptote: $x = -2$
Horizontal asymptote: $y = 0$
y-intercept: $\left(0, \ -\frac{1}{2}\right)$

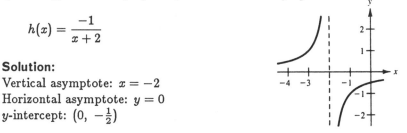

25. Sketch the graph of the following rational function. As sketching aids, check for intercepts, symmetry, vertical asymptotes, and horizontal asymptotes.

$$f(x) = \frac{x + 1}{x + 2}$$

Solution:

$$f(x) = \frac{x+1}{x+2} = 1 - \frac{1}{x+2}$$

Vertical asymptote: $x = -2$
Horizontal asymptote: $y = 1$
x-intercept: $(-1, 0)$
y-intercept: $\left(0, \frac{1}{2}\right)$

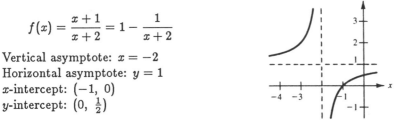

29. Sketch the graph of the following rational function. As sketching aids, check for intercepts, symmetry, vertical asymptotes, and horizontal asymptotes.

$$f(t) = \frac{3t+1}{t}$$

Solution:

$$f(t) = \frac{3t+1}{t} = 3 + \frac{1}{t}$$

Vertical asymptote: $x = 0$
Horizontal asymptote: $y = 3$
x-intercept: $\left(-\frac{1}{3}, 0\right)$

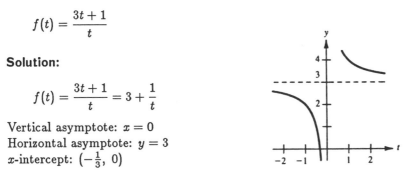

33. Sketch the graph of the following rational function. As sketching aids, check for intercepts, symmetry, vertical asymptotes, and horizontal asymptotes.

$$C(x) = \frac{5+2x}{1+x}$$

Solution:

$$C(x) = \frac{5+2x}{1+x} = 2 + \frac{3}{1+x}$$

Vertical asymptote: $x = -1$
Horizontal asymptote: $y = 2$
x-intercept: $\left(-\frac{5}{2}, 0\right)$
y-intercept: $(0, 5)$

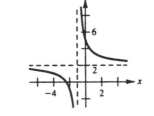

37. Sketch the graph of the following rational function. As sketching aids, check for intercepts, symmetry, vertical asymptotes, and horizontal asymptotes.

$$h(x) = \frac{x^2}{x^2 - 9}$$

Solution:

$$h(x) = \frac{x^2}{x^2 - 9} = 1 + \frac{9}{x^2 - 9}$$

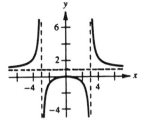

Vertical asymptotes: $x = \pm 3$
Horizontal asymptote: $y = 1$
Intercept: $(0, 0)$
y-axis symmetry

41. Sketch the graph of the following rational function. As sketching aids, check for intercepts, symmetry, vertical asymptotes, and horizontal asymptotes.

$$f(x) = -\frac{1}{(x - 2)^2}$$

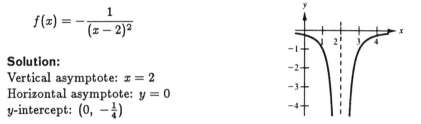

Solution:
Vertical asymptote: $x = 2$
Horizontal asymptote: $y = 0$
y-intercept: $\left(0, -\frac{1}{4}\right)$

45. Sketch the graph of the following rational function. As sketching aids, check for intercepts, symmetry, vertical asymptotes, and slant asymptotes.

$$f(x) = \frac{2x^2 + 1}{x}$$

Solution:

$$f(x) = \frac{2x^2 + 1}{x} = 2x + \frac{1}{x}$$

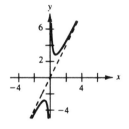

Vertical asymptote: $x = 0$
Slant asymptote: $y = 2x$
Origin symmetry

49. Sketch the graph of the following rational function. As sketching aids, check for intercepts, symmetry, vertical asymptotes, and slant asymptotes.

$$f(x) = \frac{x^3}{x^2 - 1}$$

Solution:

$$f(x) = \frac{x^3}{x^2 - 1} = x + \frac{x}{x^2 - 1}$$

Vertical asymptotes: $x = \pm 1$
Slant asymptote: $y = x$
Intercept: $(0, 0)$
Origin symmetry

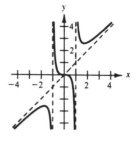

51. Sketch the graph of the following rational function. As sketching aids, check for intercepts, symmetry, vertical asymptotes, and slant asymptotes.

$$f(x) = \frac{x^2 - x + 1}{x - 1}$$

Solution:

$$f(x) = \frac{x^2 - x + 1}{x - 1} = x + \frac{1}{x - 1}$$

Vertical asymptote: $x = 1$
Slant asymptote: $y = x$
y-intercept: $(0, -1)$

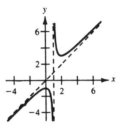

55. The game commission introduces 50 deer into newly acquired state game lands. The population of the herd is given by

$$N = \frac{10(5 + 3t)}{1 + 0.04t}, \qquad 0 \le t$$

where t is time in years.

(a) Find the population when t is 5, 10, and 25.
(b) What is the limiting size of the herd as time increases?

Solution:

$$N = \frac{10(5 + 3t)}{1 + 0.04t} = 750 - \frac{700}{1 + 0.04t}$$

(a) $N(5) \approx 167$ deer
   $N(10) = 250$ deer
   $N(25) = 400$ deer
(b) As $t \to \infty$, $N \to 750$ deer.

59. A right triangle is formed in the first quadrant by the x-axis, the y-axis, and a line segment through the point $(2, 3)$, as shown in the figure.

(a) Show that an equation of the line segment is

$$y = \frac{3(x - a)}{2 - a}, \qquad 0 \le x \le a.$$

(b) Show that the area of the triangle is

$$A = \frac{-3a^2}{2(2 - a)}.$$

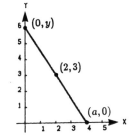

(c) Sketch the graph of the area function of part (b), and from the graph estimate the value of a that yields a minimum area.

Solution:

(a) The line passes through the points $(a, 0)$ and $(2, 3)$.

$$m = \frac{3 - 0}{2 - a} = \frac{3}{2 - a}$$

$$y - 0 = \frac{3}{2 - a}(x - a) \qquad \text{By the point slope equation}$$

$$y = \frac{3(x - a)}{2 - a}$$

(b) The area of a triangle is $A = \frac{1}{2}bh$.

$$b = a$$

$$h = y \text{ when } x = 0, \text{ so } h = \frac{3(0 - a)}{2 - a} = \frac{-3a}{2 - a}$$

$$A = \left(\frac{1}{2}a\right)\left(\frac{-3a}{2 - a}\right)$$

$$= \frac{-3a^2}{2(2 - a)}$$

(c) $A = \dfrac{-3a^2}{2(2 - a)} = \dfrac{3}{2}a + 3 + \dfrac{6}{a - 2}, \quad a > 2$

A is minimum when $a \approx 4$.

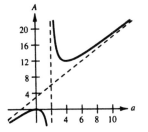

SECTION 5.2

Partial Fractions

- You should know how to decompose a rational function $\dfrac{N(x)}{D(x)}$ into partial fractions.

  (a) If the fraction is improper, divide to obtain

  $$\frac{N(x)}{D(x)} = p(x) + \frac{N_1(x)}{D(x)}$$

  where $p(x)$ is a polynomial.

  (b) Factor the denominator completely into linear and irreducible (over the reals) quadratic factors.

  (c) For each factor of the form $(px+q)^m$, the partial fraction decomposition includes the terms

  $$\frac{A_1}{(px+q)} + \frac{A_2}{(px+q)^2} + \cdots + \frac{A_m}{(px+q)^m}.$$

  (d) For each factor of the form $(ax^2+bx+c)^n$, the partial fraction decomposition includes the terms

  $$\frac{B_1 x + C_1}{ax^2+bx+c} + \frac{B_2 x + C_2}{(ax^2+bx+c)^2} + \cdots + \frac{B_n x + C_n}{(ax^2+bx+c)^n}.$$

- You should know how to determine the values of the constants in the numerators.

  (a) Set $\dfrac{N_1(x)}{D(x)}$ = partial fraction decomposition.

  (b) Multiply both sides by $D(x)$. This is called the basic equation.

  (c) For distinct linear factors, substitute the roots of the distinct linear factors into the basic equation.

  (d) For repeated linear factors, use the coefficients found in part (c) to rewrite the basic equation. Then use other values of x to solve for the remaining coefficients.

  (e) For quadratic factors, expand the basic equation, collect like terms, and then equate the coefficients of like powers.

Solutions to Selected Exercises

3. Write the partial fraction decomposition for the rational expression

$$\frac{1}{x^2 + x}.$$

Solution:
Since $x^2 + x = x(x + 1)$,

$$\frac{1}{x^2 + x} = \frac{A}{x} + \frac{B}{x + 1}$$
$$1 = A(x + 1) + Bx.$$

Let $x = 0$: $1 = A$

Let $x = -1$: $1 = -B \Rightarrow B = -1$

Thus, $\dfrac{1}{x^2 + x} = \dfrac{1}{x} - \dfrac{1}{x + 1}.$

7. Write the partial fraction decomposition for the rational expression

$$\frac{3}{x^2 + x - 2}.$$

Solution:
Since $x^2 + x - 2 = (x - 1)(x + 2)$,

$$\frac{3}{x^2 + x - 2} = \frac{A}{x - 1} + \frac{B}{x + 2}$$
$$3 = A(x + 2) + B(x - 1).$$

Let $x = 1$: $3 = 3A$

$1 = A$

Let $x = -2$: $3 = -3B$

$-1 = B$

Thus, $\dfrac{3}{x^2 + x - 2} = \dfrac{1}{x - 1} - \dfrac{1}{x + 2}.$

11. Write the partial fraction decomposition for the rational expression

$$\frac{x^2 + 12x + 12}{x^3 - 4x}.$$

Solution:

Since $x^3 - 4x = x(x+2)(x-2)$,

$$\frac{x^2 + 12x + 12}{x^3 - 4x} = \frac{A}{x} + \frac{B}{x+2} + \frac{C}{x-2}$$

$$x^2 + 12x + 12 = A(x+2)(x-2) + Bx(x-2) + Cx(x+2).$$

Let $x = 0$: $12 = -4A$

                 $-3 = A$

Let $x = -2$: $-8 = 8B$

                 $-1 = B$

Let $x = 2$: $40 = 8C$

                 $5 = C$

Thus, $\dfrac{x^2 + 12x + 12}{x^3 - 4x} = -\dfrac{3}{x} - \dfrac{1}{x+2} + \dfrac{5}{x-2}.$

13. Write the partial fraction decomposition for the rational expression

$$\frac{4x^2 + 2x - 1}{x^2(x+1)}.$$

Solution:

$$\frac{4x^2 + 2x - 1}{x^2(x+1)} = \frac{A}{x} + \frac{B}{x^2} + \frac{C}{x+1}$$

$$4x^2 + 2x - 1 = Ax(x+1) + B(x+1) + Cx^2$$

Let $x = 0$: $-1 = B$

Let $x = -1$: $1 = C$

Let $x = 1$: $5 = 2A + 2B + C$

                 $5 = 2A - 2 + 1$

                 $6 = 2A$

                 $3 = A$

Thus, $\dfrac{4x^2 + 2x - 1}{x^2(x+1)} = \dfrac{3}{x} - \dfrac{1}{x^2} + \dfrac{1}{x+1}.$

Note: $x^2 = (x - 0)^2$ and is a linear factor squared. It is not an irreducible quadratic factor.

Do not write $\dfrac{Bx + C}{x^2}$ in the partial fraction decomposition.

19. Write the partial fraction decomposition for the rational expression

$$\frac{x^2 - 1}{x(x^2 + 1)}.$$

Solution:

$$\frac{x^2 - 1}{x(x^2 + 1)} = \frac{A}{x} + \frac{Bx + C}{x^2 + 1}$$

$$x^2 - 1 = A(x^2 + 1) + (Bx + C)x$$

Let $x = 0$: $\quad -1 = A$

$$x^2 - 1 = Ax^2 + A + Bx^2 + Cx = -x^2 - 1 + Bx^2 + Cx = x^2(B - 1) + Cx - 1$$

Equating coefficients of like powers,

$$1 = B - 1$$

$$2 = B \quad \text{and} \quad 0 = C$$

Thus, $\dfrac{x^2 - 1}{x(x^2 + 1)} = \dfrac{-1}{x} + \dfrac{2x}{x^2 + 1}.$

23. Write the partial fraction decomposition for the rational expression

$$\frac{x}{16x^4 - 1}.$$

Solution:
Since $16x^4 - 1 = (4x^2 + 1)(2x + 1)(2x - 1)$,

$$\frac{x}{16x^4 - 1} = \frac{A}{2x + 1} + \frac{B}{2x - 1} + \frac{Cx + D}{4x^2 + 1}$$

$$x = A(2x - 1)(4x^2 + 1) + B(2x + 1)(4x^2 + 1) + (Cx + D)(2x + 1)(2x - 1).$$

Let $x = -\frac{1}{2}$: $\quad -\frac{1}{2} = -4A$

$$\frac{1}{8} = A$$

Let $x = \frac{1}{2}$: $\quad \frac{1}{2} = 4B$

$$\frac{1}{8} = B$$

Let $x = 0$: $\quad 0 = -A + B - D$

$$0 = -\frac{1}{8} + \frac{1}{8} - D$$

$$0 = D$$

Let $x = 1$: $\quad 1 = 5A + 15B + 3C + 3D$

$$1 = \tfrac{5}{8} + \tfrac{15}{8} + 3C + 0$$

$$1 = \tfrac{20}{8} + 3C$$

$$-\tfrac{3}{2} = 3C$$

$$-\tfrac{1}{2} = C$$

Thus, $\dfrac{x}{16x^4 - 1} = \dfrac{1/8}{2x+1} + \dfrac{1/8}{2x-1} - \dfrac{x/2}{4x^2+1} = \dfrac{1}{8}\left[\dfrac{1}{2x+1} + \dfrac{1}{2x-1} - \dfrac{4x}{4x^2+1}\right].$

27. Write the partial fraction decomposition for the rational expression

$$\frac{x^2 + 5}{(x+1)(x^2 - 2x + 3)}.$$

Solution:

$$\frac{x^2 + 5}{(x+1)(x^2 - 2x + 3)} = \frac{A}{x+1} + \frac{Bx + C}{x^2 - 2x + 3}$$

$$x^2 + 5 = A(x^2 - 2x + 3) + (Bx + C)(x + 1)$$

Let $x = -1$: $\quad 6 = 6A$

$$1 = A$$

$$x^2 + 5 = x^2 - 2x + 3 + Bx^2 + Bx + Cx + C$$
$$= x^2(1 + B) + x(-2 + B + C) + (3 + C)$$

Equating coefficients of like powers,

$$1 = 1 + B, \qquad 0 = -2 + B + C, \qquad \text{and} \qquad 5 = 3 + C$$
$$0 = B \qquad\qquad\qquad\qquad\qquad\qquad\qquad\qquad 2 = C$$

Thus, $\dfrac{x^2 + 5}{(x+1)(x^2 - 2x + 3)} = \dfrac{1}{x+1} + \dfrac{2}{x^2 - 2x + 3}.$

31. Write the partial fraction decomposition for the rational expression

$$\frac{x^4}{(x-1)^3}.$$

Solution:

$$\frac{x^4}{(x-1)^3} = \frac{x^4}{x^3 - 3x^2 + 3x - 1} \qquad \text{By division}$$

$$= x + 3 + \frac{6x^2 - 8x + 3}{(x-1)^3}$$

$$\frac{6x^2 - 8x + 3}{(x-1)^3} = \frac{A}{x-1} + \frac{B}{(x-1)^2} + \frac{C}{(x-1)^3}$$

$$6x^2 - 8x + 3 = A(x-1)^2 + B(x-1) + C$$

Let $x = 1:$ $1 = C$

Let $x = 0:$ $3 = A - B + C$

$$3 = A - B + 1$$

$$2 = A - B$$

Let $x = -1:$ $17 = 4A - 2B + C$

$$17 = 4A - 2B + 1$$

$$16 = 4A - 2B$$

$$8 = 2A - B$$

$$-2 = -A + B$$

$$6 = A$$

$$2 = A - B$$

$$2 = 6 - B$$

$$4 = B$$

Thus, $\dfrac{x^4}{(x-1)^3} = x + 3 + \dfrac{6}{x-1} + \dfrac{4}{(x-1)^2} + \dfrac{1}{(x-1)^3}.$

35. Write the partial fraction decomposition for the rational expression

$$\frac{1}{y(L-y)}, \qquad L \text{ is a constant.}$$

Solution:

$$\frac{1}{y(L-y)} = \frac{A}{y} + \frac{B}{L-y}$$

$$1 = A(L-y) + By$$

Let $y = 0:$ $1 \quad = LA$

$$1/L = A$$

Let $y = L:$ $1 \quad = LB$

$$1/L = B$$

Thus, $\dfrac{1}{y(L-y)} = \dfrac{1/L}{y} + \dfrac{1/L}{L-y} = \dfrac{1}{L}\left(\dfrac{1}{y} + \dfrac{1}{L-y}\right).$

SECTION 5.3

Conic Sections

You should know the following basic definitions of conic sections.

■ A circle is the set of all points (x, y) that are equidistant from a fixed point (h, k).

(a) Standard Equation: $(x - h)^2 + (y - k)^2 = r^2$

(b) Center: (h, k)

(c) Radius: r

■ A parabola is the set of all points (x, y) that are equidistant from a fixed line (directrix) and a fixed point (focus) not on the line.

(a) Standard Equation with Vertex $(0, 0)$ and Directrix $y = -p$ (vertical axis): $x^2 = 4py$

(b) Standard Equation with Vertex $(0, 0)$ and Directrix $x = -p$ (horizontal axis): $y^2 = 4px$

(c) The focus lies on the axis p units (directed distance) from the vertex.

■ An ellipse is the set of all points (x, y) the sum of whose distances from two distinct fixed points (foci) is constant.

(a) Standard Equation of an Ellipse with Center $(0, 0)$, Major Axis Length $2a$, and Minor Axis Length $2b$:

1. Horizontal Major Axis: $\dfrac{x^2}{a^2} + \dfrac{y^2}{b^2} = 1$

2. Vertical Major Axis: $\dfrac{x^2}{b^2} + \dfrac{y^2}{a^2} = 1$

(b) The foci lie on the major axis, c units from the center, where a, b, and c are related by the equation $c^2 = a^2 - b^2$.

(c) The vertices are

1. Horizontal Axis: $(\pm a, 0)$ and $(0, \pm b)$
2. Vertical Axis: $(0, \pm a)$ and $(\pm b, 0)$

- A hyperbola is the set of all points (x, y) the difference of whose distances from two distinct points (foci) is constant.

(a) Standard Equation of a Hyperbola with Center $(0, 0)$

    1. Horizontal Transverse Axis: $\dfrac{x^2}{a^2} - \dfrac{y^2}{b^2} = 1$

    2. Vertical Transverse Axis: $\dfrac{y^2}{a^2} - \dfrac{x^2}{b^2} = 1$

(b) The vertices and foci are a and c units from the center and $b^2 = c^2 - a^2$.

(c) The asymptotes of the hyperbola are

    1. Horizontal Transverse Axis: $y = \pm\dfrac{b}{a}x$

    2. Vertical Transverse Axis: $y = \pm\dfrac{a}{b}x$

Solutions to Selected Exercises

7. Match the following equation with its graph.

$$\frac{x^2}{1} - \frac{y^2}{4} = 1$$

Solution:
This is the standard equation of a hyperbola with vertices $(\pm 1, 0)$ and thus matches the graph shown in (e).

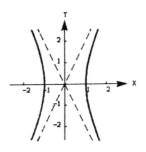

11. Find the vertex and focus of $y^2 = -6x$ and sketch its graph.

Solution:

$$y^2 = -6x$$
$$y^2 = 6\left(-\tfrac{3}{2}\right)y; \quad p = -\tfrac{3}{2}$$

Vertex: $(0, 0)$
Focus: $\left(-\tfrac{3}{2}, 0\right)$

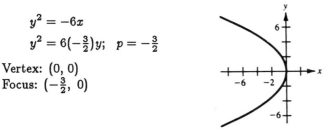

15. Find the vertex and focus of $y^2 - 8x = 0$ and sketch its graph.

Solution:

$$y^2 - 8x = 0$$
$$y^2 = 8x$$
$$y^2 = 4(2)x; \quad p = 2$$

Vertex: $(0, 0)$
Focus: $(2, 0)$

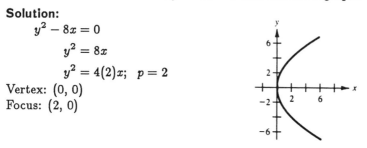

17. Find an equation of the parabola with vertex at the origin and focus $\left(0, -\frac{3}{2}\right)$.

Solution:

Vertex: $(0, 0)$
Focus: $\left(0, -\frac{3}{2}\right)$
$p = -\frac{3}{2}, \quad$ Axis vertical

$$x^2 = 4py$$
$$x^2 = 4\left(-\frac{3}{2}\right)y$$
$$x^2 = -6y$$

21. Find an equation of the parabola with vertex at the origin and directrix $y = -1$.

Solution:

Vertex: $(0, 0)$
Directrix: $y = -1$
$p = 1, \quad$ Vertical axis

$$x^2 = 4(1)y$$
$$x^2 = 4y$$

25. Find an equation of the parabola with vertex at the origin, horizontal axis, and passes through the point $(4, 6)$.

Solution:

Vertex: $(0, 0)$
Axis horizontal, passes through the point $(4, 6)$

$$y^2 = 4px \quad \text{Since the axis is horizontal}$$
$$6^2 = 4p(4) \quad \text{Since } (4, 6) \text{ is on the graph}$$
$$36 = 16p$$
$$p = \frac{36}{16}$$
$$p = \frac{9}{4}$$

Thus,
$$y^2 = 4\left(\tfrac{9}{4}\right)x$$
$$y^2 = 9x$$
$$y^2 - 9x = 0.$$

29. Find the center and vertices of the following ellipse and sketch its graph.

$$\frac{x^2}{16} + \frac{y^2}{25} = 1$$

Solution:
Vertical major axis
$a = 5, \ b = 4, \ c = \sqrt{25 - 16} = 3$
Center: $(0, 0)$
Vertices: $(0, \pm 5)$

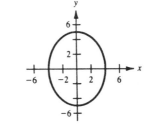

33. Find the center and vertices of $5x^2 + 3y^2 = 15$ and sketch its graph.

Solution:

$$5x^2 + 3y^2 = 15$$
$$\frac{x^2}{3} + \frac{y^2}{5} = 1$$

Vertical major axis
$a = \sqrt{5}, \ b = \sqrt{3}, \ c = \sqrt{5 - 3} = \sqrt{2}$
Center: $(0, 0)$
Vertices $(0, \pm\sqrt{5})$

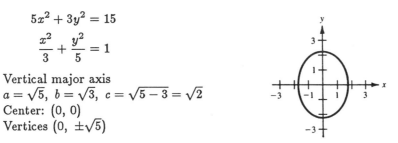

37. Find an equation of the ellipse with center at the origin, vertices at $(\pm 5, 0)$, and foci at $(\pm 2, 0)$.

Solution:
Vertices: $(5, 0), (-5, 0)$
Foci: $(2, 0), (-2, 0)$
$a = 5, \ c = 2, \ b = \sqrt{25 - 4} = \sqrt{21}$

$$\frac{x^2}{a^2} + \frac{y^2}{b^2} = 1$$
$$\frac{x^2}{25} + \frac{y^2}{21} = 1$$

41. Find an equation of the ellipse with center at the origin, vertices at $(0, \pm 5)$, and passes through the point $(4, 2)$.

Solution:

Vertices: $(0, \pm5)$; passes through $(4, 2)$

$a = 5$

$$\frac{x^2}{b^2} + \frac{y^2}{a^2} = 1$$

$$\frac{x^2}{b^2} + \frac{y^2}{25} = 1$$

$$\frac{16}{b^2} + \frac{4}{25} = 1$$

$$\frac{16}{b^2} = \frac{21}{25}$$

$$b^2 = \frac{(16)(25)}{21} = \frac{400}{21}$$

$$\frac{x^2}{400/21} + \frac{y^2}{25} = 1$$

$$\frac{21x^2}{400} + \frac{y^2}{25} = 1$$

45. Find the center and vertices of the following hyperbola and sketch its graph, using asymptotes as an aid.

$$\frac{y^2}{1} - \frac{x^2}{4} = 1$$

Solution:

$\dfrac{y^2}{1} - \dfrac{x^2}{4} = 1$; Vertical transverse axis

$a = 1,\ b = 2,\ c = \sqrt{1+4} = \sqrt{5}$

Center: $(0, 0)$

Vertices: $(0, \pm1)$

Asymptotes: $y = \pm\frac{1}{2}x$

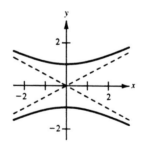

49. Find the center and vertices of $2x^2 - 3y^2 = 6$ and sketch its graph, using asymptotes as an aid.

Solution:

$2x^2 - 3y^2 = 6$

$\dfrac{x^2}{3} - \dfrac{y^2}{2} = 1$; Horizontal transverse axis

$a = \sqrt{3},\ b = \sqrt{2},\ c = \sqrt{3+2} = \sqrt{5}$

Center: $(0, 0)$

Vertices: $(\pm\sqrt{3}, 0)$

Asymptotes: $y = \pm\sqrt{2/3}\,x = \pm(\sqrt{6}/3)x$

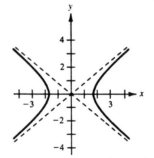

53. Find an equation of the hyperbola with center at the origin, vertices at $(\pm1, 0)$ and asymptotes $y = \pm3x$.

Solution:

Vertices: $(\pm 1, \ 0)$

Asymptotes: $y = \pm 3x$

Horizontal transverse axis

$a = 1$

$3 = \dfrac{b}{a} = \dfrac{b}{1}, \quad b = 3$

$\dfrac{x^2}{a^2} - \dfrac{y^2}{b^2} = 1$

$\dfrac{x^2}{1} - \dfrac{y^2}{9} = 1$

57. Find an equation of the hyperbola with center at the origin, vertices at $(0, \ \pm 3)$ and passes through the point $(-2, \ 5)$.

Solution:

Vertices: $(0, \ \pm 3)$; passes through $(-2, \ 5)$

Vertical transverse axis; $a = 3$

$\dfrac{y^2}{a^2} - \dfrac{x^2}{b^2} = 1$

$\dfrac{y^2}{9} - \dfrac{x^2}{b^2} = 1$

$\dfrac{25}{9} - \dfrac{4}{b^2} = 1$

$-\dfrac{4}{b^2} = -\dfrac{16}{9}$

$b^2 = \dfrac{(4)(9)}{16} = \dfrac{9}{4}$

$\dfrac{y^2}{9} - \dfrac{x^2}{9/4} = 1$

$\dfrac{y^2}{9} - \dfrac{4x^2}{9} = 1$

61. A fireplace arch is to be constructed in the shape of a semi-ellipse. The opening is to have a height of 2 feet at the center and a width of 5 feet along the base, as shown in the figure. The contractor draws the outline of the ellipse by the method shown in Figure 5.20. Where should the tacks be placed and what should be the length of the piece of string?

Solution:

$a = 2.5, \quad b = 2, \quad c^2 = (2.5)^2 - (2)^2, \quad c = \sqrt{2.25} = 1.5$

The tacks should be placed at $(\pm 1.5, \ 0)$.

The length of the string should be $2a = 5$ feet.

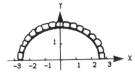

SECTION 5.4

Conic Sections and Translations

You should know the following basic facts about conic sections.

- **Parabola with Vertex** (h, k)

  (a) Vertical Axis
    1. Standard Equation: $(x - h)^2 = 4p(y - k)$
    2. Focus: $(h, k + p)$
    3. Directrix: $y = k - p$

  (b) Horizontal Axis
    1. Standard Equation: $(y - k)^2 = 4p(x - h)$
    2. Focus: $(h + p, k)$
    3. Directrix: $x = h - p$

- **Circle with Center** (h, k) **and Radius** r

  (a) Standard Equation: $(x - h)^2 + (y - k)^2 = r^2$

- **Ellipse with Center** (h, k)

  (a) Horizontal Major Axis:
    1. Standard Equation: $\dfrac{(x - h)^2}{a^2} + \dfrac{(y - k)^2}{b^2} = 1$
    2. Vertices: $(h \pm a, k)$
    3. Foci: $(h \pm c, k)$
    4. Eccentricity: $e = \dfrac{c}{a}$

  (b) Vertical Major Axis:
    1. Standard Equation: $\dfrac{(x - h)^2}{b^2} + \dfrac{(y - k)^2}{a^2} = 1$
    2. Vertices: $(h, k \pm a)$
    3. Foci: $(h, k \pm c)$
    4. Eccentricity: $e = \dfrac{c}{a}$

- Hyperbola with Center (h, k)

  (a) Horizontal Transverse Axis:

    1. Standard Equation: $\dfrac{(x-h)^2}{a^2} - \dfrac{(y-k)^2}{b^2} = 1$

    2. Vertices: $(h \pm a, k)$

    3. Foci: $(h \pm c, k)$

    4. Asymptotes: $y - k = \pm\dfrac{b}{a}(x - h)$

  (b) Vertical Transverse Axis:

    1. Standard Equation: $\dfrac{(y-k)^2}{a^2} - \dfrac{(x-h)^2}{b^2} = 1$

    2. Vertices: $(h, k \pm a)$

    3. Foci: $(h, k \pm c)$

    4. Asymptotes: $y - k = \pm\dfrac{a}{b}(x - h)$

Solutions to Selected Exercises

3. Find the vertex, focus, and directrix of $(y + \frac{1}{2})^2 = 2(x - 5)$, and sketch its graph.

Solution:

$$\left(y + \tfrac{1}{2}\right)^2 = 2(x - 5)$$
$$\left(y + \tfrac{1}{2}\right)^2 = 4\left(\tfrac{1}{2}\right)(x - 5); \quad p = \tfrac{1}{2}$$

Vertex: $(5, -\frac{1}{2})$
Focus: $(5 + \frac{1}{2}, -\frac{1}{2}) = (\frac{11}{2}, -\frac{1}{2})$
Directrix: $x = 5 - \frac{1}{2} = \frac{9}{2}$

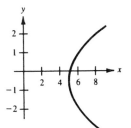

7. Find the vertex, focus, and directrix of $4x - y^2 - 2y - 33 = 0$, and sketch its graph.

Solution:

$$4x - y^2 - 2y - 33 = 0$$
$$4x - 33 + 1 = y^2 + 2y + 1$$
$$4x - 32 = (y + 1)^2$$
$$4(x - 8) = (y + 1)^2; \quad p = 1$$

Vertex: $(8, -1)$
Focus: $(9, -1)$
Directrix: $x = 7$

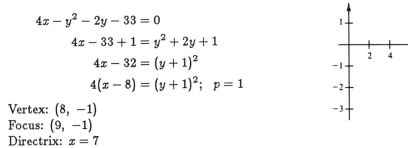

11. Find the vertex, focus, and directrix of $y^2 - 4y - 4x = 0$, and sketch its graph.

Solution:

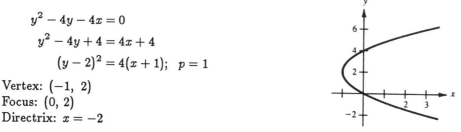

$$y^2 - 4y - 4x = 0$$
$$y^2 - 4y + 4 = 4x + 4$$
$$(y-2)^2 = 4(x+1); \quad p = 1$$

Vertex: $(-1,\ 2)$
Focus: $(0,\ 2)$
Directrix: $x = -2$

15. Find an equation of the parabola with vertex at $(0,\ 4)$ and directrix $y = 2$.

Solution:
Vertical axis
$$y = 4 - p = 2; \quad p = 2$$

$$(h,\ k) = (0,\ 4)$$
$$(x - 0)^2 = 4(2)(y - 4)$$
$$x^2 = 8(y - 4)$$

19. Find an equation of the parabola shown.

Solution:
Vertex: $(0,\ 4)$
Opens downward and passes through $(\pm 2,\ 0)$

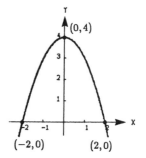

$$(x - 0)^2 = 4p(y - 4)$$
$$x^2 = 4p(y - 4)$$
$$4 = 4p(0 - 4)$$
$$4 = -16p$$
$$p = -\tfrac{1}{4}$$
$$x^2 = 4(-\tfrac{1}{4})(y - 4)$$
$$x^2 = -(y - 4)$$

23. Find the center, foci, and vertices of $9x^2 + 4y^2 + 36x - 24y + 36 = 0$, and sketch its graph.

Solution:

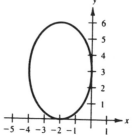

$$9x^2 + 4y^2 + 36x - 24y + 36 = 0$$
$$9(x^2 + 4x + 4) + 4(y^2 - 6y + 9) = -36 + 36 + 36$$
$$9(x + 2)^2 + 4(y - 3)^2 = 36$$
$$\frac{(x + 2)^2}{4} + \frac{(y - 3)^2}{9} = 1$$

$a = 3$, $b = 2$, $c = \sqrt{9 - 4} = \sqrt{5}$
Vertical major axis
Center: $(-2, 3)$
Foci: $(-2, 3 \pm \sqrt{5})$
Vertices: $(-2, 6)$ and $(-2, 0)$

27. Find the center, foci, and vertices of $12x^2 + 20y^2 - 12x + 40y - 37 = 0$, and sketch its graph.

Solution:

$$12x^2 + 20y^2 - 12x + 40y - 37 = 0$$

$$12\left(x^2 - x + \frac{1}{4}\right) + 20(y^2 + 2y + 1) = 37 + 3 + 20$$

$$12\left(x - \frac{1}{2}\right)^2 + 20(y + 1)^2 = 60$$

$$\frac{(x - 1/2)^2}{5} + \frac{(y + 1)^2}{3} = 1$$

$a = \sqrt{5}$, $b = \sqrt{3}$, $c = \sqrt{2}$
Horizontal major axis
Center: $\left(\frac{1}{2}, -1\right)$
Foci: $\left(\frac{1}{2} \pm \sqrt{2}, -1\right)$
Vertices: $\left(\frac{1}{2} \pm \sqrt{5}, -1\right)$

31. Find an equation of the ellipse with foci at $(0, 0)$ and $(0, 8)$, and a major axis of length 16.

Solution:
Center: $(0, 4)$; $c = 4$
$2a = 16$, $a = 8$, $b = \sqrt{64 - 16} = \sqrt{48}$
Vertical major axis

$$\frac{(x - 0)^2}{48} + \frac{(y - 4)^2}{64} = 1$$

$$\frac{x^2}{48} + \frac{(y - 4)^2}{64} = 1$$

35. Find an equation of the ellipse with center at $(0, 4)$, $a = 2c$, and vertices at $(-4, 4)$ and $(4, 4)$.

Solution:
Center: $(0, 4)$; $a = 2c$
Vertices: $(-4, 4)$, $(4, 4)$; $a = 4$,
$4 = 2c \Rightarrow c = 2$; $b = \sqrt{16 - 4} = \sqrt{12}$
Horizontal major axis

$$\frac{x^2}{16} + \frac{(y - 4)^2}{12} = 1$$

39. Find the center, vertices, and foci of $(y+6)^2 - (x-2)^2 = 1$, and sketch its graph, using asymptotes as an aid.

Solution:

$(y+6)^2 - (x-2)^2 = 1$

$a = b = 1, \quad c = \sqrt{1+1} = \sqrt{2}$

Center: $(2, -6)$

Vertical transverse axis

Foci: $(2, -6 \pm \sqrt{2})$

Vertices: $(2, -5)$ and $(2, -7)$

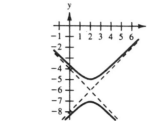

43. Find the center, vertices, and foci of $9y^2 - x^2 + 2x + 54y + 62 = 0$, and sketch its graph, using asymptotes as an aid.

Solution:

$$9y^2 - x^2 + 2x + 54y + 62 = 0$$

$$9(y^2 + 6y + 9) - (x^2 - 2x + 1) = -62 + 81 - 1$$

$$9(y+3)^2 - (x-1)^2 = 18$$

$$\frac{(y+3)^2}{2} - \frac{(x-1)^2}{18} = 1$$

Center: $(1, -3)$

$a = \sqrt{2}, \ b = \sqrt{18}, \ c = \sqrt{20} = 2\sqrt{5}$

Vertical transverse axis

Foci: $(1, -3 \pm 2\sqrt{5})$

Vertices: $(1, -3 \pm \sqrt{2})$

49. Find an equation for the hyperbola with vertices at $(4, 1)$ and $(4, 9)$, and foci at $(4, 0)$ and $(4, 10)$.

Solution:

Center: $(4, 5)$

Horizontal transverse axis

$a = 4, \ c = 5, \ b = \sqrt{25 - 16} = 3$

$$\frac{(x-4)^2}{16} - \frac{(y-5)^2}{9} = 1$$

53. Find an equation for the hyperbola with vertices at $(0, 2)$ and $(6, 2)$ and asymptotes $y = \frac{2}{3}x$ and $y = 4 - \frac{2}{3}x$.

Solution:

Horizontal transverse axis

Center: $(3, 2)$, $a = 3$

Asymptotes: $y - 2 = \pm\dfrac{b}{3}(x - 3)$

$$y = \pm\frac{b}{3}x \mp b + 2$$

$$b = 2$$

$$\frac{(x - 3)^2}{9} - \frac{(y - 2)^2}{4} = 1$$

55. Classify the graph of $x^2 + y^2 - 6x + 4y + 9 = 0$ as a circle, a parabola, an ellipse, or a hyperbola.

Solution:

$$x^2 + y^2 - 6x + 4y + 9 = 0$$
$$(x^2 - 6x + 9) + (y^2 + 4y + 4) = -9 + 9 + 4$$
$$(x - 3)^2 + (y + 2)^2 = 4$$

Circle

59. Classify the graph of $4x^2 + 3y^2 + 8x - 24y + 51 = 0$ as a circle, a parabola, an ellipse, or a hyperbola.

Solution:

$$4x^2 + 3y^2 + 8x - 24y + 51 = 0$$
$$4(x^2 + 2x + 1) + 3(y^2 - 8y + 16) = -51 + 4 + 48$$
$$4(x + 1)^2 + 3(y - 4)^2 = 1$$
$$\frac{(x + 1)^2}{1/4} + \frac{(y - 4)^2}{1/3} = 1$$

Ellipse

63. An earth satellite in a 100-mile high circular orbit around the earth has a velocity of approximately 17,500 miles per hour. If this velocity is multiplied by $\sqrt{2}$, then the satellite will have the minimum velocity necessary to escape the earth's gravity and it will follow a parabolic path with the center of the earth as the focus, as shown in the figure.

(a) Find the escape velocity of the satellite.
(b) Find an equation of its path (assume the radius of the earth is 4000 miles).

Solution:

(a) $V = 17,500\sqrt{2}$ mi/hr

$\approx 24,750$ mi/hr

(b) $p = -4100$, $(h,\ k) = (0,\ 4100)$

$(x - 0)^2 = 4(-4100)(y - 4100)$

$x^2 = -16,400(y - 4100)$

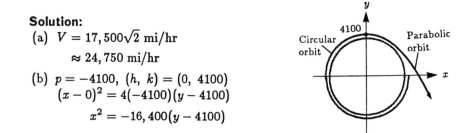

67. The earth moves in an elliptical orbit with the sun at one of the foci. The length of half of the major axis is 93 million miles and the eccentricity is 0.017. Find the least and greatest distances of the earth from the sun.

Solution:

$a = 93$ million mi

$e = c/a = 0.017$

$c = 1,581,000$ mi

Least distance: $a - c = 91,419,000$ mi

Greatest distance: $a + c = 94,581,000$ mi

REVIEW EXERCISES FOR CHAPTER 5

Solutions to Selected Exercises

5. Analyze the following equation and sketch its graph.

$$y = \frac{x^2}{x^2 + 1}$$

Solution:

$$y = \frac{x^2}{x^2 + 1} = 1 - \frac{1}{x^2 + 1}$$

Intercept: $(0, 0)$
y-axis symmetry
Horizontal asymptote: $y = 1$

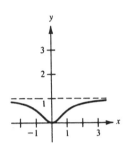

9. Analyze the following equation and sketch its graph.

$$y = \frac{2x^2}{x^2 - 4}$$

Solution:

$$y = \frac{2x^2}{x^2 - 4} = 2 + \frac{8}{x^2 - 4}$$

Intercept: $(0, 0)$
y-axis symmetry
Vertical asymptotes: $x = 2$ and $x = -2$
Horizontal asymptote: $y = 2$

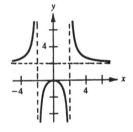

13. Analyze $5y^2 - 4x^2 = 20$ and sketch its graph.

Solution:

$$5y^2 - 4x^2 = 20$$

$$\frac{y^2}{4} - \frac{x^2}{5} = 1$$

Hyperbola
Vertical transverse axis
Center: $(0, 0)$
Vertices: $(0, \pm 2)$

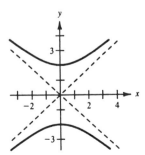

17. Analyze $x^2 + y^2 - 2x - 4y + 5 = 0$ and sketch its graph.

Solution:

$$x^2 + y^2 - 2x - 4y + 5 = 0$$

$$(x^2 - 2x + 1) + (y^2 - 4y + 4) = -5 + 1 + 4$$

$$(x - 1)^2 + (y - 2)^2 = 0$$

Point: $(1, 2)$

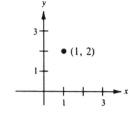

21. Write the partial fraction decomposition for $\dfrac{4 - x}{x^2 + 6x + 8}$.

Solution:

$$\frac{4 - x}{x^2 + 6x + 8} = \frac{4 - x}{(x + 2)(x + 4)}$$

$$\frac{4 - x}{(x + 2)(x - 4)} = \frac{A}{x + 2} + \frac{B}{x + 4}$$

$$4 - x = A(x + 4) + B(x + 2)$$

Let $x = -2$: $6 = 2A \Rightarrow A = 3$

Let $x = -4$: $8 = -2B \Rightarrow B = -4$

$$\frac{4 - x}{x^2 + 6x + 8} = \frac{3}{x + 2} - \frac{4}{x + 4}$$

25. Write the partial fraction decomposition for $\dfrac{x^2 + 2x}{x^3 - x^2 + x - 1}$.

Solution:

$$\frac{x^2 + 2x}{x^3 - x^2 + x - 1} = \frac{x^2 + 2x}{(x - 1)(x^2 + 1)}$$

$$\frac{x^2 + 2x}{(x - 1)(x^2 + 1)} = \frac{A}{x - 1} + \frac{Bx + C}{x^2 + 1}$$

$$x^2 + 2x = A(x^2 + 1) + (Bx + C)(x - 1)$$

Let $x = 1$: $3 = 2A,\ A = 3/2$

Let $x = 0$: $0 = A - C,\ C = 3/2$

Let $x = 2$: $8 = 5A + 2B + C$

$$8 = (15/2) + 2B + (3/2),\ B = -1/2$$

$$\frac{3/2}{x - 1} + \frac{-(1/2)x + 3/2}{x^2 + 1} = \frac{1}{2}\left(\frac{3}{x - 1} - \frac{x - 3}{x^2 + 1}\right)$$

29. Find an equation for the parabola with vertex at $(4, 2)$ and focus at $(4, 0)$.

Solution:

Vertical axis, $p = -2$

$$(x - h)^2 = 4p(y - k)$$

$$(x - 4)^2 = 4(-2)(y - 2)$$

$$(x - 4)^2 = -8(y - 2)$$

33. Find an equation for the ellipse with vertices at $(-3, 0)$ and $(7, 0)$ and foci at $(0, 0)$ and $(4, 0)$.

Solution:

Horizontal major axis

Center: $(2, 0)$

$a = 5, \ c = 2, \ b = \sqrt{25 - 4} = \sqrt{21}$

$$\frac{(x - h)^2}{a^2} + \frac{(y - k)^2}{b^2} = 1$$

$$\frac{(x - 2)^2}{25} + \frac{y^2}{21} = 1$$

37. Find an equation of the hyperbola with vertices at $(0, \pm 1)$ and foci at $(0, \pm 3)$.

Solution:

Vertical transverse axis

Center: $(0, 0)$

$a = 1, \ c = 3, \ b = \sqrt{9 - 1} = \sqrt{8}$

$$\frac{y^2}{1} - \frac{x^2}{8} = 1$$

41. The cost in millions of dollars for the government to seize $p\%$ of a certain illegal drug as it enters the country is given by

$$C = \frac{528p}{100 - p}, \quad 0 \le p < 100.$$

(a) Find the cost of seizing 25%.
(b) Find the cost of seizing 50%.
(c) Find the cost of seizing 75%.
(d) What does the cost approach as p approaches 100?

Solution:

(a) When $p = 25$, $C = \dfrac{528(25)}{100 - 25} = \$176$ million.

(b) When $p = 50$, $C = \dfrac{528(50)}{100 - 50} = \$528$ million.

(c) When $p = 75$, $C = \dfrac{528(75)}{100 - 75} = \$1584$ million.

(d) As $p \to 100$, $C \to \infty$.

Practice Test for Chapter 5

1. Sketch the graph of $f(x) = \dfrac{x-1}{2x}$ and label all intercepts and asymptotes.

2. Sketch the graph of $f(x) = \dfrac{3x^2 - 4}{x}$ and label all intercepts and asymptotes.

3. Find all the asymptotes of $f(x) = \dfrac{8x^2 - 9}{x^2 + 1}$.

4. Find all the asymptotes of $f(x) = \dfrac{4x^2 - 2x + 7}{x - 1}$.

5. Sketch the graph of $f(x) = \dfrac{x - 5}{(x - 5)^2}$.

For Exercises 6–9, write the partial fraction decomposition for the rational expression.

6. $\dfrac{1 - 2x}{x^2 + x}$

7. $\dfrac{6x}{x^2 - x - 2}$

8. $\dfrac{6x - 17}{(x - 3)^2}$

9. $\dfrac{3x^2 - x + 8}{x^3 + 2x}$

10. Find the vertex, focus, and directrix of the parabola $x^2 = 20y$.

11. Find the equation of the parabola with vertex $(0, 0)$ and focus $(7, 0)$.

12. Find the center, foci, and vertices of the ellipse $\dfrac{x^2}{144} + \dfrac{y^2}{25} = 1$.

13. Find the equation of the ellipse with foci $(\pm 4,\ 0)$ and minor axis of length 6.

14. Find the center, vertices, foci, and asymptotes of the hyperbola $\dfrac{y^2}{144} - \dfrac{x^2}{169} = 1$.

15. Find the equation of the hyperbola with vertices $(\pm 4,\ 0)$ and asymptotes $y = \pm\frac{1}{2}x$.

16. Find the equation of the parabola with vertex $(6,\ -1)$ and focus $(6,\ 3)$.

17. Find the center, foci, and vertices of the ellipse $16x^2 + 9y^2 - 96x + 36y + 36 = 0$.

18. Find the equation of the ellipse with vertices $(-1,\ 1)$ and $(7,\ 1)$ and minor axis of length 2.

19. Find the center, vertices, foci, and asymptotes of the hyperbola $4(x + 3)^2 - 9(y - 1)^2 = 1$.

20. Find the equation of the hyperbola with vertices $(3,\ 4)$ and $(3,\ -4)$ and foci $(3,\ 7)$ and $(3,\ -7)$.

CHAPTER 6

Exponential and Logarithmic Functions

SECTION 6.1

Exponential Functions

- You should know that a function of the form $y = a^x$, where $a > 0$, $a \neq 1$, is called an exponential function with base a.

- You should be able to graph exponential functions.

- You should know some properties of exponential functions where $a > 0$ and $a \neq 1$.

  (a) If $a^x = a^y$, then $x = y$.
  (b) If $a^x = b^x$ and $x \neq 0$, then $a = b$.

- You should know formulas for compound interest.

  (a) For n compoundings per year: $A = P\left(1 + \dfrac{r}{n}\right)^{nt}$.

  (b) For continuous compoundings: $A = Pe^{rt}$.

Solutions to Selected Exercises

3. Use a calculator to evaluate $1000(1.06)^{-5}$. Round your answer to three decimal places.

Solution:

$$1000(1.06)^{-5} \approx 747.258$$

7. Use a calculator to evaluate $8^{2\pi}$. Round your answer to three decimal places.

Solution:

$$8^{2\pi} \approx 472,369.379$$

11. Use a calculator to evaluate e^2. Round your answer to three decimal places.

Solution:

$$e^2 \approx 7.389$$

15. Match $f(x) = 3^x$ with its graph.

Solution:
$f(x) = 3^x$
y-intercept: $(0, 1)$
3^x increases as x increases
Matches graph (g)

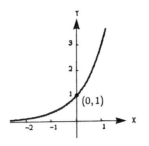

19. Match $f(x) = 3^x - 4$ with its graph.

Solution:
$f(x) = 3^x - 4$
y-intercept: $(0, -3)$
$3^x - 4$ increases as x increases
Matches graph (d)

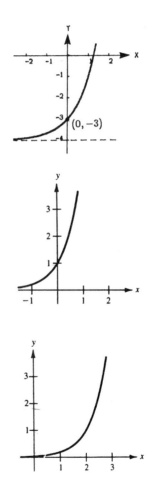

23. Sketch the graph of $g(x) = 5^x$.

Solution:
$g(x) = 5^x$

x	-2	-1	0	1	2
$g(x)$	$\frac{1}{25}$	$\frac{1}{5}$	1	5	25

27. Sketch the graph of $h(x) = 5^{x-2}$.

Solution:
$h(x) = 5^{x-2}$

x	-1	0	1	2	3
$h(x)$	$\frac{1}{125}$	$\frac{1}{25}$	$\frac{1}{5}$	1	5

31. Sketch the graph of $y = 2^{-x^2}$.

Solution:

$y = 2^{-x^2} = \left(\frac{1}{2}\right)^{x^2}$

x	0	1	-1	2	-2
y	1	$\frac{1}{2}$	$\frac{1}{2}$	$\frac{1}{16}$	$\frac{1}{16}$

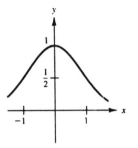

33. Sketch the graph of $y = 3^{|x|}$.

Solution:

$y = 3^{|x|}$

x	0	1	2	-1	-2
y	1	3	9	3	9

37. Sketch the graph of $f(x) = e^{2x}$.

Solution:

$f(x) = e^{2x}$

x	0	1	2	-1	-2
$f(x)$	1	7.39	54.60	0.135	0.02

43. Complete the following table to determine the balance A for \$2500 invested at 12% for 20 years and compounded n times per year.

n	1	2	4	12	365	Continuous compounding
A						

Solution:

$$A = P\left(1 + \frac{r}{n}\right)^{nt}$$

$P = 2500$, $r = 0.12$, $t = 20$

When $n = 1$, $A = 2500\left(1 + \frac{0.12}{1}\right)^{(1)(20)} \approx \$24,115.73$

When $n = 2$, $A = 2500\left(1 + \frac{0.12}{2}\right)^{(2)(20)} \approx \$25,714.29$

When $n = 4$, $A = 2500\left(1 + \frac{0.12}{4}\right)^{(4)(20)} \approx \$26,602.23$

When $n = 12$, $A = 2500\left(1 + \frac{0.12}{12}\right)^{(12)(20)} \approx \$27,231.38$

When $n = 365$, $A = 2500\left(1 + \frac{0.12}{365}\right)^{(365)(20)} \approx \$27,547.07$

For continuous compounding, $A = Pe^{rt}$, $A = 2500e^{(0.12)(20)} \approx \$27,557.94$

n	1	2	4	12	365	Continuous compounding
A	\$24,115.73	\$25,714.29	\$26,602.23	\$27,231.38	\$27,547.07	\$27,557.94

49. The demand equation for a certain product is given by $p = 500 - 0.5e^{0.004x}$. Find the price p for a demand of (a) $x = 1000$ units and (b) $x = 1500$ units.

Solution:

(a) $x = 1000$

$p = 500 - 0.5e^4$

$\approx \$472.70$

(b) $x = 1500$

$p = 500 - 0.5e^6$

$\approx \$298.29$

53. Given the exponential function $f(x) = a^x$, show that (a) $f(u + v) = f(u) \cdot f(v)$ and (b) $f(2x) = [f(x)]^2$.

Solution:

(a) $f(u + v) = a^{u+v}$

$= a^u \cdot a^v$

$= f(u) \cdot f(v)$

(b) $f(2x) = a^{2x}$

$= (a^x)^2$

$= [f(x)]^2$

SECTION 6.2

Logarithmic Functions

■ You should know that a function of the form $y = \log_b M$, where $b > 0$, $b \neq 1$, and $M > 0$, is called a logarithm of M to base B.

■ You should be able to convert from logarithmic form to exponential form and vice versa.

■ You should know the following properties of logarithms.

(a) $\log_a 1 = 0$

(b) $\log_a a = 1$

(c) $\log_a a^x = x$

■ You should know the definition of the natural logarithmic function.

$$\log_e x = \ln x, \quad x > 0$$

■ You should know the properties of the natural logarithmic function.

(a) $\ln 1 = 0$

(b) $\ln e = 1$

(c) $\ln e^x = x$

■ You should know the change of base formula.

$$\log_a x = \frac{\log_b x}{\log_b a}$$

■ You should be able to graph logarithmic functions.

Solutions to Selected Exercises

5. Evaluate $\log_{16} 4$ without using a calculator.

Solution:

$$\log_{16} 4 = \log_{16} \sqrt{16} = \log_{16} 16^{1/2} = \tfrac{1}{2}$$

9. Evaluate $\log_{10} 0.01$ without using a calculator.

Solution:

$$\log_{10} 0.01 = \log_{10} \tfrac{1}{100} = \log_{10} 10^{-2} = -2$$

13. Evaluate $\ln e^{-2}$ without using a calculator.

Solution:

$$\ln e^{-2} = -2$$

17. Use the definition of a logarithm to write $5^3 = 125$ in logarithmic form.

Solution:

$$5^3 = 125$$
$$\log_5 125 = 3$$

23. Use the definition of a logarithm to write $e^3 = 20.0855\ldots$ in logarithmic form.

Solution:

$$e^3 = 20.0855\ldots$$
$$\log_e 20.0855\ldots = 3$$
$$\ln 20.0855\ldots \approx 3$$

27. Use a calculator to evaluate $\log_{10} 345$. Round your answer to three decimal places.

Solution:

$$\log_{10} 345 = 2.537819095\ldots$$
$$\approx 2.538$$

31. Use a calculator to evaluate $\ln(1 + \sqrt{3})$. Round your answer to three decimal places.

Solution:

$$\ln(1 + \sqrt{3}) = 1.005052539\ldots$$
$$\approx 1.005$$

35. Demonstrate that $f(x) = e^x$ and $g(x) = \ln x$ are inverses of each other by sketching their graphs on the same coordinate plane.

Solution:

x	-2	-1	0	1	2	3
$f(x)$	0.135	0.368	1	2.718	7.389	20.086
$g(x)$	—	—	—	0	0.693	1.097

The graph of g is obtained by reflecting the graph of f about the line $y = x$.

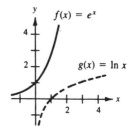

39. Use the graph of $y = \ln x$ to match $f(x) = -\ln(x + 2)$ to its graph.

Solution:
$f(x) = -\ln(x + 2)$
Vertical asymptote: $x = -2$
x-intercept: $(-1,\ 0)$
Matches graph (a)

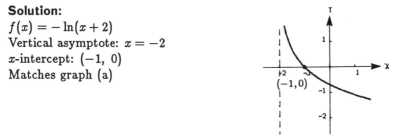

45. Find the domain, vertical asymptote, and x-intercept of $h(x) = \log_4(x - 3)$, and sketch its graph.

Solution:
Domain: $x - 3 > 0 \Rightarrow x > 3$
      The domain is $(3,\ \infty)$.

Vertical asymptote: $x - 3 = 0 \Rightarrow x = 3$
      The vertical asymptote is the line $x = 3$.

x-intercept: $\log_4(x - 3) = 0$
      $x - 3 = 1 \Rightarrow x = 4$
      The x-intercept is $(4,\ 0)$.

x	3.5	4	5	7
$h(x)$	-0.5	0	0.5	1

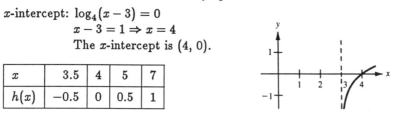

51. Use the change of base formula to write $\log_3 5$ as a multiple of a common logarithm.

Solution:

$$\log_3 5 = \frac{\log_{10} 5}{\log_{10} 3}$$

55. Use the change of base formula to write $\log_3 5$ as a multiple of a natural logarithm.

Solution:

$$\log_3 5 = \frac{\ln 5}{\ln 3}$$

59. Evaluate $\log_3 7$ using the change of base formula. Do the problem twice; once with common logarithms and once with natural logarithms. Round your answer to three decimal places.

Solution:

$$\log_3 7 = \frac{\log_{10} 7}{\log_{10} 3} = 1.771243749\ldots$$

$$\approx 1.771$$

$$\log_3 7 = \frac{\ln 7}{\ln 3} = 1.771243749\ldots$$

$$\approx 1.771$$

67. Students in a mathematics class were given an exam and then retested monthly with an equivalent exam. The average score for the class was given by the human memory model

$$f(t) = 80 - 17\log_{10}(t+1), \quad 0 \le t \le 12$$

where t is the time in months.

(a) What was the average score on the original exam $(t = 0)$?
(b) What was the average score after four months?
(c) What was the average score after ten months?

Solution:
(a) $f(0) = 80 - 17\log_{10} 1 = 80.0$
(b) $f(4) = 80 - 17\log_{10} 5 \approx 68.1$
(c) $f(10) = 80 - 17\log_{10} 11 \approx 62.3$

69. The population of a town will double in

$$t = \frac{10\ln 2}{\ln 67 - \ln 50}$$

years. Find t.

Solution:

$$t = \frac{10\ln 2}{\ln 67 - \ln 50}$$

$$t \approx \frac{6.931471806}{4.204692619 - 3.912023005}$$

$$t \approx 23.68 \text{ years}$$

73. (a) Use a calculator to complete the following table for the function

$$f(x) = \frac{\ln x}{x}.$$

x	1	5	10	10^2	10^4	10^6
$f(x)$						

(b) Use the table in part (a) to determine what $f(x)$ approaches as x increases without bound.

Solution:

(a)

x	1	5	10	10^2	10^4	10^6
$f(x)$	0	0.322	0.230	0.046	0.00092	0.0000138

(b) As $x \to \infty$, $f(x) \to 0$.

SECTION 6.3

Properties of Logarithms

■ You should know the following properties of logarithms.

(a) $\log_a(uv) = \log_a u + \log_a v$

(b) $\log_a(u/v) = \log_a u - \log_a v$

(c) $\log_a u^n = n \log_a u$

■ You should be able to rewrite logarithmic expressions.

Solutions to Selected Exercises

5. Use the properties of logarithms to write $\log_8 x^4$ as a sum, difference, or multiple of logarithms.

Solution:

$$\log_8 x^4 = 4 \log_8 x$$

9. Use the properties of logarithms to write $\log_2 xyz$ as a sum, difference, or multiple of logarithms.

Solution:

$$\log_2 xyz = \log_2[x(yz)] = \log_2 x + \log_2 yz = \log_2 x + \log_2 y + \log_2 z$$

15. Use the properties of logarithms to write the following expression as a sum, difference, or multiple of logarithms.

$$\log_b \frac{x^2}{y^2 z^3}$$

Solution:

$$\log_b \frac{x^2}{y^2 z^3} = \log_b x^2 - \log_b y^2 z^3 = \log_b x^2 - [\log_b y^2 + \log_b z^3] = 2 \log_b x - 2 \log_b y - 3 \log_b z$$

19. Use the properties of logarithms to write the following expression as a sum, difference, or multiple of logarithms.

$$\log_9 \frac{x^4 \sqrt{y}}{z^5}$$

Solution:

$$\log_9 \frac{x^4 \sqrt{y}}{z^5} = \log_9 x^4 \sqrt{y} - \log_9 z^5 = \log_9 x^4 + \log_9 \sqrt{y} - \log_9 z^5 = 4 \log_9 x + \tfrac{1}{2} \log_9 y - 5 \log_9 z$$

23. Write $\log_4 z - \log_4 y$ as the logarithm of a single quantity.

Solution:

$$\log_4 z - \log_4 y = \log_4 \frac{z}{y}$$

27. Write $\ln x - 3\ln(x+1)$ as the logarithm of a single quantity.

Solution:

$$\ln x - 3\ln(x+1) = \ln x - \ln(x+1)^3 = \ln \frac{x}{(x+1)^3}$$

33. Write $\ln x - 2[\ln(x+2) + \ln(x-2)]$ as the logarithm of a single quantity.

Solution:

$$\begin{aligned}
\ln x - 2[\ln(x+2) + \ln(x-2)] &= \ln x - 2\ln(x+2)(x-2) \\
&= \ln x - 2\ln(x^2-4) \\
&= \ln x - \ln(x^2-4)^2 \\
&= \ln \frac{x}{(x^2-4)^2}
\end{aligned}$$

37. Write $\frac{1}{3}[\ln y + 2\ln(y+4)] - \ln(y-1)$ as the logarithm of a single quantity.

Solution:

$$\begin{aligned}
\frac{1}{3}[\ln y + 2\ln(y+4)] - \ln(y-1) &= \frac{1}{3}[\ln y + \ln(y+4)^2] - \ln(y-1) \\
&= \frac{1}{3}\ln[y(y+4)^2] - \ln(y-1) \\
&= \ln \sqrt[3]{y(y+4)^2} - \ln(y-1) \\
&= \ln \frac{\sqrt[3]{y(y+4)^2}}{y-1}
\end{aligned}$$

41. Approximate $\log_b 6$ using the properties of logarithms, given $\log_b 2 \approx 0.3562$ and $\log_b 3 \approx 0.5646$.

Solution:

$$\log_b 6 = \log_b(2 \cdot 3) = \log_b 2 + \log_b 3 \approx 0.3562 + 0.5646 = 0.9208$$

47. Approximate $\log_b \sqrt{2}$ using the properties of logarithms, given $\log_b 2 \approx 0.3562$.

Solution:

$$\log_b \sqrt{2} = \log_b(2^{1/2}) = \tfrac{1}{2}\log_b 2 \approx \tfrac{1}{2}(0.3562) = 0.1781$$

51. Approximate $\log_b \frac{1}{4}$ using the properties of logarithms, given $\log_b 2 \approx 0.3562$.

Solution:
$$\log_b \tfrac{1}{4} = \log_b 1 - \log_b 4 = 0 - \log_b 2^2 = -2\log_b 2 \approx -2(0.3562) = -0.7124$$

55. Approximate the following using the properties of logarithms, given $\log_b 2 \approx 0.3562$ and $\log_b 3 \approx 0.5646$.
$$\log_b \left[\frac{(4.5)^3}{\sqrt{3}}\right]$$

Solution:
$$\log_b \left[\frac{(4.5)^3}{\sqrt{3}}\right] = 3\log_b 4.5 - \frac{1}{2}\log_b 3$$
$$= 3\log_b \frac{9}{2} - \frac{1}{2}\log_b 3$$
$$= 3[\log_b 9 - \log_b 2] - \frac{1}{2}\log_b 3$$
$$= 3[2\log_b 3 - \log_b 2] - \frac{1}{2}\log_b 3$$
$$= 3[2(0.5646) - 0.3562] - \frac{1}{2}(0.5646)$$
$$= 2.0367$$

59. Find the exact value of $\log_4 16^{1.2}$.

Solution:
$$\log_4 16^{1.2} = 1.2\log_4 16 = 1.2\log_4 4^2 = (1.2)(2)\log_4 4 = (2.4)(1) = 2.4$$

63. Use the properties of logarithms to simplify $\log_4 8$.

Solution:
$$\log_4 8 = \log_4 2^3 = 3\log_4 2 = 3\log_4 \sqrt{4} = 3\log_4 4^{1/2} = 3\left(\tfrac{1}{2}\right)\log_4 4 = \tfrac{3}{2}$$

67. Use the properties of logarithms to simplify $\log_5 \frac{1}{250}$.

Solution:
$$\log_5 \tfrac{1}{250} = \log_5 1 - \log_5 250 = 0 - \log_5 (125 \cdot 2)$$
$$= -\log_5 (5^3 \cdot 2) = -[\log_5 5^3 + \log_5 2]$$
$$= -[3\log_5 5 + \log_5 2] = -3 - \log_5 2$$

71. Prove that $\log_b \dfrac{u}{v} = \log_b u - \log_b v$.

Solution:
Let $x = \log_b u$ and $y = \log_b v$, then $b^x = u$ and $b^y = v$.
$$\frac{u}{v} = \frac{b^x}{b^y} = b^{x-y}$$
$$\log_b \left(\frac{u}{v}\right) = \log_b (b^{x-y}) = x - y = \log_b u - \log_b v$$

SECTION 6.4

Solving Exponential and Logarithmic Equations

■ You should be able to solve exponential and logarithmic equations.

■ To solve an exponential equation, take the logarithm of both sides.

■ To solve a logarithmic equation, rewrite it in exponential form.

Solutions to Selected Exercises

5. Solve $\left(\frac{3}{4}\right)^x = \frac{27}{64}$ for x.

Solution:

$$\left(\tfrac{3}{4}\right)^x = \tfrac{27}{64}$$
$$\left(\tfrac{3}{4}\right)^x = \left(\tfrac{3}{4}\right)^3$$
$$x = 3$$

9. Solve $\log_{10} x = -1$ for x.

Solution:

$$\log_{10} x = -1$$
$$x = 10^{-1} = \tfrac{1}{10}$$

13. Apply the inverse properties of $\ln x$ and e^x to simplify $e^{\ln(5x+2)}$.

Solution:

$$e^{\ln(5x+2)} = 5x + 2$$

17. Solve $10^x = 42$.

Solution:

$$10^x = 42$$
$$x = \log_{10} 42 \approx 1.6232$$

21. Solve $3(10^{x-1}) = 2$.

Solution:

$$3(10^{x-1}) = 2$$
$$10^{x-1} = \tfrac{2}{3}$$
$$x - 1 = \log_{10} \tfrac{2}{3}$$
$$x = 1 + \log_{10} \tfrac{2}{3} \approx 0.8239$$

25. Solve $500e^{-x} = 300$.

Solution:

$$500e^{-x} = 300$$
$$e^{-x} = \tfrac{3}{5}$$
$$-x = \ln \tfrac{3}{5}$$
$$x = -\ln \tfrac{3}{5} = \ln \tfrac{5}{3} \approx 0.5108$$

29. Solve $25e^{2x+1} = 962$.

Solution:

$$25e^{2x+1} = 962$$
$$e^{2x+1} = \tfrac{962}{25}$$
$$2x + 1 = \ln \tfrac{962}{25}$$
$$2x = -1 + \ln \tfrac{962}{25}$$
$$x = \tfrac{1}{2}\left[-1 + \ln \tfrac{962}{25} \right] = -\tfrac{1}{2} + \tfrac{1}{2} \ln \tfrac{962}{25} \approx 1.3251$$

35. Solve $\left(1 + \frac{0.10}{12}\right)^{12t} = 2$.

Solution:

$$\left(1 + \frac{0.10}{12}\right)^{12t} = 2$$
$$\ln\left(1 + \frac{0.10}{12}\right)^{12t} = \ln 2$$
$$12t \ln\left(1 + \frac{0.10}{12}\right) = \ln 2$$
$$t = \frac{\ln 2}{12 \ln\left(1 + \frac{0.10}{12}\right)} \approx 6.9603$$

39. Solve $\left(\frac{1}{1.0775}\right)^{N} = 0.2247$.

Solution:

$$\left(\frac{1}{1.0775}\right)^N = 0.2247$$

$$N = \frac{\ln(0.2247)}{\ln\left(\frac{1}{1.0775}\right)} = \frac{\ln(0.2247)}{\ln 1 - \ln(1.0775)} = \frac{\ln(0.2247)}{-\ln(1.0775)} \approx 20.0016$$

43. Solve $3(1 + e^{2x}) = 4$.

Solution:

$$3(1 + e^{2x}) = 4$$
$$1 + e^{2x} = \tfrac{4}{3}$$
$$e^{2x} = \tfrac{1}{3}$$
$$2x = \ln \tfrac{1}{3}$$
$$x = \tfrac{1}{2} \ln \tfrac{1}{3} \approx -0.5493$$

47. Solve $\dfrac{e^x + e^{-x}}{e^x - e^{-x}} = 2$.

Solution:

$$\frac{e^x + e^{-x}}{e^x - e^{-x}} = 2$$

$$\frac{e^x(e^x + e^{-x})}{e^x(e^x - e^{-x})} = 2$$

$$\frac{e^{2x} + 1}{e^{2x} - 1} = 2$$

$$e^{2x} + 1 = 2(e^{2x} - 1)$$

$$3 = e^{2x}$$

$$2x = \ln 3$$

$$x = \frac{1}{2} \ln 3 \approx 0.549$$

51. Solve $2 \ln x = 7$.

Solution:

$$2 \ln x = 7$$
$$\ln x = \tfrac{7}{2}$$
$$x = e^{7/2} \approx 33.1154$$

55. Solve $\log_{10}(z - 3) = 2$.

Solution:

$$\log_{10}(z - 3) = 2$$
$$z - 3 = 10^2$$
$$z = 10^2 + 3 = 103$$

59. Solve $\log_{10}(x + 4) - \log_{10} x = \log_{10}(x + 2)$.

Solution:

$$\log_{10}(x + 4) - \log_{10} x = \log_{10}(x + 2)$$

$$\log_{10}\left(\frac{x + 4}{4}\right) = \log_{10}(x + 2)$$

$$\frac{x + 4}{x} = x + 2$$

$$x + 4 = x^2 + 2x$$

$$0 = x^2 + x - 4$$

$$x = \frac{-1 \pm \sqrt{17}}{2} = -\frac{1}{2} \pm \frac{\sqrt{17}}{2} \qquad \text{Quadratic Formula}$$

63. Solve $\ln x^2 = (\ln x)^2$.

Solution:

$$\ln x^2 = (\ln x)^2$$

$$2\ln x = (\ln x)^2$$

$$0 = (\ln x)^2 - 2\ln x$$

$$0 = \ln x(\ln x - 2)$$

$$\begin{array}{ccc} \ln x = 0 & \text{or} & \ln x - 2 = 0 \\ x = e^0 & \text{or} & \ln x = 2 \\ x = 1 & \text{or} & x = e^2 \end{array}$$

67. The demand equation for a certain product is given by $p = 500 - 0.5(e^{0.004x})$. Find the demand x for a price of (a) $p = \$350$ and (b) $p = \$300$.

Solution:

(a)
$$350 = 500 - 0.5(e^{0.004x})$$
$$-150 = -0.5(e^{0.004x})$$
$$300 = e^{0.004x}$$
$$0.004x = \ln 300$$
$$x = \frac{\ln 300}{0.004} \approx 1426 \text{ units}$$

(b)
$$300 = 500 - 0.5(e^{0.004x})$$
$$-200 = -0.5(e^{0.004x})$$
$$400 = e^{0.004x}$$
$$0.004x = \ln 400$$
$$x = \frac{\ln 400}{0.004} \approx 1498 \text{ units}$$

SECTION 6.5

Applications of Exponential and Logarithmic Functions

■ You should be able to solve compound interest problems.

(a) Compound interest formulas:

  1. $A = P\left(1 + \dfrac{r}{n}\right)^{nt}$

  2. $A = Pe^{rt}$

(b) Doubling time:

  1. $t = \dfrac{\ln 2}{n\ln[1 + (r/n)]}$, n compoundings per year

  2. $t = \dfrac{\ln 2}{r}$, continuous compounding

(c) Effective yield:

  1. Effective yield $= \left(1 + \dfrac{r}{n}\right)^{n} - 1$, n compoundings per year

  2. Effective yield $= e^{r} - 1$, continuous compounding

■ You should be able to solve growth and decay problems.

$$Q(t) = Ce^{kt}$$

(a) If $k > 0$, the population grows.

(b) If $k < 0$, the population decays.

(c) Ratio of Carbon 12 to Carbon 14 is $R(t) = \dfrac{1}{10^{12}} 2^{-t/5700}$

■ You should be able to solve logistics model problems.

$$Q(t) = \dfrac{M}{1 + \left(\dfrac{M}{Q_0} - 1\right)e^{-kt}}$$

■ You should be able to solve intensity model problems.

$$S = k\log_{10}\dfrac{I}{I_0}$$

Solutions to Selected Exercises

5. $500 is deposited into an account with continuously compounded interest. If the balance is $1292.85 after ten years, find the annual percentage rate, the effective yield, and the time to double.

Solution:
$P = 500$, $A = 1292.85$, $t = 10$
$A = Pe^{rt}$

$$1292.85 = 500e^{10r}$$

$$\frac{1292.85}{500} = e^{10r}$$

$$10r = \ln\left(\frac{1292.85}{500}\right)$$

$$r = \frac{1}{10}\ln\left(\frac{1292.85}{100}\right) \approx 0.095 = 9.5\%$$

Effective yield $= e^{0.095} - 1 \approx 0.09966 \approx 9.97\%$

Time to double: $1000 = 500e^{0.095t}$

$$2 = e^{0.095t}$$

$$0.095t = \ln 2$$

$$t = \frac{\ln 2}{0.095} \approx 7.30 \text{ years}$$

9. $5000 is deposited into an account with continuously compounded interest. If the effective yield is 8.33%, find the annual percentage rate, the time to double, and the amount after 10 years.

Solution:
$P = 5000$
Effective yield $= 8.33\%$
$0.0833 = e^r - 1$

$$r = \ln 1.0833 \approx 0.0800 = 8\%$$

Time to double: $10,000 = 5000e^{0.08t}$

$$t = \frac{\ln 2}{0.08} \approx 8.66 \text{ years}$$

After 10 years: $A = 5000e^{0.08(10)} \approx \$11,127.70$

13. Determine the time necessary for $1000 to double if it is invested at 11% compounded (a) annually, (b) monthly, (c) daily, and (d) continuously.

Solution:

$P = 1000$, $r = 11\%$

(a) $n = 1$

$$t = \frac{\ln 2}{\ln(1 + 0.11)} \approx 6.642 \text{ years}$$

(b) $n = 12$

$$t = \frac{\ln 2}{12 \ln\left(1 + \frac{0.11}{12}\right)} \approx 6.330 \text{ years}$$

(c) $n = 365$

$$t = \frac{\ln 2}{365 \ln\left(1 + \frac{0.11}{365}\right)} \approx 6.302 \text{ years}$$

(d) Continuously

$$t = \frac{\ln 2}{0.11} \approx 6.301 \text{ years}$$

17. $50 is deposited monthly into a savings account at an annual rate of 7% compounded monthly. Find the balance, A, after 20 years given that

$$A = \frac{P(e^{rt} - 1)}{e^{r/12} - 1}.$$

Solution:

$p = 50$, $r = 7\%$, $t = 20$

$$A = \frac{50(e^{0.07(20)} - 1)}{e^{0.07/12} - 1} \approx \$26,111.12$$

21. The population P of a city is given by $P = 105,300e^{0.015t}$, where t is the time in years with $t = 0$ corresponding to 1985. According to this model, in what year will the city have a population of 150,000?

Solution:

$$150,000 = 105,300e^{0.015t}$$

$$0.015t = \ln\left(\frac{150,000}{105,300}\right)$$

$$t = \frac{1}{0.015} \ln\left(\frac{150,000}{105,300}\right) \approx 23.588 \text{ years}$$

$$1985 + 24 = 2009$$

The city will have a population of 150,000 in the year 2009.

25. The half-life of the isotope Ra^{226} is 1,620 years. If the initial quantity is 10 grams, how much will remain after 1000 years, and after 10,000 years?

Solution:

$$Q(t) = Ce^{kt}$$
$$Q = 10 \quad \text{when } t = 0 \Rightarrow 10 = Ce^{\circ} \Rightarrow 10 = C$$
$$Q(t) = 10e^{kt}$$
$$Q = 5 \quad \text{when } t = 1620$$
$$5 = 10e^{1620k}$$
$$k = \tfrac{1}{1620} \ln\left(\tfrac{1}{2}\right)$$
$$Q(t) = 10e^{[\ln(1/2)/1620]t}$$

When $t = 1000$, $Q(t) = 10e^{[\ln(1/2)/1620](1000)} \approx 6.52$ grams.
When $t = 10,000$, $Q(t) = 10e^{[\ln(1/2)/1620](10000)} \approx 0.14$ gram.

29. The half-life of the isotope Pu^{230} is 24,360 years. If 2.1 grams remain after 1000 years, what is the initial quantity and how much will remain after 10,000 years?

Solution:

$$y = Ce^{[\ln(1/2)/24360]t}$$
$$2.1 = Ce^{[\ln(1/2)/24360](1000)}$$
$$C \approx 2.16$$

The initial quantity is 2.16 grams.
When $t = 10,000$, $y = 2.16e^{[\ln(1/2)/24360](10000)} \approx 1.62$ grams.

33. Find the constant k such that the exponential function $y = Ce^{kt}$ passes through the points (0, 1) and (4, 10).

Solution:

$$y = Ce^{kt}$$
$$1 = Ce^{k(0)}, \quad (0,\ 1)$$
$$1 = C$$
$$y = e^{kt}$$
$$10 = e^{4k}, \quad (4,\ 10)$$
$$4k = \ln 10$$
$$k = \frac{\ln 10}{4} \approx 0.5756$$

37. The sales S (in thousands of units) of a new product after it has been on the market t years are given by

$$S(t) = 100(1 - e^{kt}).$$

(a) Find S as a function of t if 15,000 units have been sold after one year.
(b) How many units will be sold after five years?

Solution:
$S(t) = 100(1 - e^{kt}), \quad S = 15$ when $t = 1$

(a) $15 = 100(1 - e^k)$

$\quad\quad 0.15 = 1 - e^k$

$\quad\quad\quad e^k = 0.85$

$\quad\quad\quad\ k = \ln 0.85$

$\quad\quad S(t) = 100[1 - e^{(\ln 0.85)t}] = 100(1 - e^{-0.1625t})$

(b) $S(5) = 100[1 - e^{-(0.1625)(5)}] \approx 55.625$ thousands of units $= 55,625$ units

41. The intensity level β, in decibels, of a sound wave is defined by

$$\beta(I) = 10 \log_{10} \frac{I}{I_0}$$

where I_0 is an intensity of 10^{-16} watts per square centimeter, corresponding roughly to the faintest sound that can be heard. Determine $\beta(I)$ for the following conditions.

(a) $I = 10^{-14}$ watts per centimeter (whisper)
(b) $I = 10^{-9}$ watts per centimeter (busy street corner)
(c) $I = 10^{-6.5}$ watts per centimeter (air hammer)
(d) $I = 10^{-4}$ watts per centimeter (threshold of pain)

Solution:
$\beta(I) = 10 \log_{10} \dfrac{I}{I_0}$ where $I_0 = 10^{-16}$ watt/cm^2.

(a) $\beta(10^{-14}) = 10 \log_{10} \dfrac{10^{-14}}{10^{-16}} = 10 \log_{10} 10^2 = 20$

(b) $\beta(10^{-9}) = 10 \log_{10} \dfrac{10^{-9}}{10^{-16}} = 10 \log_{10} 10^7 = 70$

(c) $\beta(10^{-6.5}) = 10 \log_{10} \dfrac{10^{-6.5}}{10^{-16}} = 10 \log_{10} 10^{9.5} = 95$

(d) $\beta(10^{-4}) = 10 \log_{10} \dfrac{10^{-4}}{10^{-16}} = 10 \log_{10} 10^{12} = 120$

45. Use the acidity model $pH = -\log_{10}[H^+]$, where acidity (pH) is a measure of the hydrogen ion concentration $[H^+]$ (measured in moles of hydrogen per liter) of a solution. Find the pH if $[H^+] = 2.3 \times 10^{-5}$.

Solution:

$$pH = -\log_{10}[H^+] = -\log_{10}[2.3 \times 10^{-5}] \approx 4.64$$

49. Use **Newton's Law of Cooling** which states that the rate of change in the temperature of an object is proportional to the difference between its temperature and the temperature of its environment. If $T(t)$ is the temperature of the object at time t in minutes, T_0 is the initial temperature, and T_e is the constant temperature of the environment, then

$$T(t) = T_e + (T_0 - T_e)e^{-kt}.$$

An object in a room at $70°$ F cools from $350°$ F to $150°$ F in 45 minutes.

(a) Find the temperature of the object as a function of time.
(b) Find the temperature after it has cooled for one hour.
(c) Find the time necessary for the object to cool to $80°$ F.

Solution:
(a) $T_e = 70,\ \ T_0 = 350,\ \ T = 150$ when $t = 45$

$$150 = 70 + (350 - 70)e^{-45k}$$

$$80 = 280e^{-45k}$$

$$\frac{2}{7} = e^{-45k}$$

$$k = \frac{\ln(2/7)}{-45}$$

$$T(t) = 70 + 280e^{-[\ln(2/7)/-45]t} = 70 + 280e^{-0.02784t}$$

(b) $T(60) = 70 + 280e^{[\ln(2/7)/45](60)} \approx 122.7°$

(c) $\qquad 80 = 70 + 280e^{[\ln(2/7)/45]t}$

$$\frac{1}{28} = e^{[\ln(2/7)/45]t}$$

$$\frac{\ln(2/7)}{45}t = \ln\left(\frac{1}{28}\right)$$

$$t = \frac{45\ln(1/28)}{\ln(2/7)} \approx 119.7 \text{ minutes}$$

REVIEW EXERCISES FOR CHAPTER 6

Solutions to Selected Exercises

3. Sketch the graph of $g(x) = 6^{-x}$.

Solution:

$$g(x) = 6^{-x} = \left(\tfrac{1}{6}\right)^x$$

x	0	1	-1
$g(x)$	1	$\frac{1}{6}$	6

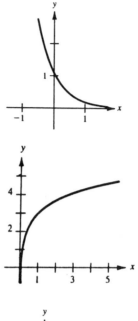

11. Sketch the graph of $f(x) = \ln x + 3$.

Solution:

$$f(x) = \ln x + 3$$

x	1	2	3	$\frac{1}{2}$	$\frac{1}{4}$
$f(x)$	3	3.69	4.10	2.31	1.61

15. Sketch the graph of $h(x) = \ln(e^{x-1})$.

Solution:

$$
\begin{aligned}
h(x) &= \ln(e^{x-1}) \\
&= (x-1)\ln e \\
&= x - 1
\end{aligned}
$$

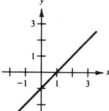

19. Use the properties of logarithms to write the following expression as a sum, difference, or multiple of logarithms.

$$\log_{10} \frac{5\sqrt{y}}{x^2}$$

Solution:

$$
\begin{aligned}
\log_{10} \frac{5\sqrt{y}}{x^2} &= \log_{10} 5\sqrt{y} - \log_{10} x^2 \\
&= \log_{10} 5 + \log_{10} \sqrt{y} - \log_{10} x^2 \\
&= \log_{10} 5 + \frac{1}{2}\log_{10} y - 2\log_{10} x
\end{aligned}
$$

23. Use the properties of logarithms to write the following expression as a sum, difference, or multiple of logarithms.

$$\ln[(x^2 + 1)(x - 1)]$$

Solution:

$$\ln[(x^2 + 1)(x - 1)] = \ln(x^2 + 1) + \ln(x - 1)$$

27. Write $\frac{1}{2} \ln |2x - 1| - 2 \ln |x + 1|$ as the logarithm of a single quantity.

Solution:

$$\frac{1}{2} \ln |2x - 1| - 2 \ln |x + 1| = \ln \sqrt{|2x - 1|} - \ln(x + 1)^2 = \ln \frac{\sqrt{|2x - 1|}}{(x + 1)^2}$$

31. Write $\ln 3 + \frac{1}{3} \ln(4 - x^2) - \ln x$ as the logarithm of a single quantity.

Solution:

$$\ln 3 + \frac{1}{3} \ln(4 - x^2) - \ln x = \ln 3 + \ln \sqrt[3]{4 - x^2} - \ln x = \ln(3\sqrt[3]{4 - x^2}) - \ln x = \ln \frac{3\sqrt[3]{4 - x^2}}{x}$$

35. Determine whether the equation $\ln(x + y) = \ln x + \ln y$ is true or false.

Solution:
False, since $\ln x + \ln y = \ln(xy)$.

39. Determine whether the following equation is true or false.

$$\frac{e^{2x} - 1}{e^x - 1} = e^x + 1$$

Solution:
True, since

$$\frac{e^{2x} - 1}{e^x - 1} = \frac{(e^x + 1)(e^x - 1)}{e^x - 1} = e^x + 1.$$

41. A solution of a certain drug contained 500 units per milliliter when prepared. It was analyzed after 40 days and found to contain 300 units per milliliter. Assuming that the rate of decomposition is proportional to the amount present, the equation giving the amount A after t days is

$$A = 500e^{-0.013t}.$$

Use this model to find A when $t = 60$.

Solution:

$$A = 500e^{-0.013(60)} \approx 229.2 \text{ units per milliliter}$$

45. A certain automobile gets 28 miles per gallon of gasoline for speeds up to 50 miles per hour. Over 50 miles per hour, the number of miles per gallon drops at the rate of 12% for each 10 miles per hour. If s is the speed and y is the number of miles per gallon, then

$$y = 28e^{0.6-0.012s}, \quad s \geq 50.$$

Use this function to complete the following table.

Speed	50	55	60	65	70
Miles per gallon					

Solution:

When $s = 50$, $y = 28e^{0.6-0.012(50)} = 28$ miles per gallon

When $s = 55$, $y = 28e^{0.6-0.012(55)} \approx 26.369$ miles per gallon

When $s = 60$, $y = 28e^{0.6-0.012(60)} \approx 24.834$ miles per gallon

When $s = 65$, $y = 28e^{0.6-0.012(65)} \approx 23.388$ miles per gallon

When $s = 70$, $y = 28e^{0.6-0.012(70)} \approx 22.026$ miles per gallon

Speed	50	55	60	65	70
Miles per gallon	28	26.4	24.8	23.4	22.0

49. Find the exponential function $y = Ce^{kt}$ that passes through the points $(0, 4)$ and $(5, \frac{1}{2})$.

Solution:

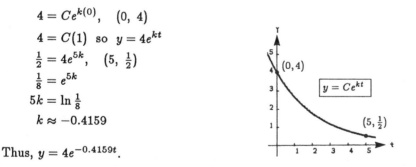

$$4 = Ce^{k(0)}, \quad (0, 4)$$
$$4 = C(1) \quad \text{so} \quad y = 4e^{kt}$$
$$\tfrac{1}{2} = 4e^{5k}, \quad (5, \tfrac{1}{2})$$
$$\tfrac{1}{8} = e^{5k}$$
$$5k = \ln \tfrac{1}{8}$$
$$k \approx -0.4159$$

Thus, $y = 4e^{-0.4159t}$.

51. The demand equation for a certain product is given by

$$p = 500 - 0.5e^{0.004x}.$$

Find the demand x for a price of (a) $p = \$450$ and (b) $p = \$400$.

Solution:

(a)
$$p = 450$$
$$450 = 500 - 0.5e^{0.004x}$$
$$0.5e^{0.004x} = 50$$
$$e^{0.004x} = 100$$
$$0.004x = \ln 100$$
$$x \approx 1151 \text{ units}$$

(b)
$$p = 400$$
$$400 = 500 - 0.5e^{0.004x}$$
$$0.5e^{0.004x} = 100$$
$$e^{0.004x} = 200$$
$$0.004x = \ln 200$$
$$x \approx 1325 \text{ units}$$

Practice Test for Chapter 6

1. Solve for x: $x^{3/5} = 8$.

2. Solve for x: $3^{x-1} = \frac{1}{81}$.

3. Graph $f(x) = 2^{-x}$.

4. Graph $g(x) = e^x + 1$.

5. If $5000 is invested at 9% interest, find the amount after three years if the interest is compounded
   (a) monthly   (b) quarterly   (c) continuously.

6. Write the equation in logarithmic form: $7^{-2} = \frac{1}{49}$.

7. Solve for x : $x - 4 = \log_2 \frac{1}{64}$.

8. Given $\log_b 2 = 0.3562$ and $\log_b 5 = 0.8271$, evaluate $\log_b \sqrt[4]{8/25}$.

9. Write $5 \ln x - \frac{1}{2} \ln y + 6 \ln z$ as a single logarithm.

10. Using your calculator and the change of base formula, evaluate $\log_9 28$.

11. Use your calculator to solve for N : $\log_{10} N = 0.6646$.

12. Graph $y = \log_4 x$.

13. Determine the domain of $f(x) = \log_3 (x^2 - 9)$.

14. Graph $y = \ln(x - 2)$.

15. True or False: $\dfrac{\ln x}{\ln y} = \ln(x - y)$.

16. Solve for x : $5^x = 41$.

17. Solve for x : $x - x^2 = \log_5 \frac{1}{25}$.

18. Solve for x : $\log_2 x + \log_2 (x - 3) = 2$.

19. Solve for x : $\dfrac{e^x + e^{-x}}{3} = 4$.

20. $6000 is deposited into a fund at an annual percentage rate of 13%. Find the time required for the investment to double if the interest is compounded continuously.

CHAPTER 7

Systems of Equations and Inequalities

SECTION 7.1

Systems of Equations

- ■ You should be able to solve systems of equations by the method of substitution.

- ■ You should be able to solve systems of equations by graphically finding points of inter-section.

Solutions to Selected Exercises

5. Solve the following system by the method of substitution.

$$x + 3y = 15$$
$$x^2 + y^2 = 25$$

Solution:

$x + 3y = 15 \Rightarrow x = 15 - 3y$

$$x^2 + y^2 = 25$$
$$(15 - 3y)^2 + y^2 = 25$$
$$225 - 90y + 10y^2 = 25$$
$$10y^2 - 90y + 200 = 0$$
$$10(y^2 - 9y + 20) = 0$$
$$10(y - 4)(y - 5) = 0$$

$y = 4 \quad \text{or} \quad y = 5$

$x = 3 \qquad \quad x = 0$

Solutions: $(3, 4), (0, 5)$

9. Solve the following system by the method of substitution.

$$x - 3y = -4$$
$$x^2 - y^3 = 0$$

Solution:

$$x - 3y = -4 \Rightarrow x = 3y - 4$$

$$x^2 - y^3 = 0$$
$$(3y - 4)^2 - y^3 = 0$$
$$y^3 - 9y^2 + 24y - 16 = 0$$
$$(y - 1)(y - 4)^2 = 0$$

$$y = 1 \quad \text{or} \quad y = 4$$
$$x = -1 \qquad\quad x = 8$$

Solutions: $(-1, \ 1), \ (8, \ 4)$

13. Solve the following system by the method of substitution.

$$2x - y + 2 = 0$$
$$4x + y - 5 = 0$$

Solution:

$$2x - y + 2 = 0 \Rightarrow y = 2x + 2$$

$$4x + y - 5 = 0$$
$$4x + (2x + 2) - 5 = 0$$
$$6x = 3$$
$$x = \tfrac{1}{2}$$
$$y = 3$$

Solution: $\left(\tfrac{1}{2}, \ 3\right)$

17. Solve the following system by the method of substitution.

$$\tfrac{1}{5}x + \tfrac{1}{2}y = \ 8$$
$$x + \ y = 20$$

Solution:

$$\tfrac{1}{5}x + \tfrac{1}{2}y = 8 \Rightarrow 2x + 5y = 80$$
$$x + y = 20 \Rightarrow y = 20 - x$$

$$2x + 5(20 - x) = 80$$
$$-3x = -20$$
$$x = \tfrac{20}{3}$$
$$y = \tfrac{40}{3}$$

Solution: $\left(\tfrac{20}{3}, \ \tfrac{40}{3}\right)$

23. Solve the following system by the method of substitution.

$$3x - 7y + 6 = 0$$
$$x^2 - y^2 = 4$$

Solution:

$$3x - 7y + 6 = 0 \Rightarrow x = \frac{7y - 6}{3}$$

$$x^2 - y^2 = 4$$

$$\left(\frac{7y - 6}{3}\right)^2 - y^2 = 4$$

$$\frac{49y^2 - 84y + 36}{9} - y^2 = 4$$

$$49y^2 - 84y + 36 - 9y^2 = 36$$

$$40y^2 - 84y = 0$$

$$4y(10y - 21) = 0$$

$$y = 0 \quad \text{or} \quad y = \frac{21}{10}$$

$$x = -2 \qquad x = \frac{29}{10}$$

Solutions: $(-2, \ 0)$, $\left(\frac{29}{10}, \ \frac{21}{10}\right)$

27. Solve the following system by the method of substitution.

$$y = x^4 - 2x^2 + 1$$
$$y = 1 - x^2$$

Solution:

$$x^4 - 2x^2 + 1 = 1 - x^2$$

$$x^4 - x^2 = 0$$

$$x^2(x^2 - 1) = 0$$

$$x^2(x + 1)(x - 1) = 0$$

$$x = 0 \quad \text{or} \quad x = -1 \quad \text{or} \quad x = 1$$

$$y = 1 \qquad \qquad y = 0 \qquad \qquad y = 0$$

Solutions: $(0, \ 1)$, $(\pm 1, \ 0)$

29. Solve the following system by the method of substitution.

$$xy - 1 = 0$$
$$2x - 4y + 7 = 0$$

Solution:

$$xy - 1 = 0$$
$$2x - 4y + 7 = 0 \Rightarrow x = \frac{4y - 7}{2}$$

$$\left(\frac{4y - 7}{2}\right)y - 1 = 0$$
$$4y^2 - 7y - 2 = 0$$
$$(4y + 1)(y - 2) = 0$$

$$y = -\frac{1}{4} \quad \text{or} \quad y = 2$$
$$x = -4 \qquad\qquad x = \frac{1}{2}$$

Solutions: $\left(-4, -\frac{1}{4}\right), \left(\frac{1}{2}, 2\right)$

33. Find all points of intersection of the graphs of the given pair of equations. [*Hint:* A graphical approach, as demonstrated in Example 5, may be helpful.]

$$2x - y + 3 = 0$$
$$x^2 + y^2 - 4x = 0$$

Solution:

$$2x - y + 3 = 0 \Rightarrow y = 2x + 3$$
$$x^2 + y^2 - 4x = 0 \Rightarrow (x - 2)^2 + y^2 = 4$$

No points of intersection

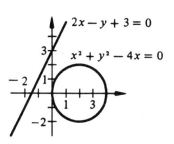

39. Find x, y, and λ satisfying the given system. These systems arise in certain optimization problems in calculus, and λ is called a Lagrange Multiplier. [*Hint:* You can reduce each system to a system of two equations in two variables by solving for λ in the first equation and substituting into the second equation.]

$$y + \lambda = 0$$
$$x + \lambda = 0$$
$$x + y - 10 = 0$$

Solution:

$$y + \lambda = 0 \Rightarrow y = -\lambda$$
$$x + \lambda = 0 \Rightarrow x = -\lambda$$
$$x + y - 10 = 0 \Rightarrow -\lambda - \lambda - 10 = 0$$
$$-2\lambda = 10$$
$$\lambda = -5$$
$$x = y = 5$$

Solution: $x = 5$, $y = 5$, $\lambda = -5$

45. A person is setting up a small business and has invested $16,000 to produce an item that will sell for $5.95. If each unit can be produced for $3.45, how many units must be sold to break even?

Solution:

Let $x =$ the number of units

$$C = 3.45x + 16,000$$
$$R = 5.95x$$

To break even: $R = C$

$$5.95x = 3.45x + 16,000$$
$$2.5x = 16,000$$
$$x = 6400 \text{ units}$$

49. What are the dimensions of a rectangle if its perimeter is 40 miles and its area is 96 square miles?

Solution:

Let $l =$ the length of the rectangle and $w =$ the width of the rectangle.

Perimeter: $2l + 2w = 40 \Rightarrow w = 20 - l$

Area: $lw = 96 \Rightarrow l(20 - l) = 96$

$$20l - l^2 = 96$$
$$0 = l^2 - 20l + 96$$
$$0 = (l - 8)(l - 12)$$

$l = 8$ or $l = 12$

$w = 12$ $w = 8$

The dimensions are 12 miles by 8 miles.

SECTION 7.2

Systems of Linear Equations in Two Variables

■ You should be able to solve a linear system by the method of elimination.

■ You should know that for a system of two linear equations, one of the following is true.

(a) There are infinitely many solutions; the lines are identical.
(b) There is no solution; the lines are parallel.
(c) There is one solution; the lines intersect at one point.

Solutions to Selected Exercises

5. Solve the linear system by elimination. Identify and label each line with the appropriate equation.

$$x - \ y = 1$$
$$-2x + 2y = 5$$

Solution:

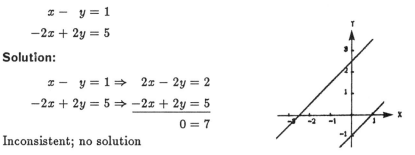

$$x - \ y = 1 \Rightarrow \ \ 2x - 2y = 2$$
$$-2x + 2y = 5 \Rightarrow \underline{-2x + 2y = 5}$$
$$0 = 7$$

Inconsistent; no solution

9. Solve the linear system by elimination. Identify and label each line with the appropriate equation.

$$9x - 3y = -1$$
$$3x + 6y = -5$$

Solution:

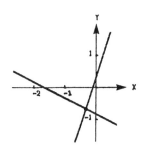

$$9x - 3y = -1 \Rightarrow 18x - 6y = -2$$
$$3x + 6y = -5 \Rightarrow \underline{\ \ 3x + 6y = -5}$$
$$21x \qquad = -7$$
$$x = -\tfrac{1}{3}$$
$$y = -\tfrac{2}{3}$$

Consistent; one solution

Solution: $\left(-\tfrac{1}{3}, \ -\tfrac{2}{3}\right)$

13. Solve the system by elimination.

$$2x + 3y = 18$$
$$5x - y = 11$$

Solution:

$$2x + 3y = 18 \Rightarrow \quad 2x + 3y = 18$$
$$5x - y = 11 \Rightarrow \underline{15x - 3y = 33}$$
$$17x \qquad = 51$$
$$x = \quad 3$$
$$y = \quad 4$$

Consistent; one solution

Solution: $(3, 4)$

17. Solve the system by elimination.

$$2u + v = 120$$
$$u + 2v = 120$$

Solution:

$$2u + v = 120 \Rightarrow -4u - 2v = -240$$
$$u + 2v = 120 \Rightarrow \underline{\quad u + 2v = \quad 120}$$
$$-3u \qquad = -120$$
$$u = \quad 40$$
$$v = \quad 40$$

Consistent; one solution

Solution: $(40, 40)$

23. Solve the system by elimination.

$$\frac{x+3}{4} + \frac{y-1}{3} = 1$$
$$2x - y = 12$$

Solution:

$$\frac{x+3}{4} + \frac{y-1}{3} = 1 \Rightarrow 3(x+3) + 4(y-1) = 12 \Rightarrow 3x + 4y = 7$$
$$2x - y = 12 \Rightarrow$$
$$\underline{8x - 4y = 48}$$
$$11x = 55$$
$$x = 5$$
$$y = -2$$

Consistent; one solution

Solution: $(5, -2)$

25. Solve the system by elimination.

$$2.5x - 3y = 1.5$$
$$10x - 12y = 6$$

Solution:

$$2.5x - 3y = 1.5 \Rightarrow 25x - 30y = 15 \Rightarrow 5x - 6y = 3$$
$$10x - 12y = 6 \Rightarrow 5x - 6y = 3 \Rightarrow \underline{-5x + 6y = -3}$$
$$0 = 0$$

Consistent; infinite solutions of the form $\left(a, \frac{5}{6}a - \frac{1}{2}\right)$

29. Solve the system by elimination.

$$4b + 3m = 3$$
$$3b + 11m = 13$$

Solution:

$$4b + 3m = 3 \Rightarrow 44b + 33m = 33$$
$$3b + 11m = 13 \Rightarrow \underline{-9b - 33m = -39}$$
$$35b = -6$$
$$b = -\frac{6}{35}$$
$$m = \frac{43}{35}$$

Consistent; one solution

Solution: $\left(-\frac{6}{35}, \frac{43}{35}\right)$

33. Find two numbers whose sum is 20 and difference is 2.

Solution:

Let $x =$ one number and $y =$ the other number.

$$x + y = 20$$
$$\underline{x - y = 2}$$
$$2x = 22$$
$$x = 11$$
$$y = 9$$

The two numbers are 11 and 9.

37. Ten gallons of a 30% acid solution are obtained by mixing a 20% solution with a 50% solution. How much of each must be used?

Solution:

Let $x =$ amount of 20% solution and $y =$ amount of 50% solution.

$$x + y = 10 \Rightarrow -2x - 2y = -20$$
$$\underline{0.2x + 0.5y = 0.3(10) \Rightarrow 2x + 5y = 30}$$
$$3y = 10$$
$$y = \tfrac{10}{3}$$
$$x = \tfrac{20}{3}$$

Solution: $\tfrac{20}{3}$ gal 20% solution, $\tfrac{10}{3}$ gal 50% solution

41. The perimeter of a rectangle is 40 feet and the length is 4 feet greater than the width. Find the dimensions of the rectangle.

Solution:

$$2l + 2w = 40 \Rightarrow l + w = 20$$
$$\underline{l = w + 4 \Rightarrow l - w = 4}$$
$$2l = 24$$
$$l = 12$$
$$w = 8$$

Solution: Length = 12 ft, width = 8 ft

45. (a) Find the least squares regression line, and (b) plot the given points and sketch the least squares regression line on the same axes. The *least squares regression line*, $y = ax + b$, for the points (x_1, y_1), (x_2, y_2), $\ldots$, (x_n, y_n) is obtained by solving the following system of linear equations for a and b.

$$nb + \left(\sum_{i=1}^{n} x_i \right) a = \sum_{i=1}^{n} y_i$$

$$\left(\sum_{i=1}^{n} x_i \right) b + \left(\sum_{i=1}^{n} x_i{}^2 \right) a = \sum_{i=1}^{n} x_i y_i$$

Use the points $(0, 4)$, $(1, 3)$, $(1, 1)$, $(2, 0)$.

Solution:

(a) $\qquad n = 4$

$$\sum_{i=1}^{4} x_i = 4$$

$$\sum_{i=1}^{4} x_i^2 = 6$$

$$\sum_{i=1}^{4} y_i = 8$$

$$\sum_{i=1}^{4} x_i y_i = 4$$

$$
\begin{aligned}
4b + 4a &= 8 \\
-(4b + 6a &= 4) \\
\hline
-2a &= 4 \\
a &= -2 \\
b &= 4
\end{aligned}
$$

$$y = -2x + 4$$

(b)

SECTION 7.3

Systems of Linear Equations in More Than Two Variables

- You should know the operations that lead to equivalent systems of equations:
  (a) Interchange any two equations.
  (b) Multiply all terms of an equation by a nonzero constant.
  (c) Replace an equation by the sum of itself and a constant multiple of any other equation in the system.
- You should be able to use the method of elimination.

Solutions to Selected Exercises

3. Solve the following system of linear equations.

$$4x + y - 3z = 11$$
$$2x - 3y + 2z = 9$$
$$x + y + z = -3$$

Handwritten:
$4x + y - 3z = 11$ ^3
$2x - 3y + 2z = 9$
$12x + 3y - 9z = 33$
$2x - 3y + 2z = 9$
$14x - 7z = 42$

Solution:

$$4x + y - 3z = 11 \qquad\qquad 2x - 3y + 2z = 9$$
$$\underline{-4x + 6y - 4z = -18} \qquad \underline{-2x - 2y - 2z = 6}$$
$$7y - 7z = -7 \qquad\qquad -5y = 15$$
$$y - z = -1 \qquad\qquad y = -3$$
$$z = y + 1$$
$$z = -2$$
$$x = 2$$

Solution: $(2, -3, -2)$

7. Solve the following system of linear equations.

$$3x - 2y + 4z = 1$$
$$x + y - 2z = 3$$
$$2x - 3y + 6z = 8$$

Solution:

$$3x - 2y + 4z = 1$$
$$\underline{-3x - 3y + 6z = -9}$$
$$-5y + 10z = -8$$

$$-2x - 2y + 4z = -6$$
$$\underline{2x - 3y + 6z = 8}$$
$$-5y + 10z = 2$$

$$-5y + 10z = -8$$
$$\underline{5y - 10z = -2}$$
$$0 = -10$$

Inconsistent; no solution

11. Solve the following system of linear equations.

$$x + 2y - 7z = -4$$
$$2x + y + z = 13$$
$$3x + 9y - 36z = -33$$

Solution:

$$2x + 4y - 14z = -8$$
$$\underline{-2x - y - z = -13}$$
$$3y - 15z = -21$$
$$y - 5z = -7$$

$$3x + 6y - 21z = -12$$
$$\underline{-3x - 9y + 36z = 33}$$
$$-3y + 15z = 21$$
$$y - 5z = -7$$

Let $z = a$. Then

$$y = 5a - 7$$
$$x = -4 - 2(5a - 7) + 7a = -3a + 10$$

Solution: $(-3a + 10,\ 5a - 7,\ a)$, a is any real number

15. Solve the following system of linear equations.

$$x - 2y + 5z = 2$$
$$3x + 2y - z = -2$$

Solution:

$$x - 2y + 5z = 2$$
$$\underline{3x + 2y - z = -2}$$
$$4x + 4z = 0 \Rightarrow x = -z$$

Let $z = a$. Then

$$x = -a$$
$$y = \tfrac{1}{2}[-a + 5a - 2] = 2a - 1$$

Solution: $(-a,\ 2a - 1,\ a)$, a is any real number.

21. Solve the following system of linear equations.

$$x \qquad + \ 4z = \ 1$$
$$x + y + 10z = \ 10$$
$$2x - y + \ 2z = -5$$

Solution:

$-x \quad - \quad 4z = -1$	$-2x \quad - \ 8z = -2$	$y + 6z = \ 9$
$\underline{x + y + 10z = \ 10}$	$\underline{2x - y + 2z = -5}$	$\underline{-y - 6z = -7}$
$y + \ 6z = \ 9$	$-y - 6z = -7$	$0 = \ 2$

Inconsistent; no solution

23. Solve the following system of linear equations.

$$4x + 3y + 17z = 0$$
$$5x + 4y + 22z = 0$$
$$4x + 2y + 19z = 0$$

Solution:

$20x + 15y + 85z = 0$	$4x + \ 3y + 17z = 0$
$\underline{-20x - 16y - 88z = 0}$	$\underline{-4x - \ 2y - 19z = 0}$
$-y - \ 3z = 0$	$y + \ 2z = 0$
	$\underline{-y - \ 3z = 0}$
	$-z = 0$
	$z = 0 , \ y = 0, \ x = 0$

Solution: $(0, 0, 0)$

27. Find the equation of the parabola $y = ax^2 + bx + c$ that passes through the points $(0, -4)$, $(1, 1)$, and $(2, 10)$.

Solution:

$$-4 = a(0)^2 + b(0) + c \Rightarrow -4 = \qquad\qquad c$$
$$1 = a(1)^2 + b(1) + c \Rightarrow \quad 1 = \ a + \ b + c$$
$$10 = a(2)^2 + b(2) + c \Rightarrow \ 10 = 4a + 2b + c$$

$$1 = a + b - 4 \Rightarrow a + b = 5 \Rightarrow -a - b = -5$$
$$10 = 4a + 2b - 4 \Rightarrow 4a + 2b = 14 \Rightarrow \underline{2a + b = \quad 7}$$
$$a \quad = 2$$
$$b = \quad 3$$

Thus, $y = 2x^2 + 3x - 4$.

31. Find the equation of the circle $x^2 + y^2 + Dx + Ey + F = 0$ that passes through the points $(0, 0)$, $(2, -2)$, and $(4, 0)$.

Solution:

$$(0)^2 + (0)^2 + D(0) + E(0) + F = 0 \Rightarrow \qquad\qquad F = \quad 0$$
$$(2)^2 + (-2)^2 + D(2) + E(-2) + F = 0 \Rightarrow 2D - 2E + F = \quad -8$$
$$(4)^2 + (0)^2 + D(4) + E(0) + F = 0 \Rightarrow 4D \qquad + F = -16$$

$$2D - 2E + 0 = \quad -8 \Rightarrow D - E = -4$$
$$4D \qquad + 0 = -16 \Rightarrow D \qquad = -4 \Rightarrow E = 0$$

Thus, $x^2 + y^2 - 4x + 0y + 0 = 0$
$$x^2 + y^2 - 4x = 0.$$

35. Find a, v_0, and s_0 in the position equation $s = \frac{1}{2}at^2 + v_0t + s_0$.

At $t = 1$ second, $s = 128$ feet.
At $t = 2$ seconds, $s = \quad 80$ feet.
At $t = 3$ seconds, $s = \quad 0$ feet.

Solution:

$s = \frac{1}{2}at^2 + v_0t + s_0$
$(1, 128), (2, 80), (3, 0)$

$$128 = \frac{1}{2}a + \quad v_0 + s_0 \Rightarrow \quad a + 2v_0 + 2s_0 = 256$$
$$80 = 2a + 2v_0 + s_0 \Rightarrow 2a + 2v_0 + \quad s_0 = \quad 80$$
$$0 = \frac{9}{2}a + 3v_0 + s_0 \Rightarrow 9a + 6v_0 + 2s_0 = \quad 0$$

$$2a + 4v_0 + 4s_0 = 512 \qquad\qquad 18a + 18v_0 + 9s_0 = \quad 720$$
$$\underline{-2a - 2v_0 - \ s_0 = -80} \qquad\quad \underline{-18a - 12v_0 - 4s_0 = \qquad 0}$$
$$2v_0 + 3s_0 = 432 \qquad\qquad\quad 6v_0 + 5s_0 = \quad 720$$
$$\underline{-6v_0 - 9s_0 = -1296}$$
$$- \ 4s_0 = \ -576$$
$$s_0 = \qquad 144$$
$$v_0 = \qquad\quad 0$$
$$a = \quad -32$$

Thus, $s = \frac{1}{2}(-32)t^2 + (0)t + 144$

$\qquad = -16t^2 + 144.$

39. Use a system of linear equations to decompose the following rational fraction into partial fractions. (See Example 9 and Section 5.2.)

$$\frac{1}{x^3 - x} = \frac{A}{x} + \frac{B}{x-1} + \frac{C}{x+1}$$

Solution:

$$\frac{1}{x^3 - x} = \frac{A}{x} + \frac{B}{x-1} + \frac{C}{x+1}$$
$$1 = A(x+1)(x-1) + Bx(x+1) + Cx(x-1)$$
$$1 = Ax^2 - A + Bx^2 + Bx + Cx^2 - Cx$$
$$1 = (A + B + C)x^2 + (B - C)x - A$$

By equating coefficients, we have

$$0 = \quad A + B + C$$
$$0 = \quad B - C$$
$$1 = -A \qquad\qquad \Rightarrow \qquad\qquad A = -1$$
$$B + \ C = \ 1$$
$$\underline{B - \ C = \ 0}$$
$$2B = \ 1 \Rightarrow B = \tfrac{1}{2}$$
$$C = \tfrac{1}{2}$$

$$\frac{A}{x} + \frac{B}{x-1} + \frac{C}{x+1} = \frac{-1}{x} + \frac{1/2}{x-1} + \frac{1/2}{x+1}$$
$$= \frac{1}{2}\left(\frac{-2}{x} + \frac{1}{x-1} + \frac{1}{x+1}\right)$$

43. A small company that manufactures products A and B has an order for 15 units of product A and 16 units of product B. The company has trucks of three different sizes that can haul the products, as shown in the following table.

	Product	
Truck	A	B
Large	6	3
Medium	4	4
Small	0	3

How many trucks of each size are needed to deliver the order? (Give *two* possible solutions.)

Solution:

Possible solutions:
    (1) 4 medium trucks
    (2) 2 large trucks, 1 medium truck, 2 small trucks
    (3) 3 large trucks, 1 medium truck, 1 small truck
    (4) 3 large trucks, 3 small trucks

47. (a) Find the least squares regression parabola, then (b) plot the given points and sketch the least squares parabola on the same axes. The least squares regression parabola, $y = ax^2 + bx + c$, for the points (x_1, y_1), (x_2, y_2), $\ldots$, (x_n, y_n) is obtained by solving the following system of linear equations for a, b, and c.

$$nc + \left(\sum_{i=1}^{n} x_i\right) b + \left(\sum_{i=1}^{n} x_i^2\right) a = \sum_{i=1}^{n} y_1$$

$$\left(\sum_{i=1}^{n} x_i\right) c + \left(\sum_{i=1}^{n} x_i^2\right) b + \left(\sum_{i=1}^{n} x_i^3\right) a = \sum_{i=1}^{n} x_i y_i$$

$$\left(\sum_{i=1}^{n} x_i^2\right) c + \left(\sum_{i=1}^{n} x_i^3\right) b + \left(\sum_{i=1}^{n} x_i^4\right) a = \sum_{i=1}^{n} x_i^2 y_i$$

Use the points $(0, 0)$, $(2, 2)$, $(3, 6)$, $(4, 12)$.

Solution:

(a)
$$n = 4 \quad \sum y_i = 20$$
$$\sum x_i = 9 \quad \sum x_i^3 = 99$$
$$\sum x_i^2 = 29 \quad \sum x_i y_i = 70$$
$$\sum x_i^4 = 353$$
$$\sum x_i^2 y_i = 254$$

$$353a + 99b + 29c = 254$$
$$99a + 29b + 9c = 70$$
$$29a + 9b + 4c = 20$$

(b)

By solving, we get $a = 1$, $b = -1$, $c = 0$. Thus, $y = x^2 - x$.

SECTION 7.4

Systems of Inequalities

■ You should be able to sketch the graph of an inequality in two variables:

(a) Replace the inequality with an equal sign and graph the equation. Use a dashed line for < or >, a solid line for ≤ or ≥.

(b) Test a point in each region formed by the graph. If the point satisfies the inequality, shade the whole region.

Solutions to Selected Exercises

5. Match $x^2 + y^2 < 4$ with its graph.

Solution:
Since $x^2 + y^2 = 4$ is a circle with center $(0, 0)$ and radius $r = 2$, it matches graph a.

9. Sketch the graph of $x \geq 2$.

Solution:
Using a solid line, sketch the graph of the vertical line $x = 2$. Test point $(3, 0)$. Shade the half-plane to the right of $x = 2$.

13. Sketch the graph of $y < 2 - x$.

Solution:
Using a dashed line, graph $x + y = 2$, and then shade the half-plane below the line. (Use $(0, 0)$ as a test point.)

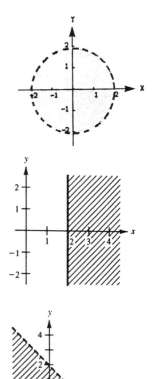

17. Sketch the graph of $(x+1)^2 + (y-2)^2 < 9$.

Solution:
Using a dashed line, sketch the circle $(x+1)^2 + (y-2)^2 = 9$.
Center: $(-1,\ 2)$
Radius: 3
Test Point: $(0,\ 0)$. Shade inside of circle.

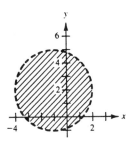

21. Sketch the graph of the solution of the system of inequalities.

$$x + y \leq 1$$
$$-x + y \leq 1$$
$$y \geq 0$$

Solution:
First, find the points of intersection of each pair of equations.

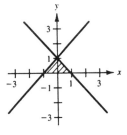

Vertex A	Vertex B	Vertex C
$x + y = 1$	$x + y = 1$	$-x + y = 1$
$-x + y = 1$	$y = 0$	$y = 0$
$(0,\ 1)$	$(1,\ 0)$	$(-1,\ 0)$

25. Sketch the graph of the solution of the system of inequalities.

$$-3x + 2y < 6$$
$$x + 4y > -2$$
$$2x + y < 3$$

Solution:
First, find the points of intersection of each pair of equations.

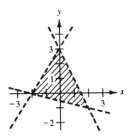

Vertex A	Vertex B	Vertex C
$-3x + 2y = 6$	$-3x + 2y = 6$	$x + 4y = -2$
$x + 4y = -2$	$2x + y = 3$	$2x + y = 3$
$(-2,\ 0)$	$(0,\ 3)$	$(2,\ -1)$

29. Sketch the graph of the solution of the system of inequalities.

$$x \geq 1$$
$$x - 2y \leq 3$$
$$3x + 2y \geq 9$$
$$x + y \leq 6$$

Solution:
The vertices of the region are
$(1, 5)$, $(1, 3)$, $(3, 0)$, and $(5, 1)$.

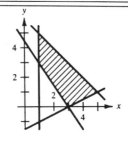

33. Sketch the graph of the solution of the system of inequalities.

$$x > y^2$$
$$x < y + 2$$

Solution:
Points of intersection:

$$y^2 = y + 2$$
$$y^2 - y - 2 = 0$$
$$(y + 1)(y - 2) = 0$$
$$y = -1, \; y = 2$$
$$(1, -1), \; (4, 2)$$

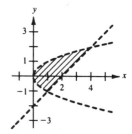

37. Sketch the graph of the solution of the system of inequalities.

$$y < x^3 - 2x + 1$$
$$y > -2x$$
$$x \leq 1$$

Solution:
Points of intersection:
$$x^3 - 2x + 1 = -2x$$
$$x^3 + 1 = 0$$
$$x = -1$$
$$(-1, 2)$$

$$
\begin{array}{ll}
x = 1 & x = 1 \\
y = x^3 - 2x + 1 & y = -2x \\
(1, 0) & (1, -2)
\end{array}
$$

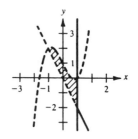

41. Derive a set of inequalities to describe the rectangular region with vertices at $(2, 1)$, $(5, 1)$, $(5, 7)$, and $(2, 7)$.

Solution:

$x \geq 2$

$x \leq 5$

$y \geq 1$

$y \leq 7$

Thus, $2 \leq x \leq 5$, $1 \leq y \leq 7$.

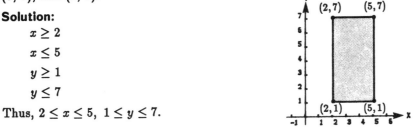

47. A furniture company can sell all the tables and chairs it produces. Each table requires 1 hour in the assembly center and $1\frac{1}{3}$ hours in the finishing center. Each chair requires $1\frac{1}{2}$ hours in the assembly center and $1\frac{1}{2}$ hours in the finishing center. The company's assembly center is available 12 hours per day, and its finishing center is available 15 hours per day. If x is the number of tables produced per day and y is the number of chairs, find a system of inequalities describing all possible production levels. Sketch the graph of the system.

Solution:

Assembly center constraint: $x + \frac{3}{2}y \leq 12$

Finishing center constraint: $\frac{4}{3}x + \frac{3}{2}y \leq 15$

Physical constraints: $x \geq 0$ and $y \geq 0$

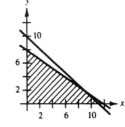

49. A person plans to invest a total of at most \$20,000 in two different interest bearing accounts. Each account is to contain at least \$5000. Moreover, one account should have at least twice the amount that is in the other account. Find a system of inequalities to describe the various amounts that can be deposited in each account, and sketch the graph of the system.

Solution:
Account constraints:

$x \geq 5,000$

$y \geq 5,000$

$2x \leq y$

$x + y \leq 20,000$

SECTION 7.5

Linear Programming

■ To solve a linear programming problem:

1. Sketch the solution set for the system of constraints.
2. Find the vertices of the region.
3. Test the objective function at each of the vertices.

Solutions to Selected Exercises

1. Find the minimum and maximum values of the objective function $C = 3x + 2y$, subject to the constraints:

$$x \geq 0$$
$$y \geq 0$$
$$x + 3y \leq 15$$
$$4x + y \leq 16.$$

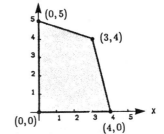

Solution:

The minimum and maximum values occur at the vertices of the constrained region.

Vertex	Value of $C = 3x + 2y$
(0, 0)	$C = 0$, minimum value
(4, 0)	$C = 12$
(0, 5)	$C = 10$
(3, 4)	$C = 17$, maximum value

7. Find the minimum and maximum values of the objective function $C = 25x + 30y$, subject to the constraints:

$$0 \leq x \leq 60$$
$$0 \leq y \leq 45$$
$$5x + 6y \leq 420.$$

Solution:

Vertex	Value of $C = 25x + 30y$
(0, 0)	$C = 0$, minimum value
(60, 0)	$C = 1500$
(60, 20)	$C = 2100$, maximum value
(30, 45)	$C = 2100$, maximum value
(0, 45)	$C = 1350$

13. Find the minimum and maximum values of the objective function $C = 4x + y$, subject to the constraints:

$$x \geq 0$$
$$y \geq 0$$
$$x + 2y \leq 40$$
$$x + y \geq 30$$
$$2x + 3y \geq 72.$$

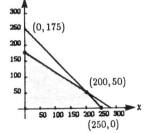

$(24, 8)$

Solution:

Vertex	Value of $C = 4x + y$
(36, 0)	$C = 144$
(40, 0)	$C = 160$, maximum value
(24, 8)	$C = 104$, minimum value

17. A merchant plans to sell two models of home computers at costs of \$250 and \$400, respectively. The \$250 model yields a profit of \$45 and the \$400 model yields a profit of \$50. The merchant estimates that the total monthly demand will not exceed 250 units. Find the number of units of each model that should be stocked in order to maximize profit. Assume that the merchant does not want to invest more than \$70,000 in computer inventory.

Solution:
Objective function:
  Maximize $P = 45x + 50y$ subject to the constraints:

$$x \geq 0$$
$$y \geq 0$$
$$x + y \leq 250$$
$$250x + 400y \leq 70,000$$

Testing the vertices shows that the profit is maximized when $x = 200$ units and $y = 50$ units.

$(0, 175)$

$(200, 50)$

$(250, 0)$

19. A farmer mixes two brands of cattle feed. Brand X costs \$25 per bag and contains 2 units of nutritional element A, 2 units of element B, and 2 units of element C. Brand Y costs \$20 per bag and contains 1 unit of nutritional element A, 9 units of element B, and 3 units of element C. Find the number of bags of each brand that should be mixed to produce a mixture having a minimum cost per bag. The minimum requirements of nutrients A, B, and C are 12 units, 36 units, and 24 units, respectively.

Solution:
Objective function:

Minimize $C = 25x + 20y$ subject to the constraints:

$$2x + y \geq 12$$
$$2x + 9y \geq 36$$
$$2x + 3y \geq 24$$
$$x \geq 0, \ y \geq 0$$

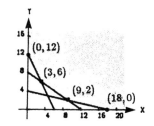

Vertex	Value of $C = 25x + 20y$
$(0, \ 12)$	$C = 240$
$(3, \ 6)$	$C = 195$, minimum value
$(9, \ 2)$	$C = 265$
$(18, \ 0)$	$C = 450$

The cost is a minimum when three bags of Brand X and six bags of Brand Y are used.

23. Sketch a graph of the solution region for the given linear programming problem and describe its unusual characteristic. (The objective function is to be maximized.)

Objective function: $C = -x + 2y$
Constraints: $x \geq 0, \ y \geq 0$
$$x \leq 10, \ x + y \leq 7$$

Solution:
The constraint $x \leq 10$ is extraneous.

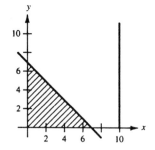

Vertex	Value of $C = -x + 2y$
$(0, \ 0)$	$C = 0$
$(7, \ 0)$	$C = -7$
$(0, \ 7)$	$C = 14$, maximum value

REVIEW EXERCISES FOR CHAPTER 7

Solutions to Selected Exercises

3. Solve the system of equations.

$$x^2 - y^2 = 9$$
$$x - y = 1$$

Solution:

$$x^2 - y^2 = 9$$
$$x - y = 1 \Rightarrow x = y + 1$$

$$(y + 1)^2 - y^2 = 9$$
$$2y + 1 = 9$$
$$y = 4$$
$$x = 5$$

Solution: $(5, 4)$

7. Solve the system of equations.

$$y^2 - 2y + x = 0$$
$$x + y = 0$$

Solution:

$$y^2 - 2y + x = 0$$
$$x + y = 0 \Rightarrow x = -y$$
$$y^2 - 2y - y = 0$$
$$y(y - 3) = 0$$

$$y = 0, \ y = 3$$
$$x = 0, \ x = -3$$

Solutions: $(0, 0), \ (-3, 3)$

11. Solve the system of equations.

$$0.2x + 0.3y = 0.14$$
$$0.4x + 0.5y = 0.20$$

Solution:

$$0.2x + 0.3y = 0.14 \Rightarrow 20x + 30y = 14 \Rightarrow \quad 20x + 30y = \quad 14$$
$$0.4x + 0.5y = 0.20 \Rightarrow 4x + 5y = 2 \Rightarrow -20x - 25y = -10$$
$$5y = \quad 4$$
$$y = \quad \tfrac{4}{5}$$
$$x = \quad -\tfrac{1}{2}$$

Solution: $\left(-\tfrac{1}{2}, \tfrac{4}{5}\right)$ or $(-0.5,\ 0.8)$

15. Solve the system of equations.

$$x + 2y + 6z = \quad 4$$
$$-3x + 2y - z = -4$$
$$4x \qquad + 2z = \quad 16$$

Solution:

$3x + 6y + 18z = 12$	$2x + 4y + 12z = 8$	$8y + 17z = 8$
$-3x + 2y - z = -4$	$-2x \quad - z = -8$	$-8y - 22z = 0$
$8y + 17z = 8$	$4y + 11z = 0$	$-5z = 8$

$$z = -\tfrac{8}{5} = -1.6$$
$$y = \tfrac{1}{8}[8 - 17(-1.6)] = 4.4$$
$$x = \tfrac{1}{2}[8 - (-1.6)] = 4.8$$

Solution: $(4.8,\ 4.4,\ -1.6)$

19. Solve the system of equations.

$$2x + 5y - 19z = 34$$
$$3x + 8y - 31z = 54$$

Solution:

$$2x + 5y - 19z = 34 \Rightarrow 6x + 15y - 57z = \quad 102$$
$$3x + 8y - 31z = 54 \Rightarrow -6x - 16y + 62z = -108$$
$$-y + 5z = \quad -6$$

Let $z = a$. Then,

$$y = 5a + 6$$
$$x = \tfrac{1}{2}[34 - 5(5a + 6) + 19a] = -3a + 2$$

Solution: $(-3a + 2,\ 5a + 6,\ a)$

23. A mixture of 6 parts of chemical A, 8 parts of chemical B, and 13 parts of chemical C is required to kill a certain destructive crop insect. Commercial spray X contains 1, 2, and 2 parts, respectively, of these chemicals. Commercial spray Y contains only chemical C. Commercial spray Z contains chemicals A, B, and C in equal amounts. How much of each type of commercial spray is needed to get the desired mixture?

Solution:
From the following chart we obtain our system of equations.

	A	B	C
Mixture X	$\frac{1}{5}$	$\frac{2}{5}$	$\frac{2}{5}$
Mixture Y	0	0	1
Mixture Z	$\frac{1}{3}$	$\frac{1}{3}$	$\frac{1}{3}$
Desired Mixture	$\frac{6}{27}$	$\frac{8}{27}$	$\frac{13}{27}$

$$\left.\begin{array}{l} \frac{1}{5}x + \frac{1}{3}z = \frac{6}{27} \\ \frac{2}{5}x + \frac{1}{3}z = \frac{8}{27} \end{array}\right\} \quad x = \frac{10}{27}, \ z = \frac{12}{27}$$

$$\frac{2}{5}x + y + \frac{1}{3}z = \frac{13}{27} \Rightarrow y = \frac{5}{27}$$

To obtain the desired mixture, the commercial sprays X, Y, and Z should be combined in a ratio of 10, 5, 12, respectively.

27. Sketch the graph of the solution of the system of inequalities.

$$3x + 2y \geq 24$$
$$x + 2y \geq 12$$
$$2 \leq x \leq 15$$
$$y \leq 15$$

Solution:

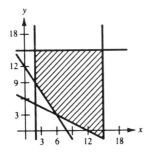

33. A Pennsylvania fruit grower has 1500 bushels of apples that are to be divided between markets in Harrisburg and Philadelphia. These two markets need at least 400 bushels and 600 bushels, respectively. Determine a system of inequalities and sketch a graph of the solution of the system.

Solution:

Let x = number of bushels for Harrisburg and y = number of bushels for Philadelphia.

$$x \geq 400$$
$$y \geq 600$$
$$x + y \leq 1500$$

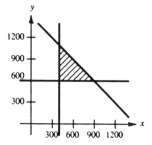

37. Minimize $C = 1.75x + 2.25y$ subject to the constraints:

$$2x + y \geq 25$$
$$3x + 2y \geq 45$$
$$x \geq 0$$
$$y \geq 0.$$

Solution:

Vertex	Value of $C = 1.75x + 2.25y$
(0, 25)	$C = 56.25$
(5, 15)	$C = 42.5$
(15, 0)	$C = 26.25$ minimum value

Practice Test for Chapter 7

For Exercises 1–3, solve the given system by the method of substitution.

1. $x + y = 1$
$3x - y = 15$

2. $x - 3y = -3$
$x^2 + 6y = 5$

3. $x + y + z = 6$
$2x - y + 3z = 0$
$5x + 2y - z = -3$

4. Find two numbers whose sum is 110 and product is 2800.

5. Find the dimensions of a rectangle if its perimeter is 170 feet and its area is 2800 square feet.

For Exercises 6–8, solve the linear system by elimination.

6. $2x + 15y = 4$
$x - 3y = 23$

7. $x + y = 2$
$38x - 19y = 7$

8. $0.4x + 0.5y = 0.112$
$0.3x - 0.7y = -0.131$

9. Herbert invests \$17,000 in two funds that pay 11% and 13% simple interest, respectively. If he receives \$2080 in yearly interest, how much is invested in each fund?

10. Find the least squares regression line for the points $(4, 3)$, $(1, 1)$, $(-1, -2)$, and $(-2, -1)$.

For Exercises 11–13, solve the system of equations.

11. $x + y = -2$
$2x - y + z = 11$
$4y - 3z = -20$

12. $4x - y + 5z = 4$

$2x + y - z = 0$

$2x + 4y + 8z = 0$

13. $3x + 2y - z = 5$

$6x - y + 5z = 2$

14. Find the equation of the parabola $y = ax^2 + bx + c$ passing through the points $(0, -1)$, $(1, 4)$ and $(2, 13)$.

15. Find the position equation $s = (1/2)at^2 + v_0t + s_0$ given that $s = 12$ feet after 1 second, $s = 5$ feet after 2 seconds, and $s = 4$ feet after 3 seconds.

16. Graph $x^2 + y^2 \geq 9$.

17. Graph the solution of the system.

$x + y \leq 6$

$x \geq 2$

$y \geq 0$

18. Derive a set of inequalities to describe the triangle with vertices $(0, 0)$, $(0, 7)$, and $(2, 3)$.

19. Find the maximum value of the objective function $C = 30x + 26y$ subject to the following constraints:

$x \geq 0$

$y \geq 0$

$2x + 3y \leq 21$

$5x + 3y \leq 30.$

20. Graph the system of inequalities.

$x^2 + y^2 \leq 4$

$(x - 2)^2 + y^2 \geq 4$

CHAPTER 8

Matrices and Determinants

SECTION 8.1

Matrices and Systems of Linear Equations

- You should be able to use elementary row operations to produce a triangular form of an augmented matrix.

- You should be able to transform a matrix into reduced row-echelon form. This is called Gauss-Jordan elimination.

Solutions to Selected Exercises

3. Determine the order of the matrix.

$$\begin{bmatrix} -9 \\ 2 \\ 36 \\ 11 \\ 3 \end{bmatrix}$$

Solution:
Since the matrix has five rows and one column, its order is 5×1.

9. Determine whether the following matrix is in row-echelon form.

$$\begin{bmatrix} 2 & 0 & 4 & 0 \\ 0 & -1 & 3 & 6 \\ 0 & 0 & 1 & 5 \end{bmatrix}$$

Solution:
Since the first nonzero entries in rows one and two are not 1, the matrix is *not* in row-echelon form.

15. Write the following matrix in row-echelon form. Remember that the row-echelon form of a matrix is not unique.

$$\begin{bmatrix} 1 & -1 & -1 & 1 \\ 5 & -4 & 1 & 8 \\ -6 & 8 & 18 & 0 \end{bmatrix}$$

Solution:

$$\begin{bmatrix} 1 & -1 & -1 & 1 \\ 5 & -4 & 1 & 8 \\ -6 & 8 & 18 & 0 \end{bmatrix} \quad \begin{matrix} -5R_1 + R_2 \to \\ 6R_1 + R_3 \to \end{matrix} \quad \begin{bmatrix} 1 & -1 & -1 & 1 \\ 0 & 1 & 6 & 3 \\ 0 & 2 & 12 & 6 \end{bmatrix}$$

$$\begin{matrix} \\ \\ -2R_2 + R_3 \to \end{matrix} \quad \begin{bmatrix} 1 & -1 & -1 & 1 \\ 0 & 1 & 6 & 3 \\ 0 & 0 & 0 & 0 \end{bmatrix}$$

19. Write the following matrix in *reduced* row-echelon form.

$$\begin{bmatrix} 1 & 2 & 3 & -5 \\ 1 & 2 & 4 & -9 \\ -2 & -4 & -4 & 3 \\ 4 & 8 & 11 & -14 \end{bmatrix}$$

Solution:

$$\begin{bmatrix} 1 & 2 & 3 & -5 \\ 1 & 2 & 4 & -9 \\ -2 & -4 & -4 & 3 \\ 4 & 8 & 11 & -14 \end{bmatrix} \quad \begin{matrix} -R_1 + R_2 \to \\ 2R_1 + R_3 \to \\ -4R_1 + R_4 \to \end{matrix} \quad \begin{bmatrix} 1 & 2 & 3 & -5 \\ 0 & 0 & 1 & -4 \\ 0 & 0 & 2 & -7 \\ 0 & 0 & -1 & 6 \end{bmatrix}$$

$$\begin{matrix} -3R_2 + R_1 \to \\ \\ -2R_2 + R_3 \to \\ R_2 + R_4 \to \end{matrix} \quad \begin{bmatrix} 1 & 2 & 0 & 7 \\ 0 & 0 & 1 & -4 \\ 0 & 0 & 0 & 1 \\ 0 & 0 & 0 & 2 \end{bmatrix}$$

$$\begin{matrix} -7R_3 + R_1 \to \\ 4R_3 + R_2 \to \\ \\ -2R_3 + R_4 \to \end{matrix} \quad \begin{bmatrix} 1 & 2 & 0 & 0 \\ 0 & 0 & 1 & 0 \\ 0 & 0 & 0 & 1 \\ 0 & 0 & 0 & 0 \end{bmatrix}$$

23. Write the system of linear equations represented by the augmented matrix.

$$\begin{bmatrix} 1 & 0 & 2 & \vdots & -10 \\ 0 & 3 & -1 & \vdots & 5 \\ 4 & 2 & 0 & \vdots & 3 \end{bmatrix}$$

Solution:

Row 1: $\quad 1x + 0y + 2z = -10 \Rightarrow \quad x \quad\quad + 2z = -10$

Row 2: $\quad 0x + 3y - 1z = \quad 5 \Rightarrow \quad\quad 3y - \ z = \quad 5$

Row 3: $\quad 4x + 2y + 0z = \quad 3 \Rightarrow 4x + 2y \quad\quad = \quad 3$

27. Determine the augmented matrix for the given system of linear equations.

$$x + 10y - 3z = 2$$
$$5x - 3y + 4z = 0$$
$$2x + 4y \qquad = 6$$

Solution:
The augmented matrix for this system is

$$\begin{bmatrix} 1 & 10 & -3 & \vdots & 2 \\ 5 & -3 & 4 & \vdots & 0 \\ 2 & 4 & 0 & \vdots & 6 \end{bmatrix}.$$

31. Solve the system of equations. Use Gaussian elimination with back-substitution or Gauss-Jordan elimination.

$$-3x + 5y = -22$$
$$3x + 4y = \quad 4$$
$$4x - 8y = \quad 32$$

Solution:

$$\begin{bmatrix} -3 & 5 & \vdots & -22 \\ 3 & 4 & \vdots & 4 \\ 4 & -8 & \vdots & 32 \end{bmatrix} \quad \begin{matrix} -\frac{1}{3}R_1 \rightarrow \\ -3R_1 + R_2 \rightarrow \\ -4R_1 + R_3 \rightarrow \end{matrix} \quad \begin{bmatrix} 1 & -\frac{5}{3} & \vdots & \frac{22}{3} \\ 0 & 9 & \vdots & -18 \\ 0 & -\frac{4}{3} & \vdots & \frac{8}{3} \end{bmatrix}$$

$$\begin{matrix} \frac{5}{3}R_2 + R_1 \rightarrow \\ \frac{1}{9}R_2 \rightarrow \\ \frac{4}{3}R_2 + R_3 \rightarrow \end{matrix} \quad \begin{bmatrix} 1 & 0 & \vdots & 4 \\ 0 & 1 & \vdots & -2 \\ 0 & 0 & \vdots & 0 \end{bmatrix}$$

Solution: $(4, -2)$

35. Solve the system of equations. Use Gaussian elimination with back-substitution or Gauss-Jordan elimination.

$$-x + 2y = 1.5$$
$$2x - 4y = 3$$

Solution:

$$\begin{bmatrix} -1 & 2 & \vdots & 1.5 \\ 2 & -4 & \vdots & 3 \end{bmatrix} \quad \begin{matrix} -R_1 \to \\ -2R_1 + R_2 \to \end{matrix} \begin{bmatrix} 1 & -2 & \vdots & -1.5 \\ 0 & 0 & \vdots & 6 \end{bmatrix}$$

The second line says $0 = 6$. This is inconsistent.

39. Solve the system of equations. Use Gaussian elimination with back-substitution or Gauss-Jordan elimination.

$$\begin{aligned} x + y - 5z &= 3 \\ x \quad\;\; - 2z &= 1 \\ 2x - y - z &= 0 \end{aligned}$$

Solution:

$$\begin{bmatrix} 1 & 1 & -5 & \vdots & 3 \\ 1 & 0 & -2 & \vdots & 1 \\ 2 & -1 & -1 & \vdots & 0 \end{bmatrix} \quad \begin{matrix} \\ -R_1 + R_2 \to \\ -2R_1 + R_3 \to \end{matrix} \begin{bmatrix} 1 & 1 & -5 & \vdots & 3 \\ 0 & -1 & 3 & \vdots & -2 \\ 0 & -3 & 9 & \vdots & -6 \end{bmatrix}$$

$$\begin{matrix} R_2 + R_1 \to \\ -R_2 \to \\ 3R_2 + R_3 \to \end{matrix} \begin{bmatrix} 1 & 0 & -2 & \vdots & 1 \\ 0 & 1 & -3 & \vdots & 2 \\ 0 & 0 & 0 & \vdots & 0 \end{bmatrix}$$

Thus, $x - 2z = 1$ and $y - 3z = 2$. By letting $z = a$, we have $y = 3a + 2$ and $x = 2a + 1$.

Solution: $(2a + 1,\ 3a + 2,\ a)$

45. Solve the system of equations. Use Gaussian elimination with back-substitution or Gauss-Jordan elimination.

$$\begin{aligned} 2x + y - z + 2w &= -6 \\ 3x + 4y \quad\;\; + w &= 1 \\ x + 5y + 2z + 6w &= -3 \\ 5x + 2y - z - w &= 3 \end{aligned}$$

Solution:

$$\begin{bmatrix} 2 & 1 & -1 & 2 & \vdots & -6 \\ 3 & 4 & 0 & 1 & \vdots & 1 \\ 1 & 5 & 2 & 6 & \vdots & -3 \\ 5 & 2 & -1 & -1 & \vdots & 3 \end{bmatrix} \qquad \begin{matrix} R_3 \to \\ \\ R_1 \to \\ \\ \end{matrix} \begin{bmatrix} 1 & 5 & 2 & 6 & \vdots & -3 \\ 3 & 4 & 0 & 1 & \vdots & 1 \\ 2 & 1 & -1 & 2 & \vdots & -6 \\ 5 & 2 & -1 & -1 & \vdots & 3 \end{bmatrix}$$

$$\begin{matrix} \\ -3R_1 + R_2 \to \\ -2R_1 + R_3 \to \\ -5R_1 + R_4 \to \end{matrix} \begin{bmatrix} 1 & 5 & 2 & 6 & \vdots & -3 \\ 0 & -11 & -6 & -17 & \vdots & 10 \\ 0 & -9 & -5 & -10 & \vdots & 0 \\ 0 & -23 & -11 & -31 & \vdots & 18 \end{bmatrix}$$

$$\begin{matrix} 5R_4 + R_1 \to \\ -11R_4 + R_2 \to \\ -9R_4 + R_3 \to \\ -2R_2 + R_4 \to \end{matrix} \begin{bmatrix} 1 & 0 & 7 & 21 & \vdots & -13 \\ 0 & 0 & -17 & -50 & \vdots & 32 \\ 0 & 0 & -14 & -37 & \vdots & 18 \\ 0 & -1 & 1 & 3 & \vdots & -2 \end{bmatrix}$$

$$\begin{matrix} -7R_3 + R_1 \to \\ 17R_3 + R_2 \to \\ -\frac{1}{14}R_3 \to \\ -R_4 \to \end{matrix} \begin{bmatrix} 1 & 0 & 0 & \frac{5}{2} & \vdots & -4 \\ 0 & 0 & 0 & -\frac{71}{14} & \vdots & \frac{71}{7} \\ 0 & 0 & 1 & \frac{37}{14} & \vdots & -\frac{9}{7} \\ 0 & 1 & -1 & -3 & \vdots & 2 \end{bmatrix}$$

$$\begin{matrix} \\ -\frac{14}{71}R_2 \to \\ \\ \end{matrix} \begin{bmatrix} 1 & 0 & 0 & \frac{5}{2} & \vdots & -4 \\ 0 & 0 & 0 & 1 & \vdots & -2 \\ 0 & 0 & 1 & \frac{37}{14} & \vdots & -\frac{9}{7} \\ 0 & 1 & -1 & -3 & \vdots & 2 \end{bmatrix}$$

$$x \qquad + \tfrac{5}{2}w = -4$$
$$w = -2$$
$$z + \tfrac{37}{14}w = -\tfrac{9}{7}$$
$$y - z - 3w = 2$$

Thus,

$$w = -2$$
$$x = -4 - \tfrac{5}{2}(-2) = 1$$
$$z = -\tfrac{9}{7} - \tfrac{37}{14}(-2) = 4$$
$$y = 2 + 4 + 3(-2) = 0.$$

Solution: $(1,\ 0,\ 4,\ -2)$

49. Solve the system of equations. Use Gaussian elimination with back-substitution or Gauss-Jordan elimination.

$$x + y + z = 0$$
$$2x + 3y + z = 0$$
$$3x + 5y + z = 0$$

Solution:

$$\begin{bmatrix} 1 & 1 & 1 & \vdots & 0 \\ 2 & 3 & 1 & \vdots & 0 \\ 3 & 5 & 1 & \vdots & 0 \end{bmatrix} \begin{matrix} \\ -2R_1 + R_2 \to \\ -3R_1 + R_3 \to \end{matrix} \begin{bmatrix} 1 & 1 & 1 & \vdots & 0 \\ 0 & 1 & -1 & \vdots & 0 \\ 0 & 2 & -2 & \vdots & 0 \end{bmatrix}$$

$$\begin{matrix} -R_2 + R_1 \to \\ \\ -2R_2 + R_3 \to \end{matrix} \begin{bmatrix} 1 & 0 & 2 & \vdots & 0 \\ 0 & 1 & -1 & \vdots & 0 \\ 0 & 0 & 0 & \vdots & 0 \end{bmatrix}$$

Thus, $x + 2z = 0$ and $y - z = 0$. By letting $z = a$, we have $x = -2a$ and $y = a$.

Solution: $(-2a, \ a, \ a)$

51. A small corporation borrowed \$1,500,000 to expand its product line. Some of the money was borrowed at 8%, some at 9%, and some at 12%. How much was borrowed at each rate if the annual interest was \$133,000 and the amount borrowed at 8% was 4 times the amount borrowed at 12%?

Solution:

Let $x = 8\%$ amount
    $y = 9\%$ amount
    $z = 12\%$ amount

$$\begin{aligned} x + y + z &= 1,500,000 \\ 0.08x + 0.09y + 0.12z &= 133,000 \\ x - 4z &= 0 \end{aligned}$$

$$\begin{bmatrix} 1 & 1 & 1 & \vdots & 1,500,000 \\ 8 & 9 & 12 & \vdots & 13,300,000 \\ 1 & 0 & -4 & \vdots & 0 \end{bmatrix}$$

$$\begin{array}{c} \\ -8R_1 + R_2 \rightarrow \\ -R_1 + R_3 \rightarrow \end{array} \begin{bmatrix} 1 & 1 & 1 & \vdots & 1,500,000 \\ 0 & 1 & 4 & \vdots & 1,300,000 \\ 0 & -1 & -5 & \vdots & -1,500,000 \end{bmatrix}$$

$$\begin{array}{c} -R_2 + R_1 \rightarrow \\ \\ R_2 + R_3 \rightarrow \end{array} \begin{bmatrix} 1 & 0 & -3 & \vdots & 200,000 \\ 0 & 1 & 4 & \vdots & 1,300,000 \\ 0 & 0 & -1 & \vdots & -200,000 \end{bmatrix}$$

$$\begin{array}{c} 3R_3 + R_1 \rightarrow \\ -4R_3 + R_2 \rightarrow \\ -R_3 \rightarrow \end{array} \begin{bmatrix} 1 & 0 & 0 & \vdots & 800,000 \\ 0 & 1 & 0 & \vdots & 500,000 \\ 0 & 0 & 1 & \vdots & 200,000 \end{bmatrix}$$

Thus,
$$\begin{aligned} x &= \$800,000 \\ y &= \$500,000 \\ z &= \$200,000. \end{aligned}$$

55. Find D, E, and F such that $(1, 1)$, $(3, 3)$, and $(4, 2)$ are solution points of the equation $x^2 + y^2 + Dx + Ey + F = 0$. [*Hint:* See Example 8 in Section 7.3.]

Solution:

At $(1, 1)$: $(1)^2 + (1)^2 + D(1) + E(1) + F = 0 \Rightarrow D + E + F = -2$

At $(3, 3)$: $(3)^2 + (3)^2 + D(3) + E(3) + F = 0 \Rightarrow 3D + 3E + F = -18$

At $(4, 2)$: $(4)^2 + (2)^2 + D(4) + E(2) + F = 0 \Rightarrow 4D + 2E + F = -20$

$$\begin{bmatrix} 1 & 1 & 1 & -2 \\ 3 & 3 & 1 & -18 \\ 4 & 2 & 1 & -20 \end{bmatrix} \begin{array}{c} \\ -3R_1 + R_2 \rightarrow \\ -4R_1 + R_3 \rightarrow \end{array} \begin{bmatrix} 1 & 1 & 1 & \vdots & -2 \\ 0 & 0 & -2 & \vdots & -12 \\ 0 & -2 & -3 & \vdots & -12 \end{bmatrix}$$

$$\begin{array}{c} -R_2 + R_1 \rightarrow \\ -\frac{1}{2}R_2 \rightarrow \\ 3R_2 + R_3 \rightarrow \end{array} \begin{bmatrix} 1 & 1 & 0 & \vdots & -8 \\ 0 & 0 & 1 & \vdots & 6 \\ 0 & -2 & 0 & \vdots & 6 \end{bmatrix}$$

$$\begin{aligned} D + E &= -8 \Rightarrow D = -5 \\ F &= 6 \Rightarrow F = 6 \\ -2E &= 6 \Rightarrow E = -3 \end{aligned}$$

The equation of the circle is $x^2 + y^2 - 5x - 3y + 6 = 0$.

SECTION 8.2

Operations with Matrices

- $A = B$ if and only if they have the same order and $a_{ij} = b_{ij}$.

- You should be able to perform the operations of matrix addition, scalar multiplication, and matrix multiplication.

- Some properties of matrix addition, scalar multiplication, and matrix multiplication are:
  - (a) $A + B = B + A$
  - (b) $A + (B + C) = (A + B) + C$
  - (c) $(cd)A = c(dA)$
  - (d) $1A = A$
  - (e) $c(A + B) = cA + cB$
  - (f) $(c + d)A = cA + dA$
  - (g) $A(BC) = (AB)C$
  - (h) $A(B + C) = AB + AC$
  - (i) $(A + B)C = AC + BC$
  - (j) $c(AB) = (cA)B = A(cB)$

- You should remember that $AB \neq BA$ in general.

Solutions to Selected Exercises

3. Find x and y.

$$\begin{bmatrix} 16 & 4 & 5 & 4 \\ -3 & 13 & 15 & 6 \\ 0 & 2 & 4 & 0 \end{bmatrix} = \begin{bmatrix} 16 & 4 & 2x + 1 & 4 \\ -3 & 13 & 15 & 3x \\ 0 & 2 & 3y - 5 & 0 \end{bmatrix}$$

Solution:

$$\left. \begin{array}{l} 5 = 2x + 1 \\ 6 = 3x \end{array} \right\} \Rightarrow x = 2$$

$$4 = 3y - 5 \quad \Rightarrow y = 3$$

Solution: $x = 2$, $y = 3$

9. Find (a) $A + B$, (b) $A - B$, (c) $3A$, and (d) $3A - 2B$.

$$A = \begin{bmatrix} 2 & 2 & -1 & 0 & 1 \\ 1 & 1 & -2 & 0 & -1 \end{bmatrix}, \quad B = \begin{bmatrix} 1 & 1 & -1 & 1 & 0 \\ -3 & 4 & 9 & -6 & -7 \end{bmatrix}$$

Solution:

(a) $A + B = \begin{bmatrix} 3 & 3 & -2 & 1 & 1 \\ -2 & 5 & 7 & -6 & -8 \end{bmatrix}$

(b) $A - B = \begin{bmatrix} 1 & 1 & 0 & -1 & 1 \\ 4 & -3 & -11 & 6 & 6 \end{bmatrix}$

(c) $3A = \begin{bmatrix} 6 & 6 & -3 & 0 & 3 \\ 3 & 3 & -6 & 0 & -3 \end{bmatrix}$

(d) $3A - 2B = \begin{bmatrix} 4 & 4 & -1 & -2 & 3 \\ 9 & -5 & -24 & 12 & 11 \end{bmatrix}$

13. Find (a) AB, (b) BA, and if possible (c) A^2.

$$A = \begin{bmatrix} 3 & -1 \\ 1 & 3 \end{bmatrix}, \quad B = \begin{bmatrix} 1 & -3 \\ 3 & 1 \end{bmatrix}$$

Solution:

(a) $AB = \begin{bmatrix} 0 & -10 \\ 10 & 0 \end{bmatrix}$

(b) $BA = \begin{bmatrix} 0 & -10 \\ 10 & 0 \end{bmatrix}$

(c) $A^2 = \begin{bmatrix} 8 & -6 \\ 6 & 8 \end{bmatrix}$

17. Find AB, if possible.

$$A = \begin{bmatrix} 2 & 1 \\ -3 & 4 \\ 1 & 6 \end{bmatrix}, \quad B = \begin{bmatrix} 0 & -1 & 0 \\ 4 & 0 & 2 \\ 8 & -1 & 7 \end{bmatrix}$$

Solution:
A is 3×2 and B is 3×3. Since the number of columns of A does not equal the number of rows of B, the multiplication is not possible.

Note: BA is possible.

21. Find AB, if possible.

$$A = \begin{bmatrix} 5 & 0 & 0 \\ 0 & -8 & 0 \\ 0 & 0 & 7 \end{bmatrix}, \quad B = \begin{bmatrix} \frac{1}{5} & 0 & 0 \\ 0 & -\frac{1}{8} & 0 \\ 0 & 0 & \frac{1}{2} \end{bmatrix}$$

Solution:

$$AB = \begin{bmatrix} 5 & 0 & 0 \\ 0 & -8 & 0 \\ 0 & 0 & 7 \end{bmatrix} \begin{bmatrix} \frac{1}{5} & 0 & 0 \\ 0 & -\frac{1}{8} & 0 \\ 0 & 0 & \frac{1}{2} \end{bmatrix} = \begin{bmatrix} 1 & 0 & 0 \\ 0 & 1 & 0 \\ 0 & 0 & \frac{7}{2} \end{bmatrix}$$

25. Solve for X in $X = 3A - 2B$, given

$$A = \begin{bmatrix} -2 & -1 \\ 1 & 0 \\ 3 & -4 \end{bmatrix} \quad \text{and} \quad B = \begin{bmatrix} 0 & 3 \\ 2 & 0 \\ -4 & -1 \end{bmatrix}.$$

Solution:

$$X = 3A - 2B = \begin{bmatrix} -6 & -3 \\ 3 & 0 \\ 9 & -12 \end{bmatrix} - \begin{bmatrix} 0 & 6 \\ 4 & 0 \\ -8 & -2 \end{bmatrix} = \begin{bmatrix} -6 & -9 \\ -1 & 0 \\ 17 & 10 \end{bmatrix}$$

29. Find matrices A, X, and B such that the given system of linear equations can be written as the matrix equation $AX = B$. Solve the system of equations.

$$-x + y = 4$$
$$-2x + y = 0$$

Solution:

$$A = \begin{bmatrix} -1 & 1 \\ -2 & 1 \end{bmatrix}, \quad X = \begin{bmatrix} x \\ y \end{bmatrix}, \quad B = \begin{bmatrix} 4 \\ 0 \end{bmatrix}$$

By Gauss-Jordan elimination on

$$\begin{bmatrix} -1 & 1 & \vdots & 4 \\ -2 & 1 & \vdots & 0 \end{bmatrix} \quad \begin{matrix} -R_1 \rightarrow \\ 2R_1 + R_2 \rightarrow \end{matrix} \quad \begin{bmatrix} 1 & -1 & \vdots & -4 \\ 0 & -1 & \vdots & -8 \end{bmatrix}$$

$$\begin{matrix} R_2 + R_1 \rightarrow \\ -R_2 \rightarrow \end{matrix} \quad \begin{bmatrix} 1 & 0 & \vdots & 4 \\ 0 & 1 & \vdots & 8 \end{bmatrix},$$

we have $x = 4$ and $y = 8$.

35. If A and B are real numbers, then the following equations are true. If A and B are $n \times n$ matrices, are they true? Give reasons for your answers.

(a) $(A + B)(A - B) = A^2 - B^2$

(b) $(A + B)(A + B) = A^2 + 2AB + B^2$

Solution:

Since $AB \neq BA$ in general, neither equation is true.

(a) $(A + B)(A - B) = A^2 + BA - AB - B^2$

(b) $(A + B)(A + B) = A^2 + BA + AB + B^2$

39. Find $f(A)$, given

$$f(x) = x^2 - 5x + 2 \quad \text{and} \quad A = \begin{bmatrix} 2 & 0 \\ 4 & 5 \end{bmatrix}.$$

Solution:

$$f(A) = \begin{bmatrix} 2 & 0 \\ 4 & 5 \end{bmatrix} \begin{bmatrix} 2 & 0 \\ 4 & 5 \end{bmatrix} - 5 \begin{bmatrix} 2 & 0 \\ 4 & 5 \end{bmatrix} + 2 \begin{bmatrix} 1 & 0 \\ 0 & 1 \end{bmatrix}$$

$$= \begin{bmatrix} 4 & 0 \\ 28 & 25 \end{bmatrix} - \begin{bmatrix} 10 & 0 \\ 20 & 25 \end{bmatrix} + \begin{bmatrix} 2 & 0 \\ 0 & 2 \end{bmatrix}$$

$$= \begin{bmatrix} -4 & 0 \\ 8 & 2 \end{bmatrix}$$

SECTION 8.3

The Inverse of a Matrix

■ You should be able to find the inverse, if it exists, of a matrix.

■ You should be able to use inverse matrices to solve systems of equations.

Solutions to Selected Exercises

7. Find the inverse of the following matrix.

$$\begin{bmatrix} 1 & -2 \\ 2 & -3 \end{bmatrix}$$

Solution:

$$\begin{bmatrix} 1 & -2 & \vdots & 1 & 0 \\ 2 & -3 & \vdots & 0 & 1 \end{bmatrix} \quad -2R_1 + R_2 \rightarrow \begin{bmatrix} 1 & -2 & \vdots & 1 & 0 \\ 0 & 1 & \vdots & -2 & 1 \end{bmatrix}$$

$$2R_2 + R_1 \rightarrow \begin{bmatrix} 1 & 0 & \vdots & -3 & 2 \\ 0 & 1 & \vdots & -2 & 1 \end{bmatrix}$$

$$A^{-1} = \begin{bmatrix} -3 & 2 \\ -2 & 1 \end{bmatrix}$$

11. Find the inverse of the following matrix, (if it exists).

$$\begin{bmatrix} 2 & 4 \\ 4 & 8 \end{bmatrix}$$

Solution:

$$\begin{bmatrix} 2 & 4 & \vdots & 1 & 0 \\ 4 & 8 & \vdots & 0 & 1 \end{bmatrix} \quad \begin{array}{c} \frac{1}{2}R_1 \rightarrow \\ -4R_1 + R_2 \rightarrow \end{array} \begin{bmatrix} 1 & 2 & \vdots & \frac{1}{2} & 0 \\ 0 & 0 & \vdots & -2 & 1 \end{bmatrix}$$

Since the left side does not reduce to I_2, the inverse does not exist.

15. Find the inverse of the following matrix.

$$\begin{bmatrix} 1 & 1 & 1 \\ 3 & 5 & 4 \\ 3 & 6 & 5 \end{bmatrix}$$

Solution:

$$\begin{bmatrix} 1 & 1 & 1 & \vdots & 1 & 0 & 0 \\ 3 & 5 & 4 & \vdots & 0 & 1 & 0 \\ 3 & 6 & 5 & \vdots & 0 & 0 & 1 \end{bmatrix} \begin{array}{c} \\ -3R_1 + R_2 \rightarrow \\ -3R_1 + R_3 \rightarrow \end{array} \begin{bmatrix} 1 & 1 & 1 & \vdots & 1 & 0 & 0 \\ 0 & 2 & 1 & \vdots & -3 & 1 & 0 \\ 0 & 3 & 2 & \vdots & -3 & 0 & 1 \end{bmatrix}$$

$$\begin{array}{c} -R_2 + R_1 \rightarrow \\ \tfrac{1}{2}R_2 \rightarrow \\ -3R_2 + R_3 \rightarrow \end{array} \begin{bmatrix} 1 & 0 & \tfrac{1}{2} & \vdots & -\tfrac{5}{2} & -\tfrac{1}{2} & 0 \\ 0 & 1 & \tfrac{1}{2} & \vdots & -\tfrac{3}{2} & \tfrac{1}{2} & 0 \\ 0 & 0 & \tfrac{1}{2} & \vdots & \tfrac{3}{2} & -\tfrac{3}{2} & 1 \end{bmatrix}$$

$$\begin{array}{c} -R_3 + R_1 \rightarrow \\ -R_3 + R_2 \rightarrow \\ 2R_3 \rightarrow \end{array} \begin{bmatrix} 1 & 0 & 0 & \vdots & 1 & 1 & -1 \\ 0 & 1 & 0 & \vdots & -3 & 2 & -1 \\ 0 & 0 & 1 & \vdots & 3 & -3 & 2 \end{bmatrix}$$

$$A^{-1} = \begin{bmatrix} 1 & 1 & -1 \\ -3 & 2 & -1 \\ 3 & -3 & 2 \end{bmatrix}$$

19. Find the inverse of the following matrix.

$$\begin{bmatrix} 1 & -2 & -1 & -2 \\ 3 & -5 & -2 & -3 \\ 2 & -5 & -2 & -5 \\ -1 & 4 & 4 & 11 \end{bmatrix}$$

Solution:

$$\left[\begin{array}{cccc:cccc}
1 & -2 & -1 & -2 & 1 & 0 & 0 & 0 \\
3 & -5 & -2 & -3 & 0 & 1 & 0 & 0 \\
2 & -5 & -2 & -5 & 0 & 0 & 1 & 0 \\
-1 & 4 & 4 & 11 & 0 & 0 & 0 & 1
\end{array}\right]$$

$$\begin{array}{l}
-3R_1 + R_2 \;\rightarrow \\
-2R_1 + R_3 \;\rightarrow \\
R_1 + R_4 \;\rightarrow
\end{array}
\left[\begin{array}{cccc:cccc}
1 & -2 & -1 & -2 & 1 & 0 & 0 & 0 \\
0 & 1 & 1 & 3 & -3 & 1 & 0 & 0 \\
0 & -1 & 0 & -1 & -2 & 0 & 1 & 0 \\
0 & 2 & 3 & 9 & 1 & 0 & 0 & 1
\end{array}\right]$$

$$\begin{array}{l}
2R_2 + R_1 \;\rightarrow \\
\\
R_2 + R_3 \;\rightarrow \\
-2R_2 + R_4 \;\rightarrow
\end{array}
\left[\begin{array}{cccc:cccc}
1 & 0 & 1 & 4 & -5 & 2 & 0 & 0 \\
0 & 1 & 1 & 3 & -3 & 1 & 0 & 0 \\
0 & 0 & 1 & 2 & -5 & 1 & 1 & 0 \\
0 & 0 & 1 & 3 & 7 & -2 & 0 & 1
\end{array}\right]$$

$$\begin{array}{l}
-R_3 + R_1 \;\rightarrow \\
-R_3 + R_2 \;\rightarrow \\
\\
-R_3 + R_4 \;\rightarrow
\end{array}
\left[\begin{array}{cccc:cccc}
1 & 0 & 0 & 2 & 0 & 1 & -1 & 0 \\
0 & 1 & 0 & 1 & 2 & 0 & -1 & 0 \\
0 & 0 & 1 & 2 & -5 & 1 & 1 & 0 \\
0 & 0 & 0 & 1 & 12 & -3 & -1 & 1
\end{array}\right]$$

$$\begin{array}{l}
-2R_4 + R_1 \;\rightarrow \\
-R_4 + R_2 \;\rightarrow \\
-2R_4 + R_3 \;\rightarrow
\end{array}
\left[\begin{array}{cccc:cccc}
1 & 0 & 0 & 0 & -24 & 7 & 1 & -2 \\
0 & 1 & 0 & 0 & -10 & 3 & 0 & -1 \\
0 & 0 & 1 & 0 & -29 & 7 & 3 & -2 \\
0 & 0 & 0 & 1 & 12 & -3 & -1 & 1
\end{array}\right]$$

$$A^{-1} = \begin{bmatrix}
-24 & 7 & 1 & -2 \\
-10 & 3 & 0 & -1 \\
-29 & 7 & 3 & -2 \\
12 & -3 & -1 & 1
\end{bmatrix}$$

23. Find the inverse of the following matrix.

$$\begin{bmatrix}
0.1 & 0.2 & 0.3 \\
-0.3 & 0.2 & 0.2 \\
0.5 & 0.4 & 0.4
\end{bmatrix}$$

Solution:

$$\begin{bmatrix} 0.1 & 0.2 & 0.3 & \vdots & 1 & 0 & 0 \\ -0.3 & 0.2 & 0.2 & \vdots & 0 & 1 & 0 \\ 0.5 & 0.4 & 0.4 & \vdots & 0 & 0 & 1 \end{bmatrix} \quad \begin{matrix} 10R_1 \to \\ 10R_2 \to \\ 10R_3 \to \end{matrix} \begin{bmatrix} 1 & 2 & 3 & \vdots & 10 & 0 & 0 \\ -3 & 2 & 2 & \vdots & 0 & 10 & 0 \\ 5 & 4 & 4 & \vdots & 0 & 0 & 10 \end{bmatrix}$$

$$\begin{matrix} \\ 3R_1 + R_2 \to \\ -5R_1 + R_3 \to \end{matrix} \begin{bmatrix} 1 & 2 & 3 & \vdots & 10 & 0 & 0 \\ 0 & 8 & 11 & \vdots & 30 & 10 & 0 \\ 0 & -6 & -11 & \vdots & -50 & 0 & 10 \end{bmatrix}$$

$$\begin{matrix} \\ R_3 + R_2 \to \\ 3R_2 + R_3 \to \end{matrix} \begin{bmatrix} 1 & 2 & 3 & \vdots & 10 & 0 & 0 \\ 0 & 2 & 0 & \vdots & -20 & 10 & 10 \\ 0 & 0 & -11 & \vdots & -110 & 30 & 40 \end{bmatrix}$$

$$\begin{matrix} -R_2 + R_1 \to \\ \frac{1}{2}R_2 \to \\ -\frac{1}{11}R_3 \to \end{matrix} \begin{bmatrix} 1 & 0 & 3 & \vdots & 30 & -10 & -10 \\ 0 & 1 & 0 & \vdots & -10 & 5 & 5 \\ 0 & 0 & 1 & \vdots & 10 & -\frac{30}{11} & -\frac{40}{11} \end{bmatrix}$$

$$\begin{matrix} \\ -3R_3 + R_1 \to \\ \\ \end{matrix} \begin{bmatrix} 1 & 0 & 0 & \vdots & 0 & -\frac{20}{11} & \frac{10}{11} \\ 0 & 1 & 0 & \vdots & -10 & 5 & 5 \\ 0 & 0 & 1 & \vdots & 10 & -\frac{30}{11} & -\frac{40}{11} \end{bmatrix}$$

$$A^{-1} = \begin{bmatrix} 0 & -\frac{20}{11} & \frac{10}{11} \\ -10 & 5 & 5 \\ 10 & -\frac{30}{11} & -\frac{40}{11} \end{bmatrix} = \frac{5}{11} \begin{bmatrix} 0 & -4 & 2 \\ -22 & 11 & 11 \\ 22 & -6 & -8 \end{bmatrix}$$

27. Find the inverse of the following matrix.

$$\begin{bmatrix} 1 & 0 & 0 \\ 3 & 4 & 0 \\ 2 & 5 & 5 \end{bmatrix}$$

Solution:

$$\left[\begin{array}{ccc:ccc} 1 & 0 & 0 & 1 & 0 & 0 \\ 3 & 4 & 0 & 0 & 1 & 0 \\ 2 & 5 & 5 & 0 & 0 & 1 \end{array}\right] \begin{array}{c} \\ -3R_1 + R_2 \rightarrow \\ -2R_1 + R_3 \rightarrow \end{array} \left[\begin{array}{ccc:ccc} 1 & 0 & 0 & 1 & 0 & 0 \\ 0 & 4 & 0 & -3 & 1 & 0 \\ 0 & 5 & 5 & -2 & 0 & 1 \end{array}\right]$$

$$\begin{array}{c} \frac{1}{4}R_2 \rightarrow \\ -5R_2 + R_3 \rightarrow \end{array} \left[\begin{array}{ccc:ccc} 1 & 0 & 0 & 1 & 0 & 0 \\ 0 & 1 & 0 & -0.75 & 0.25 & 0 \\ 0 & 0 & 5 & 1.75 & -1.25 & 1 \end{array}\right]$$

$$\begin{array}{c} \\ \frac{1}{5}R_3 \rightarrow \end{array} \left[\begin{array}{ccc:ccc} 1 & 0 & 0 & 1 & 0 & 0 \\ 0 & 1 & 0 & -0.75 & 0.25 & 0 \\ 0 & 0 & 1 & 0.35 & -0.25 & 0.2 \end{array}\right]$$

$$A^{-1} = \left[\begin{array}{ccc} 1 & 0 & 0 \\ -0.75 & 0.25 & 0 \\ 0.35 & -0.25 & 0.2 \end{array}\right]$$

33. Use an inverse matrix to solve the following systems. (See Exercise 19.)

(a)
$$\begin{aligned} x_1 - 2x_2 - x_3 - 2x_4 &= 0 \\ 3x_1 - 5x_2 - 2x_3 - 3x_4 &= 1 \\ 2x_1 - 5x_2 - 2x_3 - 5x_4 &= -1 \\ -x_1 + 4x_2 + 4x_3 + 11x_4 &= 2 \end{aligned}$$

(b)
$$\begin{aligned} x_1 - 2x_2 - x_3 - 2x_4 &= 1 \\ 3x_1 - 5x_2 - 2x_3 - 3x_4 &= -2 \\ 2x_1 - 5x_2 - 2x_3 - 5x_4 &= 0 \\ -x_1 + 4x_2 + 4x_3 + 11x_4 &= -3 \end{aligned}$$

Solution:
From Exercise 19, we have that the inverse of

$$\left[\begin{array}{cccc} 1 & -2 & -1 & -2 \\ 3 & -5 & -2 & -3 \\ 2 & -5 & -2 & -5 \\ -1 & 4 & 4 & 11 \end{array}\right] \text{ is } A^{-1} = \left[\begin{array}{cccc} -24 & 7 & 1 & -2 \\ -10 & 3 & 0 & -1 \\ -29 & 7 & 3 & -2 \\ 12 & -3 & -1 & 1 \end{array}\right].$$

(a)
$$\left[\begin{array}{c} x_1 \\ x_2 \\ x_3 \\ x_4 \end{array}\right] = \left[\begin{array}{cccc} -24 & 7 & 1 & -2 \\ -10 & 3 & 0 & -1 \\ -29 & 7 & 3 & -2 \\ 12 & -3 & -1 & 1 \end{array}\right] \left[\begin{array}{c} 0 \\ 1 \\ -1 \\ 2 \end{array}\right] = \left[\begin{array}{c} 2 \\ 1 \\ 0 \\ 0 \end{array}\right]$$

Solution: $(2, 1, 0, 0)$

(b)
$$\left[\begin{array}{c} x_1 \\ x_2 \\ x_3 \\ x_4 \end{array}\right] = \left[\begin{array}{cccc} -24 & 7 & 1 & -2 \\ -10 & 3 & 0 & -1 \\ -29 & 7 & 3 & -2 \\ 12 & -3 & -1 & 1 \end{array}\right] \left[\begin{array}{c} 1 \\ -2 \\ 0 \\ -3 \end{array}\right] = \left[\begin{array}{c} -32 \\ -13 \\ -37 \\ 15 \end{array}\right]$$

Solution: $(-32, -13, -37, 15)$

SECTION 8.4

The Determinant of a Matrix

- You should be able to determine the determinant of a matrix of order 2 or of order 3 by using the products of the diagonals.

- You should be able to use expansion by cofactors to find the determinant of a matrix of order 3 or greater.

- The determinant of a triangular matrix equals the product of the entries on the main diagonal.

Solutions to Selected Exercises

7. Find the determinant of

$$\begin{bmatrix} -7 & 6 \\ \frac{1}{2} & 3 \end{bmatrix}.$$

Solution:

$$\begin{vmatrix} -7 & 6 \\ \frac{1}{2} & 3 \end{vmatrix} = -7(3) - 6\left(\frac{1}{2}\right) = -24$$

11. Find the determinant of

$$\begin{bmatrix} 2 & -1 & 0 \\ 4 & 2 & 1 \\ 4 & 2 & 1 \end{bmatrix}.$$

Solution:

$$\begin{vmatrix} 2 & -1 & 0 \\ 4 & 2 & 1 \\ 4 & 2 & 1 \end{vmatrix} \begin{matrix} 2 & -1 \\ 4 & 2 \\ 4 & 2 \end{matrix} = 4 + (-4) + 0 - 4 - (-4) = 0$$

15. Find the determinant of

$$\begin{bmatrix} 1 & 4 & -2 \\ 3 & 6 & -6 \\ -2 & 1 & 4 \end{bmatrix}.$$

Solution:

$$\begin{vmatrix} 1 & 4 & -2 \\ 3 & 6 & -6 \\ -2 & 1 & 4 \end{vmatrix} \begin{matrix} 1 & 4 \\ 3 & 6 \\ -2 & 1 \end{matrix} = 24 + 48 + (-6) - 24 - (-6) - 48 = 0$$

19. Find the determinant of

$$\begin{bmatrix} x & y & 1 \\ -2 & -2 & 1 \\ 1 & 5 & 1 \end{bmatrix}.$$

Solution:

$$\begin{vmatrix} x & y & 1 \\ -2 & -2 & 1 \\ 1 & 5 & 1 \end{vmatrix} \begin{matrix} x & y \\ -2 & -2 \\ 1 & 5 \end{matrix} = -2x + y + (-10) - (-2) - 5x - (-2y) = -7x + 3y - 8$$

25. Find the determinant of the following matrix by the method of expansion by cofactors. Expand using (a) Row 1 and (b) Column 2.

$$\begin{bmatrix} -3 & 2 & 1 \\ 4 & 5 & 6 \\ 2 & -3 & 1 \end{bmatrix}$$

Solution:
(a) Expansion along the first row:

$$\begin{vmatrix} -3 & 2 & 1 \\ 4 & 5 & 6 \\ 2 & -3 & 1 \end{vmatrix} = -3C_{11} + 2C_{12} + 1C_{13} = -3(23) + 2(8) + 1(-22)$$
$$= -69 + 16 - 22$$
$$= -75$$

(b) Expansion along the second column:

$$\begin{vmatrix} -3 & 2 & 1 \\ 4 & 5 & 6 \\ 2 & -3 & 1 \end{vmatrix} = 2C_{12} + 5C_{22} - 3C_{32} = 2(8) + 5(-5) - 3(22)$$
$$= 16 - 25 - 66$$
$$= -75$$

31. Find the determinant of

$$\begin{bmatrix} 1 & 4 & -2 \\ 3 & 2 & 0 \\ -1 & 4 & 3 \end{bmatrix}.$$

Solution:
Expansion along the third column:

$$\begin{vmatrix} 1 & 4 & -2 \\ 3 & 2 & 0 \\ -1 & 4 & 3 \end{vmatrix} = -2\begin{vmatrix} 3 & 2 \\ -1 & 4 \end{vmatrix} + 0 + 3\begin{vmatrix} 1 & 4 \\ 3 & 2 \end{vmatrix}$$

$$= -2(14) + 3(-10)$$
$$= -28 - 30$$
$$= -58$$

35. Find the determinant of

$$\begin{bmatrix} 3 & 6 & -5 & 4 \\ -2 & 0 & 6 & 0 \\ 1 & 1 & 2 & 2 \\ 0 & 3 & -1 & -1 \end{bmatrix}.$$

Solution:
Expansion along the second row:

$$\begin{vmatrix} 3 & 6 & -5 & 4 \\ -2 & 0 & 6 & 0 \\ 1 & 1 & 2 & 2 \\ 0 & 3 & -1 & -1 \end{vmatrix} = 2\begin{vmatrix} 6 & -5 & 4 \\ 1 & 2 & 2 \\ 3 & -1 & -1 \end{vmatrix} - 6\begin{vmatrix} 3 & 6 & 4 \\ 1 & 1 & 2 \\ 0 & 3 & -1 \end{vmatrix}$$

$$= 2[6(0) - 1(9) + 3(-18)] - 6[3(-7) - (-18)]$$
$$= 2[-9 - 54] - 6[-21 + 18]$$
$$= -126 + 18$$
$$= -108$$

39. Find the determinant of

$$\begin{bmatrix} 3 & 2 & 4 & -1 & 5 \\ -2 & 0 & 1 & 3 & 2 \\ 1 & 0 & 0 & 4 & 0 \\ 6 & 0 & 2 & -1 & 0 \\ 3 & 0 & 5 & 1 & 0 \end{bmatrix}.$$

Solution:
Expansion along the second column:

$$
\begin{vmatrix}
3 & 2 & 4 & -1 & 5 \\
-2 & 0 & 1 & 3 & 2 \\
1 & 0 & 0 & 4 & 0 \\
6 & 0 & 2 & -1 & 0 \\
3 & 0 & 5 & 1 & 0
\end{vmatrix}
= -2
\begin{vmatrix}
-2 & 1 & 3 & 2 \\
1 & 0 & 4 & 0 \\
6 & 2 & -1 & 0 \\
3 & 5 & 1 & 0
\end{vmatrix}
$$

$$
= -2(-2)
\begin{vmatrix}
1 & 0 & 4 \\
6 & 2 & -1 \\
3 & 5 & 1
\end{vmatrix}
$$

$$
= 4[1(7) - 0 + 4(24)]
$$

$$
= 4[7 + 96]
$$

$$
= 412
$$

43. Evaluate the determinant of

$$
\begin{bmatrix}
4u & -1 \\
-1 & 2v
\end{bmatrix}.
$$

Determinants of this type occur in calculus.

Solution:

$$
\begin{vmatrix}
4u & -1 \\
-1 & 2v
\end{vmatrix}
= 8uv - 1
$$

45. Evaluate the determinant of

$$
\begin{bmatrix}
e^{2x} & e^{3x} \\
2e^{2x} & 3e^{3x}
\end{bmatrix}.
$$

Determinants of this type occur in calculus.

Solution:

$$
\begin{vmatrix}
e^{2x} & e^{3x} \\
2e^{2x} & 3e^{3x}
\end{vmatrix}
= 3e^{5x} - 2e^{5x} = e^{5x}
$$

SECTION 8.5

Properties of Determinants

■ You should know what effect each elementary row (column) operation has on the determinant of a matrix.

■ You should know what conditions yield a determinant of zero.

■ You should be able to use determinants to find inverses, if they exist, of matrices.

Solutions to Selected Exercises

5. State the property of determinants that verifies the equation.

$$\begin{vmatrix} 1 & 3 & 4 \\ -7 & 2 & -5 \\ 6 & 1 & 2 \end{vmatrix} = - \begin{vmatrix} 1 & 4 & 3 \\ -7 & -5 & 2 \\ 6 & 2 & 1 \end{vmatrix}$$

Solution:
Interchanging Columns 2 and 3 results in a change of sign of the determinant.

9. State the property of determinants that verifies the equation.

$$\begin{vmatrix} 5 & 0 & 10 \\ 25 & -30 & 40 \\ -15 & 5 & 20 \end{vmatrix} = 5^3 \begin{vmatrix} 1 & 0 & 2 \\ 5 & -6 & 8 \\ -3 & 1 & 4 \end{vmatrix}$$

Solution:
Each row was divided by 5, thus the resulting determinant is 5^3 times the original determinant.

13. State the property of determinants that verifies the equation.

$$\begin{vmatrix} 3 & 2 & 4 \\ -2 & 1 & 5 \\ 5 & -7 & -20 \end{vmatrix} = \begin{vmatrix} 7 & 2 & -6 \\ 0 & 1 & 0 \\ -9 & -7 & 15 \end{vmatrix}$$

Solution:
Adding multiples of Column 2 to Columns 1 and 3 leaves the determinant unchanged.

17. Use elementary row (or column) operations as aids for evaluating $\begin{vmatrix} 1 & 1 & 1 \\ 2 & -1 & -2 \\ 1 & -2 & -1 \end{vmatrix}$.

Solution:

$$\begin{vmatrix} 1 & 1 & 1 \\ 2 & -1 & -2 \\ 1 & -2 & -1 \end{vmatrix} = \begin{vmatrix} 1 & 1 & 1 \\ 0 & -3 & -4 \\ 0 & -3 & -2 \end{vmatrix} = -6$$

$$-2R_1 + R_2$$
$$- R_1 + R_3$$

21. Use elementary row (or column) operations as aids for evaluating $\begin{vmatrix} 3 & 8 & -7 \\ 0 & -5 & 4 \\ 8 & 1 & 6 \end{vmatrix}$.

Solution:

$$\begin{vmatrix} 3 & 8 & -7 \\ 0 & -5 & 4 \\ 8 & 1 & 6 \end{vmatrix} = 3(-34) + 8(-3) = -126$$

Expansion along
Column 1

25. Use elementary row (or column) operations as aids for evaluating $\begin{vmatrix} 9 & -4 & 2 & 5 \\ 2 & 7 & 6 & -5 \\ 4 & 1 & -2 & 0 \\ 7 & 3 & 4 & 10 \end{vmatrix}$.

Solution:

$$\begin{vmatrix} 9 & -4 & 2 & 5 \\ 2 & 7 & 6 & -5 \\ 4 & 1 & -2 & 0 \\ 7 & 3 & 4 & 10 \end{vmatrix} = \begin{vmatrix} 9 & -4 & 2 & 5 \\ 11 & 3 & 8 & 0 \\ 4 & 1 & -2 & 0 \\ 11 & 17 & 16 & 0 \end{vmatrix} \quad \begin{matrix} R_1 + R_2 \\ 2R_2 + R_4 \end{matrix}$$

$$= -5 \begin{vmatrix} 11 & 3 & 8 \\ 4 & 1 & -2 \\ 11 & 17 & 16 \end{vmatrix} \quad \text{Expansion along Column 4}$$

$$= -5 \begin{vmatrix} 11 & 3 & 8 \\ 4 & 1 & -2 \\ 0 & 14 & 8 \end{vmatrix} \quad -R_1 + R_3$$

$$= -5 \begin{vmatrix} 11 & -11 & 0 \\ 4 & 1 & -2 \\ 0 & 14 & 8 \end{vmatrix} \quad -R_3 + R_1$$

$$= -5(11) \begin{vmatrix} 1 & -1 & 0 \\ 0 & 5 & -2 \\ 0 & 14 & 8 \end{vmatrix} \quad \begin{matrix} \frac{1}{11}R_1 \\ -4R_1 + R_2 \end{matrix}$$

$$= -55[40 + 28] = -3740$$

29. Use elementary row (or column) operations as aids for evaluating

$$\begin{vmatrix} 3 & -2 & 4 & 3 & 1 \\ -1 & 0 & 2 & 1 & 0 \\ 5 & -1 & 0 & 3 & 2 \\ 4 & 7 & -8 & 0 & 0 \\ 1 & 2 & 3 & 0 & 2 \end{vmatrix}.$$

Solution:

$$\begin{vmatrix} 3 & -2 & 4 & 3 & 1 \\ -1 & 0 & 2 & 1 & 0 \\ 5 & -1 & 0 & 3 & 2 \\ 4 & 7 & -8 & 0 & 0 \\ 1 & 2 & 3 & 0 & 2 \end{vmatrix} = \begin{vmatrix} 3 & -2 & 4 & 3 & 1 \\ -1 & 0 & 2 & 1 & 0 \\ -1 & 3 & -8 & -3 & 0 \\ 4 & 7 & -8 & 0 & 0 \\ -4 & 3 & 3 & -3 & 0 \end{vmatrix} \quad \begin{array}{c} -2R_1 + R_3 \\ -R_3 + R_5 \end{array}$$

$$= \begin{vmatrix} -1 & 0 & 2 & 1 \\ -1 & 3 & -8 & -3 \\ 4 & 7 & -8 & 0 \\ -4 & 3 & 3 & -3 \end{vmatrix} \quad \text{Expansion along Column 5}$$

$$= \begin{vmatrix} -1 & 0 & 2 & 1 \\ -4 & 3 & -2 & 0 \\ 4 & 7 & -8 & 0 \\ -3 & 0 & 11 & 0 \end{vmatrix} \quad \begin{array}{c} 3R_1 + R_3 \\ -R_2 + R_4 \end{array}$$

$$= - \begin{vmatrix} -4 & 3 & -2 \\ 4 & 7 & -8 \\ -3 & 0 & 11 \end{vmatrix} \quad \text{Expansion along Column 4}$$

$$= - \begin{vmatrix} -4 & 3 & -2 \\ 0 & 10 & -10 \\ -3 & 0 & 11 \end{vmatrix} \quad R_1 + R_2$$

$$= -[4(110) - 3(-10)]$$
$$= -[-440 + 30]$$
$$= 410$$

33. Use a determinant to determine whether the following matrix is invertible.

$$\begin{bmatrix} 14 & 7 & 0 \\ 2 & 3 & 0 \\ 1 & -5 & 2 \end{bmatrix}$$

Solution:

$$\begin{vmatrix} 14 & 7 & 0 \\ 2 & 3 & 0 \\ 1 & -5 & 2 \end{vmatrix} = 2 \begin{vmatrix} 14 & 7 \\ 2 & 3 \end{vmatrix} = 2(42 - 14) = 56 \neq 0$$

The matrix *is* invertible.

37. Show that $\begin{vmatrix} 1 & x & x^2 \\ 1 & y & y^2 \\ 1 & z & z^2 \end{vmatrix} = (y-x)(z-x)(z-y).$

Solution:

$$\begin{vmatrix} 1 & x & x^2 \\ 1 & y & y^2 \\ 1 & z & z^2 \end{vmatrix} = \begin{vmatrix} y & y^2 \\ z & z^2 \end{vmatrix} - \begin{vmatrix} x & x^2 \\ z & z^2 \end{vmatrix} + \begin{vmatrix} x & x^2 \\ y & y^2 \end{vmatrix}$$

$$= (yz^2 - y^2z) - (xz^2 - x^2z) + (xy^2 - x^2y)$$

$$= yz^2 - xz^2 - y^2z + x^2z + xy(y-x)$$

$$= z^2(y-x) - z(y^2 - x^2) + xy(y-x)$$

$$= z^2(y-x) - z(y-x)(y+x) + xy(y-x)$$

$$= (y-x)[z^2 - z(y+x) + xy]$$

$$= (y-x)[z^2 - zy - zx + xy]$$

$$= (y-x)[z^2 - zx - zy + xy]$$

$$= (y-x)[z(z-x) - y(z-x)]$$

$$= (y-x)(z-x)(z-y)$$

41. Verify the equation.

$$\begin{vmatrix} w & x \\ y & z \end{vmatrix} = - \begin{vmatrix} y & z \\ w & x \end{vmatrix}$$

Solution:

$$\begin{vmatrix} w & x \\ y & z \end{vmatrix} = wz - xy$$

$$- \begin{vmatrix} y & z \\ w & x \end{vmatrix} = -[xy - wz] = wz - xy$$

Therefore,

$$\begin{vmatrix} w & x \\ y & z \end{vmatrix} = - \begin{vmatrix} y & z \\ w & x \end{vmatrix}.$$

SECTION 8.6

Applications of Determinants and Matrices

- You should be able to use Cramer's Rule to solve a system of linear equations.

- Now you should be able to solve a system of linear equations by substitution, elimination, elementary row operations on an augmented matrix, using the inverse matrix, or Cramer's Rule.

- You should be able to find the area of a triangle in the xy-plane.

Solutions to Selected Exercises

5. Use Cramer's Rule to solve the system of equations.

$$20x + 8y = 11$$
$$12x - 24y = 21$$

Solution:

$$x = \frac{\begin{vmatrix} 11 & 8 \\ 21 & -24 \end{vmatrix}}{\begin{vmatrix} 20 & 8 \\ 12 & -24 \end{vmatrix}} = \frac{-432}{-576} = \frac{3}{4}$$

$$y = \frac{\begin{vmatrix} 20 & 11 \\ 12 & 21 \end{vmatrix}}{\begin{vmatrix} 20 & 8 \\ 12 & -24 \end{vmatrix}} = \frac{288}{-576} = -\frac{1}{2}$$

Solution: $\left(\frac{3}{4}, -\frac{1}{2}\right)$

9. Use Cramer's Rule to solve the system of equations.

$$3x + 6y = 5$$
$$6x + 14y = 11$$

Solution:

$$x = \frac{\begin{vmatrix} 5 & 6 \\ 11 & 14 \end{vmatrix}}{\begin{vmatrix} 3 & 6 \\ 6 & 14 \end{vmatrix}} = \frac{4}{6} = \frac{2}{3}$$

$$y = \frac{\begin{vmatrix} 3 & 5 \\ 6 & 11 \end{vmatrix}}{\begin{vmatrix} 3 & 6 \\ 6 & 14 \end{vmatrix}} = \frac{3}{6} = \frac{1}{2}$$

Solution: $\left(\frac{2}{3}, \frac{1}{2} \right)$

13. Use Cramer's Rule to solve the system of equations.

$$3x + 4y + 4z = 11$$
$$4x - 4y + 6z = 11$$
$$6x - 6y \qquad = 3$$

Solution:

$$x = \frac{\begin{vmatrix} 11 & 4 & 4 \\ 11 & -4 & 6 \\ 3 & -6 & 0 \end{vmatrix}}{\begin{vmatrix} 3 & 4 & 4 \\ 4 & -4 & 6 \\ 6 & -6 & 0 \end{vmatrix}} = \frac{252}{252} = 1$$

Substituting this value into the third equation gives us $y = \frac{1}{2}$. Then substituting these values back into either of the other equations gives us $z = \frac{3}{2}$.

Solution: $\left(1, \frac{1}{2}, \frac{3}{2} \right)$

19. Use Cramer's Rule to solve the system of equations.

$$7x - 3y \qquad + 2w = 41$$
$$-2x + y \qquad - w = -13$$
$$4x \qquad + z - 2w = 12$$
$$-x + y \qquad - w = -8$$

Solution:

$$x = \frac{\begin{vmatrix} 41 & -3 & 0 & 2 \\ -13 & 1 & 0 & -1 \\ 12 & 0 & 1 & -2 \\ -8 & 1 & 0 & -1 \end{vmatrix}}{\begin{vmatrix} 7 & -3 & 0 & 2 \\ -2 & 1 & 0 & -1 \\ 4 & 0 & 1 & -2 \\ -1 & 1 & 0 & -1 \end{vmatrix}} = \frac{\begin{vmatrix} 41 & -3 & -2 \\ -13 & 1 & -1 \\ -8 & 1 & -1 \end{vmatrix}}{\begin{vmatrix} 7 & -3 & -2 \\ -2 & 1 & -1 \\ -1 & 1 & -1 \end{vmatrix}} = \frac{25}{5} = 5$$

$$y = \frac{\begin{vmatrix} 7 & 41 & 0 & 2 \\ -2 & -13 & 0 & -1 \\ 4 & 12 & 1 & -2 \\ -1 & -8 & 0 & -1 \end{vmatrix}}{\begin{vmatrix} 7 & -3 & 0 & 2 \\ -2 & 1 & 0 & -1 \\ 4 & 0 & 1 & -2 \\ -1 & 1 & 0 & -1 \end{vmatrix}} = \frac{\begin{vmatrix} 7 & 41 & 2 \\ -2 & -13 & -1 \\ -1 & -8 & -1 \end{vmatrix}}{\begin{vmatrix} 7 & -3 & -2 \\ -2 & 1 & -1 \\ -1 & 1 & -1 \end{vmatrix}} = \frac{0}{5} = 0$$

Substituting these values back into Equation 4 gives us $w = 3$. Then using these values in Equation 3 gives us $z = -2$.

Solution: $(5,\ 0,\ -2,\ 3)$

23. Use a determinant to find the area of the triangle with vertices $(-2,\ -3)$, $(2,\ -3)$, and $(0,\ 4)$.

Solution:

$$A = \frac{1}{2} \begin{vmatrix} -2 & -3 & 1 \\ 2 & -3 & 1 \\ 0 & 4 & 1 \end{vmatrix} = 14$$

29. Use a determinant to determine if the points $\left(2,\ -\frac{1}{2}\right)$, $(-4,\ 4)$, and $(6,\ -3)$ are collinear.

Solution:
Since

$$\begin{vmatrix} 2 & -\frac{1}{2} & 1 \\ -4 & 4 & 1 \\ 6 & -3 & 1 \end{vmatrix} = -3 \neq 0,$$

the points are not collinear.

35. Use a determinant to find an equation of the line through the points $(-4,\ 3)$ and $(2,\ 1)$.

Solution:

$$\begin{vmatrix} x & y & 1 \\ -4 & 3 & 1 \\ 2 & 1 & 1 \end{vmatrix} = 0$$

$$2x + 6y - 10 = 0$$

$$x + 3y - 5 = 0$$

39. Write a cryptogram for LANDING SUCCESSFUL (see Example 6), using the matrix

$$A = \begin{bmatrix} 1 & 2 & 2 \\ 3 & 7 & 9 \\ -1 & -4 & -7 \end{bmatrix}.$$

Solution:

L A N D I N G − S U C C E S S F U L
[12 1 14] [4 9 14] [7 0 19] [21 3 3] [5 19 19] [6 21 12]

$$[12 \quad 1 \quad 14]A = [\quad 1 \quad -25 \quad -65]$$
$$[\ 4 \quad 9 \quad 14]A = [\quad 17 \quad 15 \quad -9]$$
$$[\ 7 \quad 0 \quad 19]A = [-12 \quad -62 \quad -119]$$
$$[21 \quad 3 \quad 3]A = [\quad 27 \quad 51 \quad 48]$$
$$[\ 5 \quad 19 \quad 19]A = [\quad 43 \quad 67 \quad 48]$$
$$[\ 6 \quad 21 \quad 12]A = [\quad 57 \quad 111 \quad 117]$$

Cryptogram:
1 −25 −65 17 15 −9 −12 −62 −119 27 51 48 43 67 48 57 111 117

43. Decode the cryptogram

20 17 −15 −12 −56 −104 1 −25 −65 62 143 181

using the inverse of the following matrix (see Example 7).

$$A = \begin{bmatrix} 1 & 2 & 2 \\ 3 & 7 & 9 \\ -1 & -4 & -7 \end{bmatrix}$$

Solution:

To find A^{-1}, use Gauss-Jordan elimination.

$$\begin{bmatrix} 1 & 2 & 2 & \vdots & 1 & 0 & 0 \\ 3 & 7 & 9 & \vdots & 0 & 1 & 0 \\ -1 & -4 & -7 & \vdots & 0 & 0 & 1 \end{bmatrix} \rightarrow \begin{bmatrix} 1 & 0 & 0 & \vdots & -13 & 6 & 4 \\ 0 & 1 & 0 & \vdots & 12 & -5 & -3 \\ 0 & 0 & 1 & \vdots & -5 & 2 & 1 \end{bmatrix}$$

$$A^{-1} = \begin{bmatrix} -13 & 6 & 4 \\ 12 & -5 & -3 \\ -5 & 2 & 1 \end{bmatrix}$$

$$\begin{bmatrix} 20 & 17 & -15 \end{bmatrix} A^{-1} = \begin{bmatrix} 19 & 5 & 14 \end{bmatrix}$$

$$\begin{bmatrix} -12 & -56 & -104 \end{bmatrix} A^{-1} = \begin{bmatrix} 4 & 0 & 16 \end{bmatrix}$$

$$\begin{bmatrix} 1 & -25 & -65 \end{bmatrix} A^{-1} = \begin{bmatrix} 12 & 1 & 14 \end{bmatrix}$$

$$\begin{bmatrix} 62 & 143 & 181 \end{bmatrix} A^{-1} = \begin{bmatrix} 5 & 19 & 0 \end{bmatrix}$$

19 5 14 4 0 16 12 1 14 5 19 0

S E N D – P L A N E S –

REVIEW EXERCISES FOR CHAPTER 8

Solutions to Selected Exercises

3. Use matrices and elementary row operations to solve the system of equations.

$$0.2x - 0.1y = 0.07$$
$$0.4x - 0.5y = -0.01$$

Solution:

$$\begin{bmatrix} 0.2 & -0.1 & \vdots & 0.07 \\ 0.4 & -0.5 & \vdots & -0.01 \end{bmatrix} \begin{matrix} 5R_1 \rightarrow \\ -2R_1 + R_2 \rightarrow \end{matrix} \begin{bmatrix} 1 & -0.5 & \vdots & 0.35 \\ 0 & -0.3 & \vdots & -0.15 \end{bmatrix}$$

$$\begin{matrix} 0.5R_2 + R_1 \rightarrow \\ -\frac{1}{0.3}R_2 \rightarrow \end{matrix} \begin{bmatrix} 1 & 0 & \vdots & 0.6 \\ 0 & 1 & \vdots & 0.5 \end{bmatrix}$$

$x = 0.6$

$y = 0.5$

Solution: $(0.6, 0.5)$

7. Use matrices and elementary row operations to solve the system of equations.

$$2x + 3y + 3z = 3$$
$$6x + 6y + 12z = 13$$
$$12x + 9y - z = 2$$

Solution:

$$\begin{bmatrix} 2 & 3 & 3 & \vdots & 3 \\ 6 & 6 & 12 & \vdots & 13 \\ 12 & 9 & -1 & \vdots & 2 \end{bmatrix} \begin{matrix} \\ -3R_1 + R_2 \rightarrow \\ -2R_2 + R_3 \rightarrow \end{matrix} \begin{bmatrix} 2 & 3 & 3 & \vdots & 3 \\ 0 & -3 & 3 & \vdots & 4 \\ 0 & -3 & -25 & \vdots & -24 \end{bmatrix}$$

$$\begin{matrix} R_2 + R_1 \rightarrow \\ \\ -R_2 + R_3 \rightarrow \end{matrix} \begin{bmatrix} 2 & 0 & 6 & \vdots & 7 \\ 0 & -3 & 3 & \vdots & 4 \\ 0 & 0 & -28 & \vdots & -28 \end{bmatrix}$$

$$\begin{matrix} \frac{1}{2}R_1 \rightarrow \\ -\frac{1}{3}R_2 \rightarrow \\ -\frac{1}{28}R_3 \rightarrow \end{matrix} \begin{bmatrix} 1 & 0 & 3 & \vdots & \frac{7}{2} \\ 0 & 1 & -1 & \vdots & -\frac{4}{3} \\ 0 & 0 & 1 & \vdots & 1 \end{bmatrix}$$

$$z = 1$$
$$x - 3z = \tfrac{7}{2} \Rightarrow x = \tfrac{1}{2}$$
$$y - z = -\tfrac{4}{3} \Rightarrow y = -\tfrac{1}{3}$$

Solution: $\left(\tfrac{1}{2}, -\tfrac{1}{3}, 1\right)$

11. Use matrices and elementary row operations to solve the system of equations.

$$x + 2y + 6z = 1$$
$$2x + 5y + 15z = 4$$
$$3x + y + 3z = -6$$

Solution:

$$\begin{bmatrix} 1 & 2 & 6 & \vdots & 1 \\ 2 & 5 & 15 & \vdots & 4 \\ 3 & 1 & 3 & \vdots & -6 \end{bmatrix} \quad \begin{matrix} \\ -2R_1 + R_2 \rightarrow \\ -3R_1 + R_3 \rightarrow \end{matrix} \quad \begin{bmatrix} 1 & 2 & 6 & \vdots & 1 \\ 0 & 1 & 3 & \vdots & 2 \\ 0 & -5 & -15 & \vdots & -9 \end{bmatrix}$$

$$-2R_2 + R_1 \rightarrow \begin{bmatrix} 1 & 0 & 0 & \vdots & -3 \\ 0 & 1 & 3 & \vdots & 2 \\ 0 & 0 & 0 & \vdots & 1 \end{bmatrix}$$
$$5R_2 + R_3 \rightarrow$$

$$x = -3$$
$$y + 3z = 2$$
$$0 = 1, \quad \text{Inconsistent}$$

15. Perform the indicated matrix operation.

$$\begin{bmatrix} 1 & 2 \\ 5 & -4 \\ 6 & 0 \end{bmatrix} \begin{bmatrix} 6 & -2 & 8 \\ 4 & 0 & 0 \end{bmatrix}$$

Solution:

$$\begin{bmatrix} 1 & 2 \\ 5 & -4 \\ 6 & 0 \end{bmatrix} \begin{bmatrix} 6 & -2 & 8 \\ 4 & 0 & 0 \end{bmatrix} = \begin{bmatrix} 14 & -2 & 8 \\ 14 & -10 & 40 \\ 36 & -12 & 48 \end{bmatrix}$$

19. Perform the indicated matrix operation.

$$\begin{bmatrix} 1 & 3 & 2 \\ 0 & 2 & -4 \\ 0 & 0 & 3 \end{bmatrix} \begin{bmatrix} 4 & -3 & 2 \\ 0 & 3 & -1 \\ 0 & 0 & 2 \end{bmatrix}$$

Solution:

$$\begin{bmatrix} 1 & 3 & 2 \\ 0 & 2 & -4 \\ 0 & 0 & 3 \end{bmatrix} \begin{bmatrix} 4 & -3 & 2 \\ 0 & 3 & -1 \\ 0 & 0 & 2 \end{bmatrix} = \begin{bmatrix} 4 & 6 & 3 \\ 0 & 6 & -10 \\ 0 & 0 & 6 \end{bmatrix}$$

23. Solve for X in $3X + 2A = B$, given

$$A = \begin{bmatrix} -4 & 0 \\ 1 & -5 \\ -3 & 2 \end{bmatrix} \quad \text{and} \quad B = \begin{bmatrix} 1 & 2 \\ -2 & 1 \\ 4 & 4 \end{bmatrix}.$$

Solution:

$$X = \frac{1}{3}[B - 2A]$$

$$= \frac{1}{3}\left(\begin{bmatrix} 1 & 2 \\ -2 & 1 \\ 4 & 4 \end{bmatrix} - 2\begin{bmatrix} -4 & 0 \\ 1 & -5 \\ -3 & 2 \end{bmatrix} \right)$$

$$= \frac{1}{3} \begin{bmatrix} 9 & 2 \\ -4 & 11 \\ 10 & 0 \end{bmatrix}$$

27. Evaluate the determinant.

$$\begin{vmatrix} 3 & 0 & -4 & 0 \\ 0 & 8 & 1 & 2 \\ 6 & 1 & 8 & 2 \\ 0 & 3 & -4 & 1 \end{vmatrix}$$

Solution:

$$\begin{vmatrix} 3 & 0 & -4 & 0 \\ 0 & 8 & 1 & 2 \\ 6 & 1 & 8 & 2 \\ 0 & 3 & -4 & 1 \end{vmatrix} = 3\begin{vmatrix} 8 & 1 & 2 \\ 1 & 8 & 2 \\ 3 & -4 & 1 \end{vmatrix} - 4\begin{vmatrix} 0 & 8 & 2 \\ 6 & 1 & 2 \\ 0 & 3 & 1 \end{vmatrix} \quad \text{Expansion along Row 1}$$

$$= 3[8(8 - (-8)) - 1(1 - 6) + 2(-4 - 24)] - 4[0 - 6(8 - 6) + 0]$$
$$= 3[128 + 5 - 56] - 4[-12]$$
$$= 279$$

31. Find the inverse of the following matrix.

$$\begin{bmatrix} 2 & 0 & 3 \\ -1 & 1 & 1 \\ 2 & -2 & 1 \end{bmatrix}$$

Solution:

$$\begin{bmatrix} 2 & 0 & 3 & \vdots & 1 & 0 & 0 \\ -1 & 1 & 1 & \vdots & 0 & 1 & 0 \\ 2 & -2 & 1 & \vdots & 0 & 0 & 1 \end{bmatrix}$$

$$\begin{matrix} R_2 + R_1 \to \\ R_1 + R_2 \to \\ -2R_1 + R_3 \to \end{matrix} \begin{bmatrix} 1 & 1 & 4 & \vdots & 1 & 1 & 0 \\ 0 & 2 & 5 & \vdots & 1 & 2 & 0 \\ 0 & -4 & -7 & \vdots & -2 & -2 & 1 \end{bmatrix}$$

$$\begin{matrix} -R_2 + R_1 \to \\ \frac{1}{2}R_2 \to \\ 4R_2 + R_3 \to \end{matrix} \begin{bmatrix} 1 & 0 & \frac{3}{2} & \vdots & \frac{1}{2} & 0 & 0 \\ 0 & 1 & \frac{5}{2} & \vdots & \frac{1}{2} & 1 & 0 \\ 0 & 0 & 3 & \vdots & 0 & 2 & 1 \end{bmatrix}$$

$$\begin{matrix} -\frac{3}{2}R_3 + R_1 \to \\ -\frac{5}{2}R_3 + R_2 \to \\ \frac{1}{3}R_3 \to \end{matrix} \begin{bmatrix} 1 & 0 & 0 & \vdots & \frac{1}{2} & -1 & -\frac{1}{2} \\ 0 & 1 & 0 & \vdots & \frac{1}{2} & -\frac{2}{3} & -\frac{5}{6} \\ 0 & 0 & 1 & \vdots & 0 & \frac{2}{3} & \frac{1}{3} \end{bmatrix}$$

Inverse: $\begin{bmatrix} \frac{1}{2} & -1 & -\frac{1}{2} \\ \frac{1}{2} & -\frac{2}{3} & -\frac{5}{6} \\ 0 & \frac{2}{3} & \frac{1}{3} \end{bmatrix}$

33. Write the system of linear equations represented by the matrix equation.

$$\begin{bmatrix} 5 & 4 \\ -1 & 1 \end{bmatrix} \begin{bmatrix} x \\ y \end{bmatrix} = \begin{bmatrix} 2 \\ -22 \end{bmatrix}$$

Solution:

$$\begin{bmatrix} 5 & 4 \\ -1 & 1 \end{bmatrix} \begin{bmatrix} x \\ y \end{bmatrix} = \begin{bmatrix} 2 \\ -22 \end{bmatrix}$$

$$\begin{bmatrix} 5x + 4y \\ -x + y \end{bmatrix} = \begin{bmatrix} 2 \\ -22 \end{bmatrix}$$

$$5x + 4y = 2$$
$$-x + y = -22$$

37. Solve the system of linear equations using (a) the inverse of the coefficient matrix and (b) Cramer's Rule.

$$-3x - 3y - 4z = 2$$
$$y + z = -1$$
$$4x + 3y + 4z = -1$$

Solution:

(a)
$$\left[\begin{array}{ccc:ccc} -3 & -3 & -4 & 1 & 0 & 0 \\ 0 & 1 & 1 & 0 & 1 & 0 \\ 4 & 3 & 4 & 0 & 0 & 1 \end{array}\right] \quad \begin{array}{c} R_3 + R_1 \rightarrow \\ \\ -4R_1 + R_3 \rightarrow \end{array} \left[\begin{array}{ccc:ccc} 1 & 0 & 0 & 1 & 0 & 1 \\ 0 & 1 & 1 & 0 & 1 & 0 \\ 0 & 3 & 4 & -4 & 0 & -3 \end{array}\right]$$

$$\begin{array}{c} \\ -R_3 + R_2 \rightarrow \\ -3R_2 + R_3 \rightarrow \end{array} \left[\begin{array}{ccc:ccc} 1 & 0 & 0 & 1 & 0 & 1 \\ 0 & 1 & 0 & 4 & 4 & 3 \\ 0 & 0 & 1 & -4 & -3 & -3 \end{array}\right]$$

$$\begin{bmatrix} x \\ y \\ z \end{bmatrix} = \begin{bmatrix} 1 & 0 & 1 \\ 4 & 4 & 3 \\ -4 & -3 & -3 \end{bmatrix} \begin{bmatrix} 2 \\ -1 \\ -1 \end{bmatrix} = \begin{bmatrix} 1 \\ 1 \\ -2 \end{bmatrix}$$

Solution: $(1, \ 1, \ -2)$

(b) $x = \dfrac{\begin{vmatrix} 2 & -3 & -4 \\ -1 & 1 & 1 \\ -1 & 3 & 4 \end{vmatrix}}{\begin{vmatrix} -3 & -3 & -4 \\ 0 & 1 & 1 \\ 4 & 3 & 4 \end{vmatrix}} = \dfrac{1}{1} = 1$

$y = \dfrac{\begin{vmatrix} -3 & 2 & -4 \\ 0 & -1 & 1 \\ 4 & -1 & 4 \end{vmatrix}}{\begin{vmatrix} -3 & -3 & -4 \\ 0 & 1 & 1 \\ 4 & 3 & 4 \end{vmatrix}} = \dfrac{1}{1} = 1$

$z = \dfrac{\begin{vmatrix} -3 & -3 & 2 \\ 0 & 1 & -1 \\ 4 & 3 & -1 \end{vmatrix}}{\begin{vmatrix} -3 & -3 & -4 \\ 0 & 1 & 1 \\ 4 & 3 & 4 \end{vmatrix}} = \dfrac{-2}{1} = -2$

Solution: $(1, \ 1, \ -2)$

41. Use a determinant to find the area of the triangle with vertices $(1, 0)$, $(5, 0)$, and $(5, 8)$.

Solution:

$$\text{Area} = \frac{1}{2} \begin{vmatrix} 1 & 0 & 1 \\ 5 & 0 & 1 \\ 5 & 8 & 1 \end{vmatrix} = \frac{1}{2}(32) = 16$$

45. Use a determinant to find the equation of the line through the points $(-4, 0)$ and $(4, 4)$.

Solution:

$$\begin{vmatrix} x & y & 1 \\ -4 & 0 & 1 \\ 4 & 4 & 1 \end{vmatrix} = 0$$

$$-4x + 8y - 16 = 0$$

$$x - 2y + 4 = 0$$

49. If A is a 3×3 matrix and $|A| = 2$, then what is the value of $|4A|$? Give the reason for your answer.

Solution:

$|4A| = 4^3(2) = 128$, since $4A$ means that each one of the three rows of A was multiplied by 4.

Practice Test for Chapter 8

1. Put the matrix in reduced echelon form.

$$\begin{bmatrix} 1 & -2 & 4 \\ 3 & -5 & 9 \end{bmatrix}$$

For Exercises 2–4, use matrices to solve the system of equations.

2. $3x + 5y = 3$

$2x - y = -11$

3. $2x + 3y = -3$

$3x + 2y = 8$

$x + y = 1$

4. $x \quad\quad + 3z = -5$

$2x + y \quad\quad = 0$

$3x + y - z = 3$

5. Multiply $\begin{bmatrix} 1 & 4 & 5 \\ 2 & 0 & -3 \end{bmatrix} \begin{bmatrix} 1 & 6 \\ 0 & -7 \\ -1 & 2 \end{bmatrix}$.

6. Given $A = \begin{bmatrix} 9 & 1 \\ -4 & 8 \end{bmatrix}$ and $B = \begin{bmatrix} 6 & -2 \\ 3 & 5 \end{bmatrix}$, find $3A - 5B$.

7. Find $f(A)$:

$$f(x) = x^2 - 7x + 8, \quad A = \begin{bmatrix} 3 & 0 \\ 7 & 1 \end{bmatrix}.$$

8. True or false: $(A + B)(A + 3B) = A^2 + 4AB + 3B^2$ where A and B are matrices.

For Exercises 9–10, find the inverse of the matrix, if it exists.

9. $\begin{bmatrix} 1 & 2 \\ 3 & 5 \end{bmatrix}$

10. $\begin{bmatrix} 1 & 1 & 1 \\ 3 & 6 & 5 \\ 6 & 10 & 8 \end{bmatrix}$

11. Use an inverse matrix to solve the systems:

(a) $x + 2y = 4$

   $3x + 5y = 1$

(b) $x + 2y = 3$

   $3x + 5y = -2$

For Exercises 12–14, find the determinant of the matrix.

12. $\begin{bmatrix} 6 & -1 \\ 3 & 4 \end{bmatrix}$

13. $\begin{bmatrix} 1 & 3 & -1 \\ 5 & 9 & 0 \\ 6 & 2 & -5 \end{bmatrix}$

14. $\begin{bmatrix} 1 & 4 & 2 & 3 \\ 0 & 1 & -2 & 0 \\ 3 & 5 & -1 & 1 \\ 2 & 0 & 6 & 1 \end{bmatrix}$

15. True or false:

$$\begin{vmatrix} 3 & 0 & 0 \\ 0 & 3 & 0 \\ 0 & 0 & 3 \end{vmatrix} = -3^3 \begin{vmatrix} 1 & 0 & 0 \\ 0 & 0 & 1 \\ 0 & 1 & 0 \end{vmatrix}$$

16. Evaluate $\begin{vmatrix} 6 & 4 & 3 & 0 & 6 \\ 0 & 5 & 1 & 4 & 8 \\ 0 & 0 & 2 & 7 & 3 \\ 0 & 0 & 0 & 9 & 2 \\ 0 & 0 & 0 & 0 & 1 \end{vmatrix}$.

17. Use cofactors to find the inverse of $\begin{bmatrix} 1 & 3 & 0 \\ 0 & 4 & 5 \\ 0 & 1 & 2 \end{bmatrix}$.

For Exercises 18–20, use Cramer's Rule to find the indicated value.

18. $6x - 7y = 4$ Find x.

   $2x + 5y = 11$

19. $3x + z = 1$ Find z.

   $\phantom{3x + {}} y + 4z = 3$

   $x - y = 2$

20. $721.4x - 29.1y = 33.77$ Find y.

   $45.9x + 105.6y = 19.85$

CHAPTER 9

Sequences, Series, and Probability

SECTION 9.1

Sequences and Summation Notation

- Given the general nth term in a sequence, you should be able to find, or list, the terms.

- You should be able to find an expression for the nth term of a sequence.

- You should be able to use sigma notation for a sum.

Solutions to Selected Exercises

5. Write the first five terms of the following sequence. (Assume n begins with 1.)

$$a_n = \frac{3^n}{n!}$$

Solution:

$$a_n = \frac{3^n}{n!}$$

$$a_1 = \frac{3^1}{1!} = 3$$

$$a_2 = \frac{3^2}{2!} = \frac{9}{2}$$

$$a_3 = \frac{3^3}{3!} = \frac{27}{6} = \frac{9}{2}$$

$$a_4 = \frac{3^4}{4!} = \frac{81}{24} = \frac{27}{8}$$

$$a_5 = \frac{3^5}{5!} = \frac{243}{120} = \frac{81}{40}$$

Solution: $3, \frac{9}{2}, \frac{9}{2}, \frac{27}{8}, \frac{81}{40}$

9. Write the first five terms of the following sequence. (Assume n begins with 1.)

$$a_n = \frac{n+1}{n}$$

Solution:

$$a_n = \frac{n+1}{n}$$

$$a_1 = \frac{2}{1} = 2$$

$$a_2 = \frac{3}{2}$$

$$a_3 = \frac{4}{3}$$

$$a_4 = \frac{5}{4}$$

$$a_5 = \frac{6}{5}$$

Solution: $2,\ \frac{3}{2},\ \frac{4}{3},\ \frac{5}{4},\ \frac{6}{5}$

13. Write the first five terms of the following sequence. (Assume n begins with 1.)

$$a_n = \frac{1 + (-1)^n}{n}$$

Solution:

$$a_n = \frac{1 + (-1)^n}{n}$$

$$a_1 = \frac{1 + (-1)}{1} = \frac{0}{1} = 0$$

$$a_2 = \frac{1 + (-1)^2}{2} = \frac{2}{2} = 1$$

$$a_3 = \frac{1 + (-1)^3}{3} = \frac{0}{3} = 0$$

$$a_4 = \frac{1 + (-1)^4}{4} = \frac{2}{4} = \frac{1}{2}$$

$$a_5 = \frac{1 + (-1)^5}{5} = \frac{0}{5} = 0$$

Solution: $0,\ 1,\ 0,\ \frac{1}{2},\ 0$

19. Write the first five terms of the sequence $a_1 = 3$ and $a_{k+1} = 2(a_k - 1)$. (Assume n begins with 1.)

Solution:

$$a_1 = 3 \text{ and } a_{k+1} = 2(a_k - 1)$$
$$a_1 = 3$$
$$a_2 = 2(3 - 1) = 4$$
$$a_3 = 2(4 - 1) = 6$$
$$a_4 = 2(6 - 1) = 10$$
$$a_5 = 2(10 - 1) = 18$$

Solution: 3, 4, 6, 10, 18

21. Simplify the ratio

$$\frac{10!}{8!}.$$

Solution:

$$\frac{10!}{8!} = \frac{10 \cdot 9 \cdot 8!}{8!} = 10 \cdot 9 = 90$$

25. Simplify the ratio

$$\frac{(2n-1)!}{(2n+1)!}.$$

Solution:

$$\frac{(2n-1)!}{(2n+1)!} = \frac{(2n-1)!}{(2n+1)(2n)(2n-1)!} = \frac{1}{(2n+1)(2n)} = \frac{1}{2n(2n+1)}$$

29. Write an expression for the nth term of the sequence 0, 3, 8, 15, 24, ... (Assume n begins with 1.)

$$a_1 = 0 = 1^2 - 1$$
$$a_2 = 3 = 2^2 - 1$$
$$a_3 = 8 = 3^2 - 1$$
$$a_4 = 15 = 4^2 - 1$$
$$a_5 = 24 = 5^2 - 1$$

Therefore, $a_n = n^2 - 1$.

35. Write an expression for the nth term of the sequence $1 + \frac{1}{1}, \; 1 + \frac{1}{2}, \; 1 + \frac{1}{3}, \; 1 + \frac{1}{4}, \; 1 + \frac{1}{5}, \; \ldots$. (Assume n begins with 1.)

Solution:

$$a_1 = 1 + \frac{1}{1}$$
$$a_2 = 1 + \frac{1}{2}$$
$$a_3 = 1 + \frac{1}{3}$$
$$a_4 = 1 + \frac{1}{4}$$
$$a_5 = 1 + \frac{1}{5}$$

Therefore, $a_n = 1 + \dfrac{1}{n}$.

39. Write an expression for the nth term of the sequence $1, \; -1, \; 1, \; -1, \; 1, \; \ldots$. (Assume n begins with 1.)

Solution:

$$a_1 = 1 = (-1)^{1-1} \quad \text{or} \quad (-1)^{1+1}$$
$$a_2 = -1 = (-1)^{2-1} \quad \text{or} \quad (-1)^{2+1}$$
$$a_3 = 1 = (-1)^{3-1} \quad \text{or} \quad (-1)^{3+1}$$
$$a_4 = -1 = (-1)^{4-1} \quad \text{or} \quad (-1)^{4+1}$$
$$a_5 = 1 = (-1)^{5-1} \quad \text{or} \quad (-1)^{5+1}$$

Therefore, $a_n = (-1)^{n-1}$ or $a_n = (-1)^{n+1}$.

43. Find the sum.

$$\sum_{k=0}^{3} \frac{1}{k^2 + 1}$$

Solution:

$$\sum_{k=0}^{3} \frac{1}{k^2 + 1} = \frac{1}{(0)^2 + 1} + \frac{1}{(1)^2 + 1} + \frac{1}{(2)^2 + 1} + \frac{1}{(3)^2 + 1}$$

$$= 1 + \frac{1}{2} + \frac{1}{5} + \frac{1}{10}$$

$$= \frac{10 + 5 + 2 + 1}{10}$$

$$= \frac{18}{10}$$

$$= \frac{9}{5}$$

49. Find the sum.

$$\sum_{i=1}^{4}(x^2 + 2i)$$

Solution:

$$\sum_{i=1}^{4}(x^2 + 2i) = (x^2 + 2(1)) + (x^2 + 2(2)) + (x^2 + 2(3)) + (x^2 + 2(4))$$

$$= x^2 + 2 + x^2 + 4 + x^2 + 6 + x^2 + 8$$

$$= 4x^2 + 20$$

51. Use sigma notation to write the sum

$$\frac{1}{3(1)} + \frac{1}{3(2)} + \frac{1}{3(3)} + \cdots + \frac{1}{3(9)}.$$

Solution:

$$\frac{1}{3(1)} + \frac{1}{3(2)} + \frac{1}{3(3)} + \cdots + \frac{1}{3(9)} = \sum_{i=1}^{9}\frac{1}{3i}$$

55. Use sigma notation to write the sum $3 - 9 + 27 - 81 + 243 - 729$.

Solution:

$$3 - 9 + 27 - 81 + 243 - 729 = 3^1 - 3^2 + 3^3 - 3^4 + 3^5 - 3^6$$

$$= \sum_{i=1}^{6}(-1)^{i+1}3^i$$

59. Use sigma notation to write the sum

$$\frac{1}{4} + \frac{3}{8} + \frac{7}{16} + \frac{15}{32} + \frac{31}{64}.$$

Solution:

$$\frac{1}{4} + \frac{3}{8} + \frac{7}{16} + \frac{15}{32} + \frac{31}{64} = \frac{2^1 - 1}{2^2} + \frac{2^2 - 1}{2^3} + \frac{2^3 - 1}{2^4} + \frac{2^4 - 1}{2^5} + \frac{2^5 - 1}{2^6}$$

$$= \sum_{i=1}^{5}\frac{2^i - 1}{2^{i+1}}$$

61. Prove that

$$\sum_{i=1}^{n}(x_i - \overline{x}) = 0, \quad \text{where} \quad \overline{x} = \frac{1}{n}\sum_{i=1}^{n}x_i.$$

Solution:

$$\sum_{i=1}^{n}(x_i - \overline{x}) = \sum_{i=1}^{n}x_i - \sum_{i=1}^{n}\overline{x}$$

$$= \sum_{i=1}^{n}x_i - n\overline{x}$$

$$= \sum_{i=1}^{n}x_i - n\left(\frac{1}{n}\sum_{i=1}^{n}x_i\right)$$

$$= 0$$

SECTION 9.2

Arithmetic Sequences

- You should be able to recognize an arithmetic sequence, find its common difference, and find its nth term.

- You should be able to find the nth partial sum of an arithmetic sequence with common difference d using the formula

$$S_n = \frac{n}{2}(a_1 + a_n) = \frac{n}{2}[2a_1 + (n-1)d].$$

Solutions to Selected Exercises

5. Determine whether the sequence $\frac{9}{4}$, 2, $\frac{7}{4}$, $\frac{3}{2}$, $\frac{5}{4}$, ... is arithmetic. If it is, find the common difference.

Solution:

$$\frac{9}{4}, \ 2, \ \frac{7}{4}, \ \frac{3}{2}, \ \frac{5}{4}, \ \ldots = \frac{9}{4}, \ \frac{8}{4}, \ \frac{7}{4}, \ \frac{6}{4}, \ \frac{5}{4}, \ \ldots$$

$$a_n = \frac{10}{4} - \frac{1}{4}n$$

Therefore, the sequence is arithmetic with $d = -\frac{1}{4}$.

9. Determine whether the sequence 5.3, 5.7, 6.1, 6.5, 6.9, ... is arithmetic. If it is, find the common difference.

Solution:

$$5.3, \ 5.7, \ 6.1, \ 6.5, \ 6.9, \ \ldots = 4.9 + 0.4, \ 4.9 + 2(0.4), \ 4.9 + 3(0.4),$$
$$4.9 + 4(0.4), \ 4.9 + 5(0.4), \ \ldots$$
$$a_n = 4.9 + 0.4n$$

Therefore, the sequence is arithmetic with $d = 0.4$.

13. Write the first five terms of the following sequence. Determine whether the sequence is arithmetic, and if it is, find the common difference.

$$a_n = \frac{1}{n+1}$$

300

Solution:

$$a_n = \frac{1}{n+1}$$

$$a_1 = \frac{1}{1+1} = \frac{1}{2}$$

$$a_2 = \frac{1}{2+1} = \frac{1}{3}$$

$$a_3 = \frac{1}{3+1} = \frac{1}{4}$$

$$a_4 = \frac{1}{4+1} = \frac{1}{5}$$

$$a_5 = \frac{1}{5+1} = \frac{1}{6}$$

The sequence is not arithmetic.

17. Write the first five terms of the sequence $a_1 = 1$, $a_2 = 1$, $a_n = a_{n-1} + a_{n-2}$, $n \geq 3$. Determine whether the sequence is arithmetic, and if it is, find the common difference.

Solution:

$$a_1 = 1, \ a_2 = 1, \ a_n = a_{n-1} + a_{n-2}, \ n \geq 3$$
$$a_1 = 1$$
$$a_2 = 1$$
$$a_3 = a_2 + a_1 = 1 + 1 = 2$$
$$a_4 = a_3 + a_2 = 2 + 1 = 3$$
$$a_5 = a_4 + a_3 = 3 + 2 = 5$$

The sequence 1, 1, 2, 3, 5, ... is not arithmetic.

21. Find a_n for the arithmetic sequence $a_1 = 100$, $d = -8$, $n = 8$.

Solution:

$$a_1 = 100, \ d = -8, \ n = 8$$
$$a_n = 100 + (n - 1)(-8)$$
$$a_8 = 100 + (8 - 1)(-8) = 100 - 56 = 44$$

25. Find a_n for the arithmetic sequence 4, $\frac{3}{2}$, -1, $-\frac{7}{2}$, $\ldots$, $n = 10$.

Solution:

$$4, \ \tfrac{3}{2}, \ -1, \ -\tfrac{7}{2}, \ \ldots, \ n = 10$$
$$a_n = 4 + (n - 1)\left(-\tfrac{5}{2}\right)$$
$$a_{10} = 4 + (10 - 1)\left(-\tfrac{5}{2}\right) = 4 - \tfrac{45}{2} = -\tfrac{37}{2}$$

29. Write the first five terms of the arithmetic sequence $a_1 = -2.6$, $d = -0.4$.

Solution:

$$a_1 = -2.6, \ d = -0.4$$
$$a_2 = -2.6 - 0.4, \ = -3$$
$$a_3 = -3 - 0.4 = -3.4$$
$$a_4 = -3.4 - 0.4 = -3.8$$
$$a_5 = -3.8 - 0.4 = -4.2$$

Solution: $-2.6, \ -3, \ -3.4, \ -3.8, \ -4.2$

35. Write the first five terms of the arithmetic sequence $a_8 = 26$, $a_{12} = 42$.

Solution:

$$a_8 = 26, \ a_{12} = 42$$
$$d = \frac{42 - 26}{4} = 4$$
$$a_n = -6 + 4n$$
$$a_1 = -2$$
$$a_2 = 2$$
$$a_3 = 6$$
$$a_4 = 10$$
$$a_5 = 14$$

Solution: $-2, \ 2, \ 6, \ 10, \ 14$

39. Find the nth partial sum of the arithmetic sequence $-6, \ -2, \ 2, \ 6, \ \ldots, \ n = 50$.

Solution:

$$-6, \ -2, \ 2, \ 6, \ \ldots, \ n = 50$$
$$d = 4$$
$$S_{50} = \frac{50}{2}[2(-6) + (50 - 1)(4)] = 25[-12 + 196] = 25(184) = 4600$$

43. Find the nth partial sum of the arithmetic sequence $a_1 = 100$, $a_{25} = 220$, $n = 25$.

Solution:

$$a_1 = 100, \ a_{25} = 220, \ n = 25$$
$$S_{25} = \frac{25}{2}(100 + 220) = \frac{25}{2}(320) = 4000$$

47. Find the sum.

$$\sum_{n=1}^{100} 5n$$

Solution:

$$a_n = 5n$$
$$a_1 = 5, \ a_{100} = 500$$
$$S_{100} = \frac{100}{2}(5 + 500) = 25,250$$

53. Find the sum.

$$\sum_{n=0}^{50}(1000 - 5n)$$

Solution:

$$\sum_{n=0}^{50}(1000 - 5n) = 1000 + \sum_{n=1}^{50}(1000 - 5n)$$
$$= 1000 + \frac{50}{2}(995 + 750) = 1000 + 43,625 = 44,625$$

1000 - 5n

59. Determine the seating capacity of an auditorium with 30 rows of seats if there are 20 seats in the first row, 24 seats in the second row, 28 seats in the third row, and so on.

Solution:

$$a_n = 16 + 4n$$
$$a_1 = 20, \ a_{30} = 136$$
$$S_{30} = \frac{30}{2}(20 + 136) = 2340 \text{ seats}$$

63. Insert three arithmetic means between the pair of numbers 3 and 6.

Solution:

3, 6; $k = 3$

3, m_1, m_2, m_3, 6

$$a_5 = 6 = 3 + 4d$$
$$d = \frac{3}{4}$$
$$m_1 = 3 + \frac{3}{4} = \frac{15}{4}$$
$$m_2 = \frac{15}{4} + \frac{3}{4} = \frac{18}{4} = \frac{9}{2}$$
$$m_3 = \frac{18}{4} + \frac{3}{4} = \frac{21}{4}$$

SECTION 9.3

Geometric Sequences and Series

- You should be able to identify a geometric sequence, find its common ratio, and find the nth term.

- You should be able to find the nth partial sum of a geometric sequence with common ratio r using the formula

$$S_n = \frac{a_1(1 - r^n)}{1 - r}, \quad r \neq 1.$$

- You should know that if $|r| < 1$, then

$$\sum_{n=0}^{\infty} a_1 r^n = \sum_{n=1}^{\infty} a_1 r^{n-1} = \frac{a_1}{1 - r}.$$

- You should be able to write a repeating decimal as the ratio of two integers.

Solutions to Selected Exercises

3. Determine whether the sequence 3, 12, 21, 30, ... is geometric. If it is, find its common ratio.

Solution:

3, 12, 21, 30, ...

$a_n = -6 + 9n$

This an arithmetic sequence, not a geometric sequence.

7. Determine whether the sequence $\frac{1}{2}$, $\frac{2}{3}$, $\frac{3}{4}$, $\frac{4}{5}$, ... is geometric. If it is, find its common ratio.

Solution:

$$\frac{1}{2}, \frac{2}{3}, \frac{3}{4}, \frac{4}{5}, \cdots$$

$$a_n = \frac{n}{n+1}$$

This is not a geometric series.

11. Write the first five terms of the geometric sequence $a_1 = 2$, $r = 3$.

Solution:

$$a_1 = 2, \; r = 3$$
$$a_2 = 2(3) = 6$$
$$a_3 = 2(3)^2 = 18$$
$$a_4 = 2(3)^3 = 54$$
$$a_5 = 2(3)^4 = 162$$

Solution: 2, 6, 18, 54, 162

15. Write the first five terms of the geometric sequence $a_1 = 5$, $r = -\frac{1}{10}$.

Solution:

$$a_1 = 5, \; r = -\frac{1}{10}$$
$$a_2 = 5\left(-\frac{1}{10}\right) = -\frac{1}{2}$$
$$a_3 = 5\left(-\frac{1}{10}\right)^2 = \frac{1}{20}$$
$$a_4 = 5\left(-\frac{1}{10}\right)^3 = -\frac{1}{200}$$
$$a_5 = 5\left(-\frac{1}{10}\right)^4 = \frac{1}{2000}$$

Solution: $5, \; -\frac{1}{2}, \; \frac{1}{20}, \; -\frac{1}{200}, \; \frac{1}{2000}, \; \cdots$

19. Find the nth term of the geometric sequence $a_1 = 4$, $r = \frac{1}{2}$, $n = 10$.

Solution:

$$a_1 = 4, \; r = \frac{1}{2}, \; n = 10$$
$$a_{10} = 4\left(\frac{1}{2}\right)^9 = \frac{1}{128} = \left(\frac{1}{2}\right)^7$$

23. Find the nth term of the geometric sequence $a_1 = 100$, $r = e^x$, $n = 9$.

Solution:

$$a_1 = 100, \; r = e^x, \; n = 9$$
$$a_9 = 100(e^x)^8 = 100e^{8x}$$

27. Find the nth term of the geometric sequence $a_1 = 16$, $a_4 = \frac{27}{4}$, $n = 3$.

Solution:

$$a_1 = 16, \quad a_4 = \frac{27}{4}, \quad n = 3$$

$$a_4 = 16r^3 = \frac{27}{4}$$

$$r^3 = \frac{27}{64}$$

$$r = \frac{3}{4}$$

$$a_3 = 16\left(\frac{3}{4}\right)^2 = 16\left(\frac{9}{16}\right) = 9$$

31. A sum of $1000 is invested at 10% interest. Find the amount after 10 years if the interest is compounded (a) annually, (b) semiannually, (c) quarterly, (d) monthly, and (e) daily.

Solution:

$$A = P\left(1 + \frac{r}{n}\right)^{nt} = 1000\left(1 + \frac{0.10}{n}\right)^{n(10)}$$

(a) $n = 1$, $\quad A = 1000(1 + 0.10)^{10}$ $\qquad = \$2593.74$

(b) $n = 2$, $\quad A = 1000\left(1 + \frac{0.10}{2}\right)^{2(10)}$ $\qquad = \$2653.30$

(c) $n = 4$, $\quad A = 1000\left(1 + \frac{0.10}{4}\right)^{4(10)}$ $\qquad = \$2685.06$

(d) $n = 12$, $\quad A = 1000\left(1 + \frac{0.10}{12}\right)^{12(10)}$ $\qquad = \$2707.04$

(e) $n = 365$, $\quad A = 1000\left(1 + \frac{0.10}{365}\right)^{365(10)}$ $\qquad = \$2717.91$

35. Find the sum.

$$\sum_{n=0}^{20} 3\left(\frac{3}{2}\right)^n$$

Solution:

$$\sum_{n=0}^{20} 3\left(\frac{3}{2}\right)^n = \frac{3\left(1 - (3/2)^{21}\right)}{1 - (3/2)} = 29,921.31$$

39. Find the sum.

$$\sum_{n=0}^{8} 2^n$$

Solution:

$$\sum_{n=0}^{8} 2^n = \frac{1-2^9}{1-2} = 511$$

43. A deposit of P dollars is made at the beginning of each month for T years in an account that pays R percent interest, compounded monthly. Let $N = 12T$ be the total number of deposits. The balance after T years is

$$A = P\left(1 + \frac{R}{12}\right) + P\left(1 + \frac{R}{12}\right)^2 + \cdots + P\left(1 + \frac{R}{12}\right)^N.$$

Show that the balance is given by

$$A = P\left[\left(1 + \frac{R}{12}\right)^N - 1\right]\left(1 + \frac{12}{R}\right).$$

Solution:

$$A = P\left(1 + \frac{R}{12}\right) + P\left(1 + \frac{R}{12}\right)^2 + \cdots + P\left(1 + \frac{R}{12}\right)^N$$

$$= \left(1 + \frac{R}{12}\right)\left[P + P\left(1 + \frac{R}{12}\right) + \cdots + P\left(1 + \frac{R}{12}\right)^{N-1}\right]$$

$$= P\left(1 + \frac{R}{12}\right)\sum_{n=1}^{N}\left(1 + \frac{R}{12}\right)^{n-1}$$

$$= P\left(1 + \frac{R}{12}\right)\frac{1 - \left(1 + \frac{R}{12}\right)^N}{1 - \left(1 + \frac{R}{12}\right)}$$

$$= P\left(1 + \frac{R}{12}\right)\left(-\frac{12}{R}\right)\left[1 - \left(1 + \frac{R}{12}\right)^N\right]$$

$$= P\left(\frac{12}{R} + 1\right)\left[-1 + \left(1 + \frac{R}{12}\right)^N\right]$$

$$= P\left[\left(1 + \frac{R}{12}\right)^N - 1\right]\left(1 + \frac{12}{R}\right)$$

47. Find the sum of the infinite geometric series .

$$\sum_{n=0}^{\infty}\left(\frac{1}{2}\right)^n = 1 + \frac{1}{2} + \frac{1}{4} + \frac{1}{8} + \cdots$$

Solution:

$$\sum_{n=0}^{\infty}\left(\frac{1}{2}\right)^n = 1 + \frac{1}{2} + \frac{1}{4} + \frac{1}{8} + \cdots = \frac{1}{1-(1/2)} = 2$$

51. Find the sum of the infinite geometric series.

$$\sum_{n=0}^{\infty}4\left(\frac{1}{4}\right)^n = 4 + 1 + \frac{1}{4} + \frac{1}{16} + \cdots$$

Solution:

$$\sum_{n=0}^{\infty}4\left(\frac{1}{4}\right)^n = 4 + 1 + \frac{1}{4} + \frac{1}{16} + \cdots = \frac{4}{1-(1/4)} = \frac{16}{3}$$

55. Find the sum of the infinite geometric series $4 - 2 + 1 - \frac{1}{2} + \cdots$.

Solution:

$$4 - 2 + 1 - \frac{1}{2} + \cdots = \sum_{n=0}^{\infty}4\left(-\frac{1}{2}\right)^n = \frac{4}{1-(-1/2)} = \frac{8}{3}$$

59. A ball is dropped from a height of 16 feet. Each time it drops h feet, it rebounds $0.81h$ feet. Find the total distance traveled by the ball.

Solution:

$$\text{Total distance} = \left[\sum_{n=0}^{\infty}32(0.81)^n\right] - 16 = \frac{32}{1-0.81} - 16 = 152.42 \text{ ft}$$

63. Write $0.363636\ldots$ as the ratio of two integers by considering it to be the sum of an infinite geometric series.

Solution:

$$0.363636\ldots = \sum_{n=0}^{\infty}0.36(0.01)^n = \frac{0.36}{1-0.01} = \frac{0.36}{0.99} = \frac{36}{99} = \frac{4}{11}$$

67. Write $1.363636\ldots$ as the ratio of two integers by considering it to be the sum of an infinite geometric series.

Solution:

$$1.363636\ldots = 1 + \sum_{n=0}^{\infty}0.36(0.01)^n$$

$$= 1 + \frac{4}{11} \quad \text{From Exercise 63}$$

$$= \frac{15}{11}$$

SECTION 9.4

Mathematical Induction

- You should be sure that you understand the principle of mathematical induction. If P_n is a statement involving the positive integer n, where P_1 is true and the truth of P_k implies the truth of P_{k+1}, then P_n is true for all positive integers n.

- You should be able to use mathematical induction to find a formula for the nth term of a sequence.

Solutions to Selected Exercises

5. Find the following sum, using the formulas for the sums of powers of integers.

$$\sum_{n=1}^{6} n^4$$

Solution:

$$\sum_{n=1}^{N} n^4 = \frac{N(N+1)(2N+1)(3N^2+3N-1)}{30}$$

$$\sum_{n=1}^{6} n^4 = \frac{6(7)(13)(125)}{30} = 2275$$

9. Find S_{k+1} for

$$S_k = \frac{k^2(k+1)^2}{4}.$$

Solution:

$$S_k = \frac{k^2(k+1)^2}{4}$$

$$S_{k+1} = \frac{(k+1)^2((k+1)+1)^2}{4}$$

$$= \frac{(k+1)^2(k+2)^2}{4}$$

13. Use mathematical induction to prove the formula for every positive integer n.

$$2 + 7 + 12 + 17 + \cdots + (5n - 3) = \frac{n}{2}(5n - 1)$$

Solution:

When $n = 1$,

$$S_1 = 2 = \frac{1}{2}(5(1) - 1).$$

Assume that

$$S_k = 2 + 7 + 12 + 17 + \cdots + (5k - 3) = \frac{k}{2}(5k - 1).$$

Then,

$$\begin{aligned}
S_{k+1} &= 2 + 7 + 12 + 17 + \cdots + (5k - 3) + [5(k + 1) - 3] \\
&= S_k + 5k + 5 - 3 \\
&= \frac{k}{2}(5k - 1) + 5k + 2 \\
&= \frac{5k^2 - k + 10k + 4}{2} \\
&= \frac{5k^2 + 9k + 4}{2} \\
&= \frac{(k + 1)(5k + 4)}{2} \\
&= \frac{(k + 1)}{2}[5(k + 1) - 1].
\end{aligned}$$

We conclude by mathematical induction that the formula is valid for all positive integer values of n.

17. Use mathematical induction to prove the formula for every positive integer n.

$$1 + 2 + 3 + 4 + \cdots + n = \frac{n(n + 1)}{2}$$

Solution:
When $n = 1$,

$$S_1 = 1 = \frac{1(1 + 1)}{2}.$$

Assume that

$$S_k = 1 + 2 + 3 + 4 + \cdots + k = \frac{k(k + 1)}{2}.$$

Then,

$$S_{k+1} = 1 + 2 + 3 + 4 + \cdots + k + k + 1$$
$$= S_k + k + 1$$
$$= \frac{k(k+1)}{2} + \frac{2(k+1)}{2}$$
$$= \frac{(k+1)(k+2)}{2}.$$

Therefore, we conclude that this formula holds for all positive integer values of n.

23. Use mathematical induction to prove the formula for every positive integer n.

$$\sum_{i=1}^{n} i(i+1) = \frac{n(n+1)(n+2)}{3}$$

Solution:
When $n = 1$,

$$S_1 = 2 = \frac{1(2)(3)}{3}.$$

Assume that

$$S_k = 1(2) + 2(3) + 3(4) + \cdots + k(k+1) = \frac{k(k+1)(k+2)}{3}.$$

Then,

$$S_{k+1} = 1(2) + 2(3) + 3(4) + \cdots + k(k+1) + (k+1)(k+2)$$
$$= S_k + (k+1)(k+2)$$
$$= \frac{k(k+1)(k+2)}{3} + \frac{3(k+1)(k+2)}{3}$$
$$= \frac{(k+1)(k+2)(k+3)}{3}.$$

Thus, this formula is valid for all positive integer values of n.

27. Find a formula for the nth partial sum of the sequence.

$$1, \frac{9}{10}, \frac{81}{100}, \frac{729}{1000}, \cdots$$

Solution:

$$S_1 = 1$$

$$S_2 = 1 + \frac{9}{10} = 1 + \left(\frac{9}{10}\right)^1$$

$$S_3 = 1 + \frac{9}{10} + \frac{81}{100} = 1 + \left(\frac{9}{10}\right)^1 + \left(\frac{9}{10}\right)^2$$

$$S_4 = 1 + \frac{9}{10} + \frac{81}{100} + \frac{729}{1000} = 1 + \left(\frac{9}{10}\right)^1 + \left(\frac{9}{10}\right)^2 + \left(\frac{9}{10}\right)^3$$

$$\vdots$$

$$S_n = 1 + \left(\frac{9}{10}\right)^1 + \left(\frac{9}{10}\right)^2 + \left(\frac{9}{10}\right)^3 + \cdots + \left(\frac{9}{10}\right)^{n-1} = \sum_{i=1}^{n} \left(\frac{9}{10}\right)^{i-1}$$

Since this is a geometric series,

$$S_n = \frac{1 - \left(\frac{9}{10}\right)^n}{1 - \frac{9}{10}} = 10[1 - (0.9)^n].$$

31. Use mathematical induction to prove the inequality, $\left(\frac{4}{3}\right)^n > n$, $n \geq 7$.

Solution:

When $n = 7$,

$$\left(\frac{4}{3}\right)^7 \approx 7.4915 > 7.$$

Assume that

$$\left(\frac{4}{3}\right)^k > k, \ k > 7.$$

Then,

$$\left(\frac{4}{3}\right)^{k+1} = \left(\frac{4}{3}\right)^k \left(\frac{4}{3}\right) > k\left(\frac{4}{3}\right) = k + \frac{k}{3} > k + 1.$$

Thus,

$$\left(\frac{4}{3}\right)^{k+1} > k + 1.$$

Therefore,

$$\left(\frac{4}{3}\right)^n > n.$$

35. Use mathematical induction to prove the property $(ab)^n = a^n b^n$ for all positive integers n.

Solution:

When $n = 1$, $(ab)^1 = a^1 b^1 = ab$.

Assume that $(ab)^k = a^k b^k$.

Then, $(ab)^{k+1} = (ab)^k (ab)$

$$= a^k b^k ab$$

$$= a^{k+1} b^{k+1}.$$

Thus, $(ab)^n = a^n b^n$.

39. Use mathematical induction to prove the Generalized Distributive Law:

$x(y_1 + y_2 + \cdots + y_n) = xy_1 + xy_2 + \cdots + xy_n$.

Solution:

When $n = 1$, $x(y_1) = xy_1$.

Assume that $x(y_1 + y_2 + \cdots + y_k) = xy_1 + xy_2 + \cdots + xy_k$.

Then, $xy_1 + xy_2 + \cdots + xy_k + xy_{k+1} = x(y_1 + y_2 + \cdots + y_k) + xy_{k+1}$

$$= x[(y_1 + y_2 + \cdots + y_k) + y_{k+1}]$$

$$= x(y_1 + y_2 + \cdots + y_k + y_{k+1}).$$

Hence, the formula holds.

SECTION 9.5

The Binomial Theorem

■ You should be able to use the formula

$$(x+y)^n = x^n + nx^{n-1}y + \frac{n(n-1)}{2!}x^{n-2}y^2 + \cdots + {}_nC_r{}^n x^{n-r}y^r + \cdots + y^n$$

where ${}_nC_r = \dfrac{n!}{(n-r)!r!}$, to expand $(x+y)^n$.

■ You should be able to use Pascal's Triangle in binomial expansion.

Solutions to Selected Exercises

3. Evaluate ${}_{12}C_0$.

Solution:

$$_{12}C_0 = \frac{12!}{(12-0)!0!} = \frac{12!}{(12!)(1)} = 1$$

7. Evaluate ${}_{100}C_{98}$.

Solution:

$$_{100}C_{98} = \frac{100!}{(100-98)!98!} = \frac{100\cdot 99\cdot 98!}{2!\cdot 98!} = \frac{100\cdot 99}{2} = 4950$$

11. Use the Binomial Theorem to expand $(x+y)^5$. Simplify your answer.

Solution:

$$\begin{aligned}
(x+y)^5 &= x^5 + 5x^4y + {}_5C_2x^3y^2 + {}_5C_3x^2y^3 + 5xy^4 + y^5 \\
&= x^5 + 5x^4y + 10x^3y^2 + 10x^2y^3 + 5xy^4 + y^5
\end{aligned}$$

15. Use the Binomial Theorem to expand $(r+3s)^6$. Simplify your answer.

Solution:

$$\begin{aligned}
(r+3s)^6 &= r^6 + 6r^5(3s) + 15r^4(3s)^2 + 20r^3(3s)^3 + 15r^2(3s)^4 + 6r(3s)^5 + (3s)^6 \\
&= r^6 + 18r^5s + 135r^4s^2 + 540r^3s^3 + 1215r^2s^4 + 1458rs^5 + 729s^6
\end{aligned}$$

19. Use the Binomial Theorem to expand $(1 - 2x)^3$. Simplify your answer.

Solution:

$$(1 - 2x)^3 = [1 + (-2x)]^3$$
$$= 1^3 + 3(1)^2(-2x) + 3(1)(-2x)^2 + (-2x)^3$$
$$= 1 - 6x + 12x^2 - 8x^3$$

23. Use the Binomial Theorem to expand the following. Simplify your answer.

$$\left(\frac{1}{x} + y\right)^5$$

Solution:

$$\left(\frac{1}{x} + y\right)^5 = \left(\frac{1}{x}\right)^5 + 5\left(\frac{1}{x}\right)^4 y + 10\left(\frac{1}{x}\right)^3 y^2 + 10\left(\frac{1}{x}\right)^2 y^3 + 5\left(\frac{1}{x}\right)y^4 + y^5$$
$$= \frac{1}{x^5} + \frac{5y}{x^4} + \frac{10y^2}{x^3} + \frac{10y^3}{x^2} + \frac{5y^4}{x} + y^5$$

27. Use the Binomial Theorem to expand $(2 - 3i)^6$. Simplify your answer by using the fact that $i^2 = -1$.

Solution:

$$(2 - 3i)^6 = 2^6 - 6(2)^5(3i) + 15(2)^4(3i)^2 - 20(2)^3(3i)^3 + 15(2)^2(3i)^4 - 6(2)(3i)^5 + (3i)^6$$
$$= 64 - 576i - 2160 + 4320i + 4860 - 2916i - 729$$
$$= 2035 + 828i$$

31. Expand $(2t - s)^5$, using Pascal's Triangle to determine the coefficients.

Solution:

$$1$$
$$1 \quad 1$$
$$1 \quad 2 \quad 1$$
$$1 \quad 3 \quad 3 \quad 1$$
$$1 \quad 4 \quad 6 \quad 4 \quad 1$$
$$1 \quad 5 \quad 10 \quad 10 \quad 5 \quad 1$$

$$(2t - s)^5 = (2t)^5 - 5(2t)^4 s + 10(2t)^3 s^2 - 10(2t)^2 s^3 + 5(2t)s^4 - s^5$$
$$= 32t^5 - 80t^4 s + 80t^3 s^2 - 40t^2 s^3 + 10ts^4 - s^5$$

35. Find the term x^5 in the expansion of $(x+3)^{12}$.

Solution:

$$_{12}C_7 x^5 (3)^7 = \frac{12!3^7}{(12-7)!7!} = 1,732,104 x^5$$

39. Find the term $x^4 y^{11}$ in the expansion of $(3x - 2y)^{15}$.

Solution:

$$_{15}C_{11}(3x)^4(-2y)^{11} = \frac{15!3^4(-2)^{11}}{(15-11)!11!} x^4 y^{11} = -226,437,120 x^4 y^{11}$$

45. Use the Binomial Theorem to expand $\left(\frac{1}{3} + \frac{2}{3}\right)^8$. In the study of probability, it is sometimes necessary to use the expansion of $(p+q)^n$, where $p + q = 1$.

Solution:

$$\left(\frac{1}{3} + \frac{2}{3}\right)^8 = \left(\frac{1}{3}\right)^8 + 8\left(\frac{1}{3}\right)^7\left(\frac{2}{3}\right) + 28\left(\frac{1}{3}\right)^6\left(\frac{2}{3}\right)^2 + 56\left(\frac{1}{3}\right)^5\left(\frac{2}{3}\right)^3 + 70\left(\frac{1}{3}\right)^4\left(\frac{2}{3}\right)^4$$
$$+ 56\left(\frac{1}{3}\right)^3\left(\frac{2}{3}\right)^5 + 28\left(\frac{1}{3}\right)^2\left(\frac{2}{3}\right)^6 + 8\left(\frac{1}{3}\right)\left(\frac{2}{3}\right)^7 + \left(\frac{2}{3}\right)^8$$
$$= \frac{1}{6561} + \frac{16}{6561} + \frac{112}{6561} + \frac{448}{6561} + \frac{1120}{6561} + \frac{1792}{6561} + \frac{1792}{6561} + \frac{1024}{6561} + \frac{256}{6561}$$

51. Prove $_{n+1}C_m = {}_nC_m + {}_nC_{m-1}$ for all integers m and n, $0 \le m \le n$.

Solution:

$$_nC_m + {}_nC_{m-1} = \frac{n!}{(n-m)!m!} + \frac{n!}{(n-m+1)!(m-1)!}$$
$$= \frac{n!(n-m+1)!(m-1)! + n!(n-m)!m!}{(n-m)!m!(n-m+1)!(m-1)!}$$
$$= \frac{n![(n-m+1)!(m-1)! + m!(n-m)!]}{(n-m)!m!(n-m+1)!(m-1)!}$$
$$= \frac{n!(m-1)![(n-m+1)! + m(n-m)!]}{(n-m)!m!(n-m+1)!(m-1)!}$$
$$= \frac{n!(n-m)![(n-m+1) + m]}{(n-m)!m!(n-m+1)!}$$
$$= \frac{n![n+1]}{m!(n-m+1)!}$$
$$= \frac{(n+1)!}{[(n+1)-m]!m!}$$
$$= {}_{n+1}C_m$$

SECTION 9.6

Counting Principles, Permutations, and Combinations

- You should know The Fundamental Principle of Counting.

- $_nP_r = \dfrac{n!}{(n-r)!}$ is the number of permutations of n elements taken r at a time.

- Given a set of n objects that has n_1 of one kind, n_2 of a second kind, and so on, the number of distinguishable permutations is

  $$\frac{n!}{n_1!n_2!\dots n_k!}.$$

- $_nC_r = \dfrac{n!}{(n-r)!r!}$ is the number of combinations of n elements taken r at a time.

Solutions to Selected Exercises

1. A small college needs two additional faculty members, a chemist and a statistician. In how many ways can these positions be filled if there are three applicants for the chemistry position and four for the position in statistics?

   Solution:

   $3 \cdot 4 = 12$ ways to fill the positions.

5. In a certain state the automobile license plates consist of two letters followed by a four-digit number. How many distinct license plate numbers can be formed?

   Solution:

   $26 \cdot 26 \cdot 10 \cdot 10 \cdot 10 \cdot 10 = 6,760,000$ distinct license plate numbers.

9. Three couples have reserved seats in a given row for a concert. In how many different ways can they be seated, given the following conditions?

   (a) There are no seating restrictions.
   (b) The two members of each couple wish to sit together.

   Solution:
   (a) $6! = 720$ different ways.
   (b) $6 \cdot 4 \cdot 2 = 48$ different ways.

13. Evaluate $_8P_3$.

Solution:

$$_8P_3 = \frac{8!}{(8-3)!} = \frac{8!}{5!} = 8 \cdot 7 \cdot 6 = 336$$

17. Evaluate $_{100}P_2$.

Solution:

$$_{100}P_2 = \frac{100!}{(100-2)!} = \frac{100!}{98!} = 100 \cdot 99 = 9900$$

21. In how many ways can five children line up in one row to have their picture taken?

Solution:

$5! = 120$ ways.

25. In order to conduct a certain experiment, four students are randomly selected from a class of 20. How many different groups of four students are possible?

$$_{20}C_4 = \frac{20!}{(20-4)!4!} = \frac{20!}{16!4!} = \frac{20 \cdot 19 \cdot 18 \cdot 17}{4 \cdot 3 \cdot 2} = 4845 \text{ different groups.}$$

29. Determine the number of three-digit numbers that can be formed from the ten digits 0, 1, 2, 3, 4, 5, 6, 7, 8, 9. (The leading digit cannot be zero.)

Solution:

$9 \cdot 10 \cdot 10 = 900$ different numbers.

35. An employer interviews eight people for four openings in the company. Three of the eight people are from a minority group. If all eight are qualified, in how many ways could the employer fill the four positions if (a) the selection is random and (b) exactly two are selected from the minority group?

Solution:

(a) $_8C_4 = \dfrac{8!}{(8-4)!4!} = \dfrac{8!}{4!4!} = \dfrac{8 \cdot 7 \cdot 6 \cdot 5}{4 \cdot 3 \cdot 2} = 70$ ways.

(b) $_3C_2 \cdot {}_5C_2 = \dfrac{3!}{(3-2)!2!} \cdot \dfrac{5!}{(5-2)!2!} = 3 \cdot 10 = 30$ ways.

37. Four people are to be selected at random from a group of four couples. In how many ways can this be done, given the following conditions?

(a) There are no restrictions.
(b) There is to be at least one couple in the group of four.
(c) The selection must include one member from each couple.

Solution:

(a) $_8C_4 = \dfrac{8!}{4!4!} = 70$ ways.

(b) There are 16 ways that a group of four can be formed without any couples in the group. Therefore, if at least one couple is to be in the group, there are $70 - 16 = 54$ ways that could occur.

(c) $2 \cdot 2 \cdot 2 \cdot 2 = 16$ ways.

41. Find the number of diagonals of an octagon.

Solution:

$$_8C_2 - 8 = \dfrac{8!}{6!2!} - 8 = 28 - 8 = 20 \text{ diagonals.}$$

45. Find the number of distinguishable permutations of the letters A, A, Y, Y, Y, Y, X, X, X.

Solution:

$$\dfrac{9!}{2!4!3!} = \dfrac{9 \cdot 8 \cdot 7 \cdot 6 \cdot 5}{2 \cdot 3 \cdot 2} = 1260 \text{ distinguishable permutations.}$$

49. Solve $14 \cdot {_nP_3} = {_{n+2}P_4}$ for n.

Solution:

$$14 \cdot {_nP_3} = {_{n+2}P_4}$$
$$\dfrac{14n!}{(n-3)!} = \dfrac{(n+2)!}{((n+2)-4)!}$$
$$14n(n-1)(n-2) = (n+2)(n+1)(n)(n-1)$$
$$0 = (n+2)(n+1)(n)(n-1) - 14n(n-1)(n-2)$$
$$0 = n(n-1)[(n+2)(n+1) - 14(n-2)]$$
$$0 = n(n-1)[n^2 + 3n + 2 - 14n + 28]$$
$$0 = n(n-1)[n^2 - 11n + 30]$$
$$0 = n(n-1)(n-5)(n-6)$$

$$n = 0, \; n = 1, \; n = 5, \; n = 6$$

Since $n \geq 3$, we have $n = 5$ or $n = 6$.

53. Prove $_nC_{n-1} = {_nC_1}$.

Solution:

$$_nC_{n-1} = \dfrac{n!}{(n-(n-1))!(n-1)!} = \dfrac{n!}{(1)!(n-1)!} = \dfrac{n!}{(n-1)!1!} = {_nC_1}$$

SECTION 9.7

Probability

You should know the following basic principles of probability.

- If an event A has $n(A)$ equally likely outcomes and its sample space has $n(S)$ equally likely outcomes, then the probability of event A is

$$P(A) = \frac{n(A)}{n(S)}.$$

- If A and B are mutually exclusive events, then $P(A \text{ or } B) = P(A) + P(B)$.

- If A and B are independent events, then the probability that both A and B will occur is $P(A)P(B)$.

- The complement of an event A is $P(A') = 1 - P(A)$.

Solutions to Selected Exercises

3. A coin is tossed three times. Find the probability of getting at least one head.

Solution:

$$S = \{HHH,\ HHT,\ HTH,\ HTT,\ THH,\ THT,\ TTH,\ TTT\}$$
$$P(TTT) = \frac{1}{8}$$
$$P(\text{at least one head}) = 1 - \frac{1}{8} = \frac{7}{8}$$

7. One card is selected from a standard deck of 52 playing cards. Find the probability of getting a black card that is not a face card.

Solution:

26 of the cards are black. Six of these are face cards (J, Q, K of clubs and spades). Therefore, there are 20 black cards that are not face cards.

$$P(A) = \frac{20}{52} = \frac{5}{13}$$

320

9. A six-sided die is tossed twice. Find the probability that the sum is 4.

Solution:

$$n(S) = 6(6) = 36$$
$$A = \{(1,\ 3),\ (2,\ 2),\ (3,\ 1)\}$$
$$P(A) = \frac{3}{36} = \frac{1}{12}$$

13. A six-sided die is tossed twice. Find the probability that the sum is odd and no more than 7.

Solution:

$$n(S) = 6 \cdot 6 = 36$$
$$A = \{(1,\ 2),\ (1,\ 4),\ (1,\ 6),\ (2,\ 1),\ (2,\ 3),\ (2,\ 5),\ (3,\ 2),\ (3,\ 4),$$
$$(4,\ 1),\ (4,\ 3),\ (5,\ 2),\ (6,\ 1)\}$$
$$P(A) = \frac{12}{36} = \frac{1}{3}$$

17. Two marbles are drawn (the first is *not* replaced before the second is drawn) from a bag containing one green, two yellow, and three red marbles. Find the probability of drawing neither yellow marble.

Solution:

$$P(A) = \frac{_4C_2}{_6C_2} = \frac{\frac{4!}{2!2!}}{\frac{6!}{4!2!}} = \frac{6}{15} = \frac{2}{5}$$

23. Two integers (between 1 and 30 inclusive) are chosen by a random number generator on a computer. What is the probability that (a) the numbers are both even, (b) one number is even and one is odd, (c) both numbers are less than 10, and (d) the same number is chosen twice?

Solution:

(a) $P(EE) = \dfrac{15}{30} \cdot \dfrac{15}{30} = \dfrac{1}{4}$

(b) $P(EO \text{ or } OE) = 2\left(\dfrac{15}{30}\right)\left(\dfrac{15}{30}\right) = \dfrac{1}{2}$

(c) $P(N_1 < 10,\ N_2 < 10) = \dfrac{9}{30} \cdot \dfrac{9}{30} = \dfrac{9}{100}$

(d) $P(N_1 N_1) = \dfrac{30}{30} \cdot \dfrac{1}{30} = \dfrac{1}{30}$

27. Four letters and envelopes are addressed to four different people. If the letters are randomly inserted into the envelopes, what is the probability that (a) exactly one will be inserted in the correct envelope and (b) at least one will be inserted in the correct envelope?

Solution:

(a) $P((C, W, W, W), (W, C, W, W), (W, W, C, W), (W, W, W, C))$
$$= 4\left(\frac{1}{4}\right)\left(\frac{4}{6}\right)\left(\frac{2}{4}\right)(1) = \frac{1}{3}$$

(b) $1 - P(W, W, W, W) = 1 - \frac{3}{4}\left(\frac{3}{6}\right) = \frac{5}{8}$

31. A space vehicle has an independent back-up system for one of its communication networks. The probability that either system will function satisfactorily for the duration of a flight is 0.985. What is the probability that during a given flight (a) both systems function satisfactorily, (b) at least one system functions satisfactorily, and (c) both systems fail?

Solution:

(a) $P(SS) = (0.985)^2 = 0.9702$

(b) $P(S) = 1 - P(FF) = 1 - (0.015)^2 = 0.9998$

(c) $P(FF) = (0.015)^2 = 0.0002$

35. A particular binomial experiment has 10 trials. The probability of success is 10%.

(a) Find the probability that all 10 trials fail.
(b) Find the probability that all 10 trials succeed.
(c) Find the probability that at least one trial succeeds.
(d) Find the probability that exactly one trial succeeds.

Solution:

(a) $P(\text{all fail}) = (0.9)^{10}$

(b) $P(\text{all succeed}) = (0.1)^{10}$

(c) $P(\text{at least one success}) = 1 - P(\text{all fail}) = 1 - (0.9)^{10}$

(d) $P(\text{one success}) = {}_{10}C_1(0.1)^1(0.9)^9 = (0.9)^9$

REVIEW EXERCISES FOR CHAPTER 9

Solutions to Selected Exercises

3. Use sigma notation to write the sum $\frac{1}{2} + \frac{2}{3} + \frac{3}{4} + \cdots + \frac{9}{10}$.

Solution:

$$\frac{1}{2} + \frac{2}{3} + \frac{3}{4} + \cdots + \frac{9}{10} = \sum_{k=1}^{9} \frac{k}{k+1}$$

7. Find the sum.

$$\sum_{j=3}^{10} (2j - 3)$$

Solution:

$$\sum_{j=3}^{10} (2j - 3) = [2(3) - 3] + [2(4) - 3] + [2(5) - 3] + [2(6) - 3] + [2(7) - 3]$$
$$+ [2(8) - 3] + [2(9) - 3] + [2(10) - 3]$$
$$= 3 + 5 + 7 + 9 + 11 + 13 + 15 + 17$$
$$= 80$$

11. Find the sum.

$$\sum_{i=0}^{\infty} \left(\frac{7}{8}\right)^i$$

Solution:

$$\sum_{i=0}^{\infty} \left(\frac{7}{8}\right)^i = \frac{1}{1 - \frac{7}{8}} = 8$$

17. Find the sum.

$$\sum_{n=0}^{10} (n^2 + 3)$$

Solution:

$$\sum_{n=0}^{10}(n^2+3) = \sum_{n=0}^{10}n^2 + \sum_{n=0}^{10}3 = \frac{10(11)(21)}{6} + 3(11) = 418$$

21. Write the first five terms of the geometric sequence, $a_1 = 4$, $r = -\frac{1}{4}$.

Solution:

$$a_1 = 4$$
$$a_2 = 4\left(-\frac{1}{4}\right) = -1$$
$$a_3 = -1\left(-\frac{1}{4}\right) = \frac{1}{4}$$
$$a_4 = \frac{1}{4}\left(-\frac{1}{4}\right) = -\frac{1}{16}$$
$$a_5 = -\frac{1}{16}\left(-\frac{1}{4}\right) = \frac{1}{64}$$

Solution: 4, -1, $\frac{1}{4}$, $-\frac{1}{16}$, $\frac{1}{64}$

25. Write $0.454545\ldots$ as the ratio of two integers by considering it to be the sum of an infinite geometric series.

Solution:

$$0.454545\ldots = \sum_{n=0}^{\infty}0.45(0.01)^n = \frac{0.45}{1-0.01} = \frac{45}{99} = \frac{5}{11}$$

29. Write $0.01333\ldots$ as the ratio of two integers by considering it to be the sum of an infinite geometric series.

Solution:

$$0.01333\ldots = 0.01 + \sum_{n=0}^{\infty}0.003(0.1)^n$$
$$= 0.01 + \frac{0.003}{1-0.1}$$
$$= \frac{1}{100} + \frac{3}{900}$$
$$= \frac{3}{300} + \frac{1}{300}$$
$$= \frac{1}{75}$$

31. Use mathematical induction to prove the formula $1 + 4 + \cdots + (3n - 2) = (n/2)(3n - 1)$ for every positive integer n.

Solution:

When $n = 1$,

$$1 = \frac{1}{2}[3(1) - 1] = 1.$$

Assume that

$$1 + 4 + 7 + \cdots + (3k - 2) = \frac{k}{2}(3k - 1).$$

Then,

$$
\begin{aligned}
1 + 4 + 7 + \cdots + (3k - 2) + [3(k + 1) - 2] &= [1 + 4 + 7 + \cdots + (3k - 2)] + (3k + 1) \\
&= \frac{k}{2}(3k - 1) + (3k + 1) \\
&= \frac{k(3k - 1)}{2} + \frac{2(3k + 1)}{2} \\
&= \frac{3k^2 + 5k + 2}{2} \\
&= \frac{(k + 1)(3k + 2)}{2} \\
&= \frac{(k + 1)}{2}[3(k + 1) - 1]
\end{aligned}
$$

Thus, the formula holds for all positive integers n.

37. Use the Binomial Theorem to expand the following binomial. Simplify your answer. [Remember that $i = \sqrt{-1}$.]

$$\left(\frac{2}{x} - 3x\right)^6$$

Solution:

$$
\begin{aligned}
\left(\frac{2}{x} - 3x\right)^6 &= \left(\frac{2}{x}\right)^6 + 6\left(\frac{2}{x}\right)^5(-3x) + 15\left(\frac{2}{x}\right)^4(-3x)^2 + 20\left(\frac{2}{x}\right)^3(-3x)^3 \\
&\quad + 15\left(\frac{2}{x}\right)^2(-3x)^4 + 6\left(\frac{2}{x}\right)(-3x)^5 + (-3x)^6 \\
&= \frac{64}{x^6} - \frac{576}{x^4} + \frac{2160}{x^2} - 4320 + 4860x^2 - 2916x^4 + 729x^6
\end{aligned}
$$

41. As a family increases in number, the number of different interpersonal relationships that exist increases at an even faster rate. Find the number of different interpersonal relationships that exist (between two people) if the number of members in the family is (a) 2, (b) 4, and (c) 6.

Solution:

(a) $_2C_2 = 1$
(b) $_4C_2 = 6$
(c) $_6C_2 = 15$

45. A man has five pairs of socks (no two pairs are the same color). If he randomly selects two socks from the drawer, what is the probability that he gets a matched pair?

Solution:

$$P(\text{pair}) = \frac{10}{10} \cdot \frac{1}{9} = \frac{1}{9}$$

49. Five cards are drawn from an ordinary deck of 52 playing cards. Find the probability of getting two pairs. (For example, the hand could be A-A-5-5-Q or 4-4-7-7-K.)

Solution:

$$P(2 \text{ pairs}) = \frac{(13)(_4C_2)(12)(_4C_2)(44)}{(2)(_{52}C_5)} = 0.0475$$

Practice Test for Chapter 9

1. Write out the first five terms of the sequence $a_n = \dfrac{2n}{(n+2)!}$.

2. Write an expression for the nth term of the sequence $\{\frac{4}{3}, \frac{5}{9}, \frac{6}{27}, \frac{7}{81}, \frac{8}{243}, \ldots\}$.

3. Find the sum $\displaystyle\sum_{i=1}^{6}(2i-1)$.

4. Write out the first five terms of the arithmetic sequence where $a_1 = 23$ and $d = -2$.

5. Find a_n for the arithmetic sequence with $a_1 = 12$, $d = 3$, and $n = 50$.

6. Find the sum of the first 200 positive integers.

7. Write out the first five terms of the geometric sequence with $a_1 = 7$ and $r = 2$.

8. Evaluate $\displaystyle\sum_{n=0}^{9}6\left(\frac{2}{3}\right)^n$.

9. Evaluate $\displaystyle\sum_{n=0}^{\infty}(0.03)^n$.

10. Use mathematical induction to prove that
$$1 + 2 + 3 + 4 + \cdots + n = \frac{n(n+1)}{2}.$$

11. Use mathematical induction to prove that $n! > 2^n$, $n \geq 4$.

12. Evaluate $_{13}C_4$.

13. Expand $(x+3)^5$.

14. Find the term involving x^7 in $(x-2)^{12}$.

15. Evaluate $_{30}P_4$.

16. How many ways can six people sit at a table with six chairs?

17. Twelve cars run in a race. How many different ways can they come in first, second, and third place? (Assume that there are no ties.)

18. Two six-sided dice are tossed. Find the probability that the total of the two dice is less than 5.

19. Two cards are selected at random from a deck of 52 playing cards. Find the probability that the first card is a King and the second card is a black ten.

20. A manufacturer has determined that for every 1000 units it produces, 3 will be faulty. What is the probability that an order of 50 units will have one or more faulty units?

CHAPTER 1

Practice Test Solutions

1. $\dfrac{42-20}{4-15} = \dfrac{+22}{-11} = -2$

2. $\dfrac{x}{z} - \dfrac{z}{y} = \dfrac{x}{z} \cdot \dfrac{y}{y} - \dfrac{z}{y} \cdot \dfrac{z}{z} = \dfrac{xy - z^2}{yz}$

3. $|x - 7| \le 4$

4. $10(-5)^3 = 10(-125) = -1250$

5. $(-4x^3)(-2x^{-5})\left(\dfrac{1}{16}x\right) = (-4)(-2)\left(\dfrac{1}{16}\right)x^{3+(-5)+1} = \dfrac{8}{16}x^{-1} = \dfrac{1}{2x}$

6. $0.0000412 = 4.12 \times 10^{-5}$

7. $125^{2/3} = \left(\sqrt[3]{125}\right)^2 = (5)^2 = 25$

8. $\sqrt[4]{64x^7y^9} = \sqrt[4]{16 \cdot 4x^4x^3y^8y}$
$$= 2xy^2\sqrt[4]{4x^3y}$$

9. $\dfrac{6}{\sqrt{12}} = \dfrac{6}{2\sqrt{3}} \cdot \dfrac{\sqrt{3}}{\sqrt{3}} = \dfrac{6\sqrt{3}}{6} = \sqrt{3}$

10. $3\sqrt{80} - 7\sqrt{500} = 3(4\sqrt{5}) - 7(10\sqrt{5})$
$$= 12\sqrt{5} - 70\sqrt{5} = -58\sqrt{5}$$

11. $\left(8x^4 - 9x^2 + 2x - 1\right) - \left(3x^3 + 5x + 4\right) = 8x^4 - 3x^3 - 9x^2 - 3x - 5$

12. $(x - 3)(x^2 + x - 7) = x^3 + x^2 - 7x - 3x^2 - 3x + 21 = x^3 - 2x^2 - 10x + 21$

13. $[(x - 2) - y]^2 = (x - 2)^2 - 2y(x - 2) + y^2$
$$= x^2 - 4x + 4 - 2xy + 4y + y^2 = x^2 + y^2 - 2xy - 4x + 4y + 4$$

14. $16x^4 - 1 = \left(4x^2 + 1\right)\left(4x^2 - 1\right) = \left(4x^2 + 1\right)(2x + 1)(2x - 1)$

15. $6x^2 + 5x - 4 = (2x - 1)(3x + 4)$

16. $x^3 - 64 = x^3 - 4^3 = (x - 4)\left(x^2 + 4x + 16\right)$

17. $-\dfrac{3}{x} + \dfrac{x}{x^2 + 2} = \dfrac{-3\left(x^2 + 2\right) + x^2}{x\left(x^2 + 2\right)} = \dfrac{-2x^2 - 6}{x\left(x^2 + 2\right)} = -\dfrac{2\left(x^2 + 3\right)}{x\left(x^2 + 2\right)}$

18. $\dfrac{x - 3}{4x} \div \dfrac{x^2 - 9}{x^2} = \dfrac{x - 3}{4x} \cdot \dfrac{x^2}{(x + 3)(x - 3)} = -\dfrac{x}{4(x + 3)}$

19. $\dfrac{1 - \dfrac{1}{x}}{1 - \dfrac{1}{1 - (1/x)}} = \dfrac{\dfrac{x - 1}{x}}{1 - \dfrac{1}{(x - 1)/x}} = \dfrac{\dfrac{x - 1}{x}}{1 - \dfrac{x}{x - 1}} = \dfrac{\dfrac{x - 1}{x}}{\dfrac{-1}{x - 1}} = \dfrac{x - 1}{x} \cdot \dfrac{x - 1}{-1} = \dfrac{-(x - 1)^2}{x}$

20. $\frac{1}{3}(x - 1)^{5/2} - \frac{1}{6}(x - 1)^{1/2} = \frac{1}{6}(x - 1)^{1/2}[2(x - 1)^2 - 1]$
$$= \frac{1}{6}(x - 1)^{1/2}\left(2x^2 - 4x + 2 - 1\right) = \frac{1}{6}(x - 1)^{1/2}\left(2x^2 - 4x + 1\right)$$

CHAPTER 2

Practice Test Solutions

1. $5x + 4 = 7x - 8$

$\quad 4 + 8 = 7x - 5x$

$\quad\quad 12 = 2x$

$\quad\quad\ x = 6$

2. $\dfrac{x}{3} - 5 = \dfrac{x}{5} + 1$

$\quad 15\left(\dfrac{x}{3} - 5\right) = 15\left(\dfrac{x}{5} + 1\right)$

$\quad\quad 5x - 75 = 3x + 15$

$\quad\quad\quad\ 2x = 90$

$\quad\quad\quad\ \ x = 45$

3. $\dfrac{3x + 1}{6x - 7} = \dfrac{2}{5}$

$\quad 5(3x + 1) = 2(6x - 7)$

$\quad\ 15x + 5 = 12x - 14$

$\quad\quad\quad 3x = -19$

$\quad\quad\quad\ x = -\dfrac{19}{3}$

4. $(x - 3)^2 + 4 = (x + 1)^2$

$\quad x^2 - 6x + 9 + 4 = x^2 + 2x + 1$

$\quad\quad\quad -8x = -12$

$\quad\quad\quad\quad x = \dfrac{-12}{-8}$

$\quad\quad\quad\quad x = \dfrac{3}{2}$

5. $A = \dfrac{1}{2}(a + b)h$

$\quad 2A = ah + bh$

$\quad 2A - bh = ah$

$\quad \dfrac{2A - bh}{h} = a$

6. $x + (x + 1) + (x + 2) = 132$

$\quad\quad\quad 3x + 3 = 132$

$\quad\quad\quad\quad 3x = 129$

$\quad\quad\quad\quad\ x = 43$

$\quad\quad\quad x + 1 = 44$

$\quad\quad\quad x + 2 = 45$

7. Percent $= \dfrac{301}{4300} = 0.07 = 7\%$

8. Let $x =$ number of quarters.

Then $53 - x =$ number of nickels.

$\quad 25x + 5(53 - x) = 605$

$\quad\quad 20x + 265 = 605$

$\quad\quad\quad\quad 20x = 340$

$\quad\quad\quad\quad\quad x = 17$ quarters

$\quad\quad\quad 53 - x = 36$ nickels

9. Let $x =$ amount in $9\frac{1}{2}\%$ fund.

Then $15,000 - x =$ amount in 11% fund.

$\quad 0.095x + 0.11(15,000 - x) = 1582.50$

$\quad\quad -0.015x + 1650 = 1582.50$

$\quad\quad\quad -0.015x = -67.5$

$\quad\quad\quad\quad x = \$4500$ @ $9\frac{1}{2}\%$

$\quad\quad 15,000 - x = \$10,500$ @ 11%

10. $28 + 5x - 3x^2 = 0$

$\quad (4 - x)(7 + 3x) = 0$

$\quad\quad x = 4$ or $x = -\dfrac{7}{3}$

11. $(x-2)^2 = 24$

$$x - 2 = \pm\sqrt{24}$$
$$x - 2 = \pm 2\sqrt{6}$$
$$x = 2 \pm 2\sqrt{6}$$

12. $x^2 - 4x - 9 = 0$

$$x^2 - 4x + 4 = 9 + 4$$
$$(x-2)^2 = 13$$
$$x - 2 = \pm\sqrt{13}$$
$$x = 2 \pm \sqrt{13}$$

13.
$$\frac{1}{x^2 - 6x + 1} = \frac{1}{x^2 - 6x + 9 - 9 + 1}$$
$$= \frac{1}{(x-3)^2 - 8}$$

14. $x^2 + 5x - 1 = 0$

$a = 1,\ b = 5,\ c = -1$

$$x = \frac{-5 \pm \sqrt{(5)^2 - 4(1)(-1)}}{2(1)}$$
$$= \frac{-5 \pm \sqrt{25 + 4}}{2}$$
$$= \frac{-5 \pm \sqrt{29}}{2}$$

15. $3x^2 - 2x + 4 = 0$

$a = 3,\ b = -2,\ c = 4$

$$x = \frac{-(-2) \pm \sqrt{(-2)^2 - 4(3)(4)}}{2(3)}$$
$$= \frac{2 \pm \sqrt{4 - 48}}{6}$$
$$= \frac{2 \pm \sqrt{-44}}{6}$$
$$= \frac{2 \pm 2i\sqrt{11}}{6}$$
$$= \frac{1 \pm i\sqrt{11}}{3}$$

16.
$$60,000 = xy$$
$$y = \frac{60,000}{x}$$
$$2x + 2y = 1100$$
$$2x + 2\left(\frac{60,000}{x}\right) = 1100$$
$$x + \frac{60,000}{x} = 550$$
$$x^2 + 60,000 = 550x$$
$$x^2 - 550x + 60,000 = 0$$
$$(x - 150)(x - 400) = 0$$
$$x = 150 \quad \text{or} \quad x = 400$$
$$y = 400 \qquad y = 150$$

Length: 400 feet
Width: 150 feet

17.
$$x(x + 2) = 624$$
$$x^2 + 2x - 624 = 0$$
$$(x - 24)(x + 26) = 0$$
$$x = 24, \ x = -26, \ \text{(extraneous solution)}$$
$$x + 2 = 26$$

18. $x^3 - 10x^2 + 24x = 0$

$$x(x^2 - 10x + 24) = 0$$
$$x(x - 4)(x - 6) = 0$$
$$x = 0, \ x = 4, \ x = 6$$

19. $\sqrt[3]{6-x} = 4$

$\quad\quad 6 - x = 64$

$\quad\quad -x = 58$

$\quad\quad x = -58$

20. $(x^2 - 8)^{2/5} = 4$

$\quad\quad x^2 - 8 = 4^{5/2}$

$\quad\quad x^2 - 8 = 32$

$\quad\quad x^2 = 40$

$\quad\quad x = \pm\sqrt{40}$

$\quad\quad x = \pm 2\sqrt{10}$

21. $\quad x^4 - x^2 - 12 = 0$

$\quad (x^2 - 4)(x^2 + 3) = 0$

$\quad x^2 = \quad 4 \text{ or } x^2 = -3$

$\quad\quad x = \pm 2 \quad\quad x = \pm\sqrt{3}\, i$

22. $4 - 3x > 16$

$\quad -3x > 12$

$\quad\quad x < -4$

23. $\quad \left| \dfrac{x-3}{2} \right| < 5$

$\quad -5 < \dfrac{x-3}{2} < 5$

$\quad -10 < x - 3 < 10$

$\quad\quad -7 < x < 13$

24. $\quad\quad\quad \dfrac{x+1}{x-3} < 2$

$\quad\quad \dfrac{x+1}{x-3} - 2 < 0$

$\quad \dfrac{x+1-2(x-3)}{x-3} < 0$

$\quad\quad\quad \dfrac{7-x}{x-3} < 0$

Solution intervals: $x < 3$ or $x \geq 7$

$$\frac{+}{-} < 0 \qquad \frac{+}{+} > 0 \qquad \frac{-}{+} < 0$$

Yes $\quad\quad$ No $\quad\quad$ Yes

25. $|3x - 4| \geq \quad 9$

$\quad 3x - 4 \leq -9 \quad \text{or} \quad 3x - 4 \geq 9$

$\quad\quad 3x \leq -5 \quad\quad\quad\quad 3x \geq 13$

$\quad\quad\quad x \leq -\dfrac{5}{3} \quad\quad\quad\quad x \geq \dfrac{13}{3}$

CHAPTER 3

Practice Test Solutions

1. $d = \sqrt{(4-0)^2 + (-1-3)^2}$

$= \sqrt{16 + 16}$

$= \sqrt{32}$

$= 4\sqrt{2}$

2. Midpoint: $\left(\dfrac{4+0}{2}, \dfrac{-1+3}{2}\right) = (2,\ 1)$

3. $6 = \sqrt{(x-0)^2 + (-2-0)^2}$

$6 = \sqrt{x^2 + 4}$

$36 = x^2 + 4$

$x^2 = 32$

$x = \pm\sqrt{32}$

$x = \pm 4\sqrt{2}$

4. x-intercept: Let $y = 0$; $\quad 0 = \dfrac{x-2}{x+3}$

$0 = x - 2$

$x = 2 \quad (2,\ 0)$

y-intercept: Let $x = 0$; $\quad y = \dfrac{0-2}{0+3}$

$y = -\dfrac{2}{3} \quad \left(0,\ -\dfrac{2}{3}\right)$

5. $\qquad xy^2 = 6$

$x(-y)^2 = 6 \Rightarrow xy^2 = 6 \qquad x\text{-axis symmetry}$

$(-x)y^2 = 6 \Rightarrow xy^2 = -6 \text{ No } y\text{-axis symmetry}$

$(-x)(-y)^2 = 6 \Rightarrow xy^2 = -6 \text{ No origin symmetry}$

6. x-intercepts: $(0,\ 0)$, $(2,\ 0)$, $(-2,\ 0)$

Origin symmetry:

x	0	1	-1	2	-2	3
y	0	-3	3	0	0	15

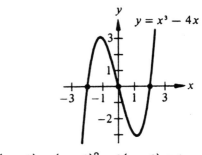

7. $\qquad x^2 + y^2 - 6x + 2y + 6 = 0$

$x^2 - 6x + \underline{9} + y^2 + 2y + \underline{1} = -6 + 9 + 1$

$(x-3)^2 + (y-1)^2 = 4$

Center: $(3,\ -1)$

Radius: 2

8. $f(x-3) = (x-3)^2 - 2(x-3) + 1$

$= x^2 - 6x + 9 - 2x + 6 + 1$

$= x^2 - 8x + 16$

9.
$$f(3) = 12 - 11 = 1$$
$$\frac{f(x) - f(3)}{x - 3} = \frac{(4x - 11) - 1}{x - 3}$$
$$= \frac{4x - 12}{x - 3}$$
$$= \frac{4(x - 3)}{x - 3}$$
$$= 4$$

11. (a) $6x - 5y + 4 = 0$
$$y = \frac{6x + 4}{5} \quad \text{function}$$

(b) $x^2 + y^2 = 9$
$$y = \pm\sqrt{9 - x^2} \quad \text{not a function}$$

(c) $y^3 = x^2 + 6$
$$y = \sqrt[3]{x^2 + 6} \quad \text{function}$$

10. $f(x) = \sqrt{36 - x^2} = \sqrt{(6 + x)(6 - x)}$
Domain: $[-6, \ 6]$
Range: $[0, \ 6]$

12. Parabola: Vertex $(0, \ -5)$
Intercepts: $(0, \ -5), \ (\pm\sqrt{5}, \ 0)$
y-axis symmetry

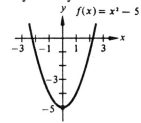

13. Intercepts: $(0, \ 3), \ (-3, \ 0)$

x	0	1	-1	2	-2	-3	-4
y	3	4	2	5	1	0	1

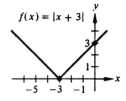

14.

x	0	1	2	3
y	1	3	5	7

x	-1	-2	0
y	2	6	0

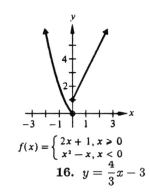

$$f(x) = \begin{cases} 2x + 1, x > 0 \\ x^2 - x, x < 0 \end{cases}$$

15.
$$m = \frac{-1 - 4}{3 - 2} = -5$$
$$y - 4 = -5(x - 2)$$
$$y - 4 = -5x + 10$$
$$y = -5x + 14$$

16. $y = \dfrac{4}{3}x - 3$

17. $2x + 3y = 0$

$$y = -\tfrac{2}{3}x$$
$$m_1 = -\tfrac{2}{3}$$
$$\perp m_2 = \tfrac{3}{2} \text{ through } (4, 1)$$
$$y - 1 = \tfrac{3}{2}(x - 4)$$
$$y - 1 = \tfrac{3}{2}x - 6$$
$$y = \tfrac{3}{2}x - 5$$

18. $(5, 32)$ and $(9, 44)$

$$m = \frac{44 - 32}{9 - 5} = \frac{12}{4} = 3$$
$$y - 32 = 3(x - 5)$$
$$y - 32 = 3x - 15$$
$$y = 3x + 17$$
When $x = 20$, $y = 3(20) + 17$
$$y = \$77$$

19. $f(g(x)) = f(2x + 3)$

$$= (2x + 3)^2 - 2(2x + 3) + 16$$
$$= 4x^2 + 12x + 9 - 4x - 6 + 16$$
$$= 4x^2 + 8x + 19$$

20.
$$f(x) = x^3 + 7$$
$$y = x^3 + 7$$
$$x = \sqrt[3]{y - 7}$$
$$f^{-1}(x) = \sqrt[3]{x - 7}$$

21. (a) $f(x) = |x - 6|$ is not one-to-one.
   For example, $f(0) = 6$ and $f(12) = 6$.
   (b) $f(x) = ax + b$, $a \neq 0$ is one-to-one.
   (c) $f(x) = x^3 - 19$ is one-to-one.

22.
$$f(x) = \sqrt{\frac{3 - x}{x}}, \quad 0 < x \leq 3$$
$$y = \sqrt{\frac{3 - x}{x}}$$
$$y^2 = \frac{3 - x}{x}$$
$$xy^2 = 3 - x$$
$$xy^2 + x = 3$$
$$x(y^2 + 1) = 3$$
$$x = \frac{3}{y^2 + 1}$$
$$f^{-1}(x) = \frac{3}{x^2 + 1}$$

23. $y = kx$ and $y = 30$ when $x = 5$

$$30 = k(5)$$
$$6 = k$$
$$y = 6x$$

24. $y = k/x$ and $y = 0.5$ when $x = 14$

$$0.5 = k/14$$
$$7 = k$$
$$y = 7/x$$

25. $z = \dfrac{kx^2}{y}$ and $z = 3$ when $x = 3$, $y = -6$

$$3 = \frac{k(3)^2}{-6}$$
$$-18 = 9k$$
$$-2 = k$$
$$z = \frac{-2x^2}{y}$$

CHAPTER 4

Practice Test Solutions

1. x-intercepts: $(1, 0)$, $(5, 0)$

y-intercept: $(0, 5)$

Vertex: $(3, -4)$

2. $a = 0.01$, $b = -90$

$$\frac{-b}{2a} = \frac{90}{2(.01)} = 4500 \text{ units}$$

3. Vertex $(1, 7)$ opening downward

through $(2, 5)$

$\quad y = a(x - 1)^2 + 7 \quad$ Standard form

$\quad 5 = a(2 - 1)^2 + 7$

$\quad 5 = a + 7$

$\quad a = -2$

$\quad y = -2(x - 1)^2 + 7$

$\quad\quad = -2(x^2 - 2x + 1) + 7$

$\quad\quad = -2x^2 + 4x + 5$

4. $y = \pm(x - 2)(3x - 4)$

$\quad y = \pm(3x^2 - 10x + 8)$

5. Leading coefficient: -3

Degree: 5

Moves down to the right and up to the left

6. $0 = x^5 - 5x^3 + 4x$

$\quad = x(x^4 - 5x^2 + 4)$

$\quad = x(x^2 - 1)(x^2 - 4)$

$\quad = x(x + 1)(x - 1)(x + 2)(x - 2)$

$\quad x = 0, \ x = \pm 1, \ x = \pm 2$

7. $f(x) = x(x - 3)(x + 2)$

$\quad\quad = x(x^2 - x - 6)$

$\quad\quad = x^3 - x^2 - 6x$

8. Intercepts: $(0, 0)$, $(0, \pm 2\sqrt{3})$

Origin symmetry

Moves up to the right.

Moves down to the left.

x	-2	-1	0	1	2
y	16	11	0	-11	-16

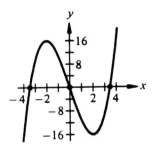

9.

$$\begin{array}{r} 3x^3 + 9x^2 + 20x + 62 + \dfrac{176}{x-3} \\ x-3\overline{)\,3x^4 + 0x^3 - 7x^2 + 2x - 10} \\ \underline{3x^4 - 9x^3} \\ 9x^3 - 7x^2 \\ \underline{9x^3 - 27x^2} \\ 20x^2 + 2x \\ \underline{20x^2 - 60x} \\ 62x - 10 \\ \underline{62x - 186} \\ 176 \end{array}$$

10.

$$\begin{array}{r} x - 2 + \dfrac{5x-13}{x^2+2x-1} \\ x^2+2x-1\overline{)\,x^3 + 0x^2 + 0x - 11} \\ \underline{x^3 + 2x^2 - x} \\ -2x^2 + x - 11 \\ \underline{-2x^2 - 4x + 2} \\ 5x - 13 \end{array}$$

11.

$$\begin{array}{r|rrrrr} -5 & 3 & 13 & 0 & 0 & 12 & -1 \\ & & -15 & 10 & -50 & 250 & -1310 \\ \hline & 3 & -2 & 10 & -50 & 262 & -1311 \end{array}$$

$$\frac{3x^5 + 13x^4 + 12x - 1}{x+5} = 3x^4 - 2x^3 + 10x^2 - 50x + 262 - \frac{1311}{x+5}$$

12.

$$\begin{array}{r|rrrr} -6 & 7 & 40 & -12 & 15 \\ & & -42 & 12 & 0 \\ \hline & 7 & -2 & 0 & 15 \end{array}$$

$$f(-6) = 15$$

13. $0 = x^3 - 19x - 30$

Possible Rational Roots: $\pm 1, \ \pm 2, \ \pm 3, \ \pm 5, \ \pm 6, \ \pm 10, \ \pm 15, \ \pm 30$

$$\begin{array}{r|rrrr} -2 & 1 & 0 & -19 & -30 \\ & & -2 & 4 & 30 \\ \hline & 1 & -2 & -15 & 0 \end{array} \qquad -2 \text{ is a zero.}$$

$0 = (x+2)(x^2 - 2x - 15)$

$0 = (x+2)(x+3)(x-5)$

Zeros: $x = -2, \ x = -3, \ x = 5$

14. $0 = x^4 + x^3 - 8x^2 - 9x - 9$

Possible Rational Roots: $\pm 1,\ \pm 3,\ \pm 9$

$$
\begin{array}{r|rrrrr}
3 & 1 & 1 & -8 & -9 & -9 \\
& & 3 & 12 & 12 & 9 \\
\hline
& 1 & 4 & 4 & 3 & 0
\end{array}
\qquad x = 3 \text{ is a zero.}
$$

$0 = (x - 3)(x^3 + 4x^2 + 4x + 3)$

Possible Rational Roots of $x^3 + 4x^2 + 4x + 3$: $\pm 1,\ \pm 3$

$$
\begin{array}{r|rrrr}
-3 & 1 & 4 & 4 & 3 \\
& & -3 & -3 & -3 \\
\hline
& 1 & 1 & 1 & 0
\end{array}
\qquad x = -3 \text{ is a zero.}
$$

$0 = (x - 3)(x + 3)(x^2 + x + 1)$

There are no real zeros of $x^2 + x + 1$.

Zeros: $x = 3,\ x = -3$

15. $0 = 6x^3 - 5x^2 + 4x - 15$

Possible Rational Roots: $\pm 1,\ \pm 3,\ \pm 5,\ \pm 15,\ \pm\frac{1}{2},\ \pm\frac{3}{2},\ \pm\frac{5}{2},\ \pm\frac{15}{2},\ \pm\frac{1}{3},\ \pm\frac{5}{3},\ \pm\frac{1}{6},\ \pm\frac{5}{6}$

16. $0 = x^3 - \frac{20}{3}x^2 + 9x - \frac{10}{3}$

$0 = 3x^3 - 20x^2 + 27x - 10$

Possible Rational Roots: $\pm 1,\ \pm 2,\ \pm 5,\ \pm 10,\ \pm\frac{1}{3},\ \pm\frac{2}{3},\ \pm\frac{5}{3},\ \pm\frac{10}{3}$

$$
\begin{array}{r|rrrr}
1 & 3 & -20 & 27 & -10 \\
& & 3 & -17 & 10 \\
\hline
& 3 & -17 & 10 & 0
\end{array}
$$

$0 = (x - 1)(3x^2 - 17x + 10)$

$0 = (x - 1)(3x - 2)(x - 5)$

Zeros: $x = 1,\ x = \frac{2}{3},\ x = 5$

17. Possible Rational Roots: $\pm 1,\ \pm 2,\ \pm 5,\ \pm 10$

$$
\begin{array}{r|rrrrr}
1 & 1 & 1 & 3 & 5 & -10 \\
  &   & 1 & 2 & 5 & 10 \\
\hline
  & 1 & 2 & 5 & 10 & 0
\end{array}
\qquad x = 1 \text{ is a zero.}
$$

$$
\begin{array}{r|rrrr}
-2 & 1 & 2 & 5 & 10 \\
   &   & -2 & 0 & -10 \\
\hline
   & 1 & 0 & 5 & 0
\end{array}
\qquad x = -2 \text{ is a zero.}
$$

$$
\begin{aligned}
f(x) &= (x-1)(x+2)(x^2+5) \\
     &= (x-1)(x+2)(x+5i)(x-5i)
\end{aligned}
$$

18.
$$
\begin{aligned}
f(x) &= (x-2)[x-(3+i)][x-(3-i)] \\
     &= (x-2)[x^2 - x(3-i) - x(3+i) + (3+i)(3-i)] \\
     &= (x-2)[x^2 - 6x + 10] \\
     &= x^3 - 8x^2 + 22x - 20
\end{aligned}
$$

19.
$$
\begin{array}{r|rrrr}
3i & 1 & 4 & 9 & 36 \\
   &   & 3i & 12i-9 & -36 \\
\hline
   & 1 & 4+3i & 12i & 0
\end{array}
$$

20.

Iteration	a	c	b	$f(a)$	$f(c)$	$f(b)$	Error
1	0	0.5	1	-1	0.125	2	0.5
2	0	0.25	0.5	-1	-0.4844	0.125	0.25
3	0.25	0.375	0.5	-0.4844	-0.1973	0.125	0.125
4	0.375	0.4375	0.5	-0.1973	-0.0413	0.125	0.0625
5	0.4375	0.4688	0.5	-0.0413	0.0405	0.125	0.0313
6	0.4375	0.4531	0.4688	-0.0413	-0.0007	0.0405	0.0156
7	0.4531	0.4610	0.4688	-0.0007	0.0198	0.0405	0.0078
8	0.4531	0.4570	0.4610	-0.0007	0.0095	0.0198	0.0039
9	0.4531	0.4550	0.4570	-0.0007	0.0043	0.0095	0.0020
10	0.4531	0.4541	0.4550	-0.0007	0.0018	0.0043	0.0010

$x \approx 0.454$

CHAPTER 5

Practice Test Solutions

1. Vertical asymptote: $x = 0$
Horizontal asymptote: $y = \frac{1}{2}$
x-intercept: $(1, 0)$

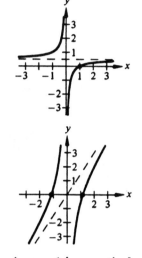

2. Vertical asymptote: $x = 0$
Slant asymptote: $y = 3x$
x-intercepts: $\left(\pm\dfrac{2}{\sqrt{3}}, 0\right)$

3. $\lim\limits_{x \to \infty} f(x) = 8$ so $y = 8$
is a horizontal asymptote.
There are no vertical asymptotes.

4. $x = 1$ is a vertical asymptote.
$$\frac{4x^2 - 2x + 7}{x - 1} = 4x + 2 + \frac{9}{x - 1}$$
so $y = 4x + 2$ is a slant asymptote.

5. $f(x) = \dfrac{x - 5}{(x - 5)^2} = \dfrac{1}{x - 5}$
Vertical asymptote: $x = 5$
Horizontal asymptote: $y = 0$
y-intercept: $\left(0, -\frac{1}{5}\right)$

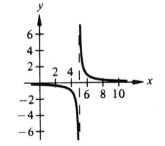

6. $\dfrac{1 - 2x}{x^2 + x} = \dfrac{1 - 2x}{x(x + 1)} = \dfrac{A}{x} + \dfrac{B}{x + 1}$
$1 - 2x = A(x + 1) + Bx$
When $x = 0$, $1 = A$.
When $x = -1$, $3 = -B \Rightarrow B = -3$.
$\dfrac{1 - 2x}{x^2 + x} = \dfrac{1}{x} - \dfrac{3}{x + 1}$

7. $\dfrac{6x}{x^2 - x - 2} = \dfrac{6x}{(x+1)(x-2)} = \dfrac{A}{x+1} + \dfrac{B}{x-2}$

$\qquad 6x = A(x-2) + B(x+1)$

When $x = -1$, $-6 = -3A \Rightarrow A = 2$.

When $x = 2$, $12 = 3B \Rightarrow B = 4$.

$\dfrac{6x}{x^2 - x - 2} = \dfrac{2}{x+1} + \dfrac{4}{x-2}$

8. $\dfrac{6x - 17}{(x-3)^2} = \dfrac{A}{x-3} + \dfrac{B}{(x-3)^2}$

$\qquad 6x - 17 = A(x-3) + B$

When $x = 3$, $1 = B$.

When $x = 0$, $-17 = -3A + B \Rightarrow A = 6$.

$\dfrac{6x - 17}{(x-3)^2} = \dfrac{6}{x-3} + \dfrac{1}{(x-3)^2}$

9. $\dfrac{3x^2 - x + 8}{x^3 + 2x} = \dfrac{3x^2 - x + 8}{x(x^2 + 2)} = \dfrac{A}{x} + \dfrac{Bx + C}{x^2 + 2}$

$\qquad 3x^2 - x + 8 = A(x^2 + 2) + (Bx + C)x$

When $x = 0$, $8 = 2A \Rightarrow A = 4$.

When $x = 1$, $10 = 3A + B + C \Rightarrow -2 = B + C$.

When $x = -1$, $12 = 3A + B - C \Rightarrow \underline{0 = B - C}$

$\qquad\qquad\qquad\qquad\qquad\qquad -2 = 2B \qquad \Rightarrow B = -1$

$\qquad\qquad\qquad\qquad\qquad\qquad\qquad\qquad\qquad\quad C = -1$

$\dfrac{3x^2 - x + 8}{x^3 + 2x} = \dfrac{4}{x} - \dfrac{x+1}{x^2 + 2} = \dfrac{4}{x} - \dfrac{x}{x^2 + 2} - \dfrac{1}{x^2 + 2}$

10. $(x - 0)^2 = 4(5)(y - 0)$

Vertex: $(0, 0)$

Focus: $(0, 5)$

Directrix: $y = -5$

11. $(y - 0)^2 = 4(7)(x - 0)$

$\qquad y^2 = 28x$

$\qquad y^2 - 28x = 0$

12. $a = 12$, $b = 5$, $h = k = 0$,

$\qquad c = \sqrt{144 - 25} = \sqrt{119}$

Center: $(0, 0)$

Foci: $(\pm\sqrt{119},\ 0)$

Vertices: $(\pm 12,\ 0)$

13. Center: $(0, 0)$

$c = 4, \ 2b = 6 \Rightarrow b = 3,$

$a = \sqrt{16 + 9} = 5$

$\dfrac{x^2}{25} + \dfrac{y^2}{9} = 1$

14. $a = 12, \ b = 13, \ c = \sqrt{144 + 169} = \sqrt{313}$

Center: $(0, 0)$

Foci: $(0, \pm\sqrt{313})$

Vertices: $(0, \pm 12)$

Asymptotes: $y = \pm\dfrac{12}{13}x$

15. Center: $(0, 0)$

$a = 4, \ \pm\dfrac{1}{2} = \pm\dfrac{b}{4} \Rightarrow b = 2$

$\dfrac{x^2}{16} - \dfrac{y^2}{4} = 1$

16. $p = 4$

$(x - 6)^2 = 4(4)(y + 1)$

$x^2 - 12x + 36 = 16y + 16$

$x^2 - 12x - 16y + 20 = 0$

17.

$16x^2 - 96x + 9y^2 + 36y = -36$

$16(x^2 - 6x + 9) + 9(y^2 + 4y + 4) = -36 + 144 + 36$

$16(x - 3)^2 + 9(y + 2)^2 = 144$

$\dfrac{(x - 3)^2}{9} + \dfrac{(y + 2)^2}{16} = 1$

$a = 4, \ b = 3, \ c = \sqrt{16 - 9} = \sqrt{7}$

Center: $(3, -2)$

Foci: $(3, -2 \pm \sqrt{7})$

Vertices: $(3, -2 \pm 4)$ or $(3, 2)$ and $(3, -6)$

18. Center: $(3, 1)$

$a = 4, \ 2b = 2 \Rightarrow b = 1$

$\dfrac{(x - 3)^2}{16} + \dfrac{(y - 1)^2}{1} = 1$

19. Center: $(-3, 1)$

Vertices: $\left(-3 \pm \dfrac{1}{2}, \ 1\right)$

Foci: $\left(-3 \pm \dfrac{\sqrt{13}}{6}, \ 1\right)$

Asymptotes: $y = \pm\dfrac{1/3}{1/2}(x + 3) + 1$

$= \pm\dfrac{2}{3}(x + 3) + 1$

$a = \dfrac{1}{2}, \ b = \dfrac{1}{3}, \ c = \sqrt{\dfrac{1}{4} + \dfrac{1}{9}} = \dfrac{\sqrt{13}}{6}$

$\dfrac{(x + 3)^2}{1/4} - \dfrac{(y - 1)^2}{1/9} = 1$

20. Center: $(3, 0)$

$a = 4, \ c = 7, \ b = \sqrt{49 - 16} = \sqrt{33}$

$\dfrac{y^2}{16} - \dfrac{(x - 3)^2}{33} = 1$

CHAPTER 6

Practice Test Solutions

1. $x^{3/5} = 8$

$\quad x = 8^{5/3} = (\sqrt[3]{8})^5 = 2^5 = 32$

2. $3^{x-1} = \frac{1}{81}$

$\quad 3^{x-1} = 3^{-4}$

$\quad x - 1 = -4$

$\quad x = -3$

3. $f(x) = 2^{-x} = \left(\frac{1}{2}\right)^x$

x	-2	-1	0	1	2
$f(x)$	4	2	1	$\frac{1}{2}$	$\frac{1}{4}$

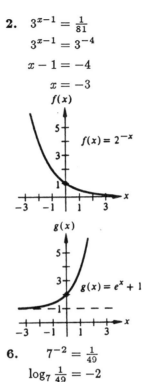

4. $g(x) = e^x + 1$

x	-2	-1	0	1	2
$g(x)$	1.14	1.37	2	3.72	8.39

5. $A = P\left(1 + \dfrac{r}{n}\right)^{nt}$

(a) $A = 5000\left(1 + \dfrac{0.09}{12}\right)^{12(3)} \approx \$6543.23$

(b) $A = 5000\left(1 + \dfrac{0.09}{4}\right)^{4(3)} \approx \$6530.25$

(c) $A = 5000e^{(0.09)(3)} \approx \$6549.82$

6. $\quad 7^{-2} = \frac{1}{49}$

$\quad \log_7 \frac{1}{49} = -2$

7. $x - 4 = \log_2 \frac{1}{64}$

$\quad 2^{x-4} = \frac{1}{64}$

$\quad 2^{x-4} = 2^{-6}$

$\quad x - 4 = -6$

$\quad x = -2$

8. $\log_b \sqrt[4]{8/25} = \frac{1}{4} \log_b \frac{8}{25}$

$\quad = \frac{1}{4}[\log_b 8 - \log_b 25]$

$\quad = \frac{1}{4}[\log_b 2^3 - \log_b 5^2]$

$\quad = \frac{1}{4}[3\log_b 2 - 2\log_b 5]$

$\quad = \frac{1}{4}[3(0.3562) - 2(0.8271)]$

$\quad = -0.1464$

9. $5\ln x - \dfrac{1}{2}\ln y + 6\ln z = \ln x^5 - \ln \sqrt{y} + \ln z^6$

$\qquad\qquad = \ln\left(\dfrac{x^5 z^6}{\sqrt{y}}\right)$

10. $\log_9 28 = \dfrac{\log 28}{\log 9} \approx 1.5166$

11. $\log N = 0.6646$

$N = 10^{0.6646} \approx 4.62$

12.

13. Domain: $\quad x^2 - 9 > 0$

$(x + 3)(x - 3) > 0$

$x < -3 \text{ or } x > 3$

14.

$y = \ln(x - 2)$

15. $\dfrac{\ln x}{\ln y} \neq \ln(x - y)$ since $\dfrac{\ln x}{\ln y} = \log_y x$

16. $5^x = 41$

$x = \log_5 41 = \dfrac{\ln 41}{\ln 5} \approx 2.3074$

17. $x - x^2 = \log_5 \frac{1}{25}$

$5^{x - x^2} = \frac{1}{25}$

$5^{x - x^2} = 5^{-2}$

$x - x^2 = -2$

$0 = x^2 - x - 2$

$0 = (x + 1)(x - 2)$

$x = -1 \text{ or } x = 2$

18. $\log_2 x + \log_2 (x - 3) = 2$

$\log_2 [x(x - 3)] = 2$

$x(x - 3) = 2^2$

$x^2 - 3x = 4$

$x^2 - 3x - 4 = 0$

$(x + 1)(x - 4) = 0$

$x = 4$

$x = -1 \text{ (extraneous solution)}$

19. $\dfrac{e^x + e^{-x}}{3} = 4$

$e^x(e^x + e^{-x}) = 12e^x$

$e^{2x} + 1 = 12e^x$

$e^{2x} - 12e^x + 1 = 0$

$e^x = \dfrac{12 \pm \sqrt{144 - 4}}{2}$

$e^x = 11.9161 \quad \text{or} \quad e^x = 0.0839$

$x = \ln 11.9161 \qquad x = \ln 0.0839$

$x \approx 2.4779 \qquad\quad x \approx -2.4779$

20. $A = Pe^{rt}$

$12,000 = 6,000e^{0.13t}$

$2 = e^{0.13t}$

$0.13t = \ln 2$

$t = \dfrac{\ln 2}{0.13}$

$t \approx 5.3319 \text{ yrs or 5 yrs 4 months}$

CHAPTER 7

Practice Test Solutions

1. $x + y = 1$

$3x - y = 15 \Rightarrow y = 3x - 15$

$x + (3x - 15) = 1$

$4x = 16$

$x = 4$

$y = -3$

2. $x - 3y = -3 \Rightarrow x = 3y - 3$

$x^2 + 6y = 5$

$(3y - 3)^2 + 6y = 5$

$9y^2 - 18y + 9 + 6y = 5$

$9y^2 - 12y + 4 = 0$

$(3y - 2)^2 = 0$

$y = \frac{2}{3}$

$x = -1$

3. $x + y + z = 6 \Rightarrow z = 6 - x - y$

$2x - y + 3z = 0 \qquad 2x - y + 3(6 - x - y) = 0 \quad \Rightarrow -x - 4y = -18$

$5x + 2y - z = -3 \qquad 5x + 2y - (6 - x - y) = -3 \Rightarrow 6x + 3y = 3$

$x = 18 - 4y$

$6(18 - 4y) + 3y = 3$

$-21y = -105$

$y = 5$

$x = 18 - 4y = -2$

$z = 6 - x - y = 3$

4. $x + y = 110 \quad \Rightarrow \quad y = 110 - x$

$xy = 2800$

$x(110 - x) = 2800$

$0 = x^2 - 110x + 2800$

$0 = (x - 40)(x - 70)$

$x = 40 \quad$ or $\quad x = 70$

$y = 70 \qquad\quad y = 40$

5. $2x + 2y = 170 \Rightarrow y = \dfrac{170 - 2x}{2} = 85 - x$

$xy = 2800$

$x(85 - x) = 2800$

$\qquad 0 = x^2 - 85x + 2800$

$\qquad 0 = (x - 25)(x - 60)$

$\qquad x = 25 \quad \text{or} \quad x = 60$

$\qquad y = 60 \qquad\quad\ y = 25$

Dimensions: $60' \times 25'$

6.
$$
\begin{array}{rcl}
2x + 15y = 4 & \Rightarrow & 2x + 15y = 4 \\
x - 3y = 23 & \Rightarrow & \underline{5x - 15y = 115} \\
& & 7x \qquad\quad = 119 \\
& & \quad x = 17 \\
& & \quad y = \dfrac{x - 23}{3} \\
& & \quad\ \ = -2
\end{array}
$$

7.
$$
\begin{array}{rcl}
x + y = 2 & \Rightarrow & 19x + 19y = 38 \\
38x - 19y = 7 & \Rightarrow & \underline{38x - 19y = \ \ 7} \\
& & 57x \qquad\quad = 45
\end{array}
$$

$\qquad x = \dfrac{45}{57} = \dfrac{15}{19}$

$\qquad y = 2 - x = \dfrac{38}{19} - \dfrac{15}{19} = \dfrac{23}{19}$

8.
$$
\begin{array}{rcl}
0.4x + 0.5y = \ \ 0.112 & \Rightarrow & 0.28x + 0.35y = \ \ 0.0784 \\
0.3x - 0.7y = -0.131 & \Rightarrow & \underline{0.15x - 0.35y = -0.0655} \\
& & 0.43x \qquad\qquad = \ \ 0.0129
\end{array}
$$

$\qquad x = \dfrac{0.0129}{0.43} = 0.03$

$\qquad y = \dfrac{0.112 - 0.4x}{0.5} = 0.20$

9. Let $x =$ amount in 11% fund and $y =$ amount in 13% fund.

$x + y = 17000 \Rightarrow y = 17000 - x$

$0.11x + 0.13y = 2080$

$0.11x + 0.13(17000 - x) = 2080$

$\qquad\qquad\qquad -0.02x = -130$

$\qquad\qquad\qquad\qquad x = \$6500$

$\qquad\qquad\qquad\qquad y = \$10,500$

10. $(4, 3), (1, 1), (-1, -2), (-2, -1)$

$$n = 4, \quad \sum_{i=1}^{4} x_i = 2, \quad \sum_{i=1}^{4} y_i = 1, \quad \sum_{i=1}^{4} x_i{}^2 = 22, \quad \sum_{i=1}^{4} x_i y_i = 17$$

$$
\begin{aligned}
4b + 2a &= 1 \quad \Rightarrow \quad 4b + 2a = 1 \\
2b + 22a &= 17 \quad \Rightarrow \quad \underline{-4b - 44a = -34} \\
&\qquad\qquad\qquad\qquad -42a = -33
\end{aligned}
$$

$$a = \frac{33}{42} = \frac{11}{14}$$

$$b = \frac{1}{4}\left(1 - 2\left(\frac{33}{42}\right)\right) = -\frac{1}{7}$$

$$y = ax + b = \frac{11}{14}x - \frac{1}{7}$$

11.

$$
\begin{array}{lll}
x + y = -2 & \Rightarrow \quad -2x - 2y = 4 & -9y + 3z = 45 \\
2x - y + z = 11 & \quad\;\; \underline{2x - y + z = 11} & \underline{4y - 3z = -20} \\
\quad\;\; 4y - 3z = -20 & \qquad\quad -3y + z = 15 & -5y \quad\;\; = 25 \\
& & y = -5 \\
& & x = 3 \\
& & z = 0
\end{array}
$$

12.

$$
\begin{array}{ll}
4x - y + 5z = 4 & \Rightarrow \quad 4x - y + 5z = 4 \\
2x + y - z = 0 & \Rightarrow \quad \underline{-4x - 2y + 2z = 0} \\
2x + 4y + 8z = 0 & \qquad\quad -3y + 7z = 4
\end{array}
$$

$$
\begin{aligned}
2x + 4y + 8z &= 0 \\
\underline{-2x - y + z} &= 0 \\
3y + 9z &= 0 \\
\underline{-3y + 7z} &= 4 \\
16z &= 4 \\
z &= \tfrac{1}{4} \\
y &= -\tfrac{3}{4} \\
x &= \tfrac{1}{2}
\end{aligned}
$$

13. $3x + 2y - z = 5 \quad \Rightarrow \quad 6x + 4y - 2z = 10$

$ 6x - y + 5z = 2 \quad \Rightarrow \quad \underline{-6x + y - 5z = -2}$

$$5y - 7z = 8$$

$$y = \frac{8 + 7z}{5}$$

$3x + 2y - z = 5$

$\underline{12x - 2y + 10z = 4}$

$15x + 9z = 9$

$$x = \frac{9 - 9z}{15} = \frac{3 - 3z}{5}$$

Let $z = a$, then $x = \dfrac{3 - 3a}{5}$ and $y = \dfrac{8 + 7a}{5}$.

14. $y = ax^2 + bx + c$ passes through $(0, -1)$, $(1, 4)$, and $(2, 13)$.

At $(0, -1)$, $\quad -1 = a(0)^2 + b(0) + c \quad \Rightarrow \quad c = -1$

At $(1, \quad 4)$, $\quad 4 = a(1)^2 + b(1) - 1 \quad \Rightarrow \quad 5 = a + b \quad \Rightarrow \quad 5 = a + b$

At $(2, 13)$, $\quad 13 = a(2)^2 + b(2) - 1 \quad \Rightarrow \quad 14 = 4a + 2b \quad \Rightarrow \quad \underline{-7 = -2a - b}$

$$-2 = -a$$

$$a = 2$$

$$b = 3$$

Thus, $y = 2x^2 + 3x - 1$.

15. $s = \frac{1}{2}at^2 + v_0 t + s_0$ passes through $(1, 12)$, $(2, 5)$, and $(3, 4)$.

At $(1, 12)$, $\quad 12 = \frac{1}{2}a + v_0 + s_0 \quad \Rightarrow \quad 24 = a + 2v_0 + 2s_0$

At $(2, \quad 5)$, $\quad 5 = 2a + 2v_0 + s_0 \quad \Rightarrow \quad \underline{-5 = -2a - 2v_0 - s_0}$

At $(3, \quad 4)$, $\quad 4 = \frac{9}{2}a + 3v_0 + s_0 \quad\quad\quad\quad 19 = -a + s_0$

$$15 = 6a + 6v_0 + 3s_0$$

$$\underline{-8 = -9a - 6v_0 - 2s_0}$$

$$7 = -3a + s_0$$

$$\underline{-19 = a - s_0}$$

$$-12 = -2a$$

$$a = 6$$

$$s_0 = 25$$

$$v_0 = -16$$

Thus, $s = \frac{1}{2}(6)t^2 - 16t + 25 = 3t^2 - 16t + 25$.

16. $x^2 + y^2 \geq 9$

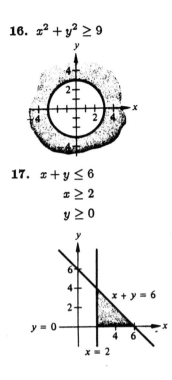

17. $x + y \leq 6$

$\qquad x \geq 2$

$\qquad y \geq 0$

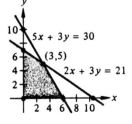

18. Line through $(0, 0)$ and $(0, 7)$:

$\qquad x = 0$

Line through $(0, 0)$ and $(2, 3)$:

$\qquad y = \frac{3}{2}x$ or $3x - 2y = 0$

Line through $(0, 7)$ and $(2, 3)$:

$\qquad y = -2x + 7$ or $2x + y = 7$

Inequalities: $\qquad x \geq 0$

$\qquad\qquad\qquad 3x - 2y \leq 0$

$\qquad\qquad\qquad 2x + y \leq 7$

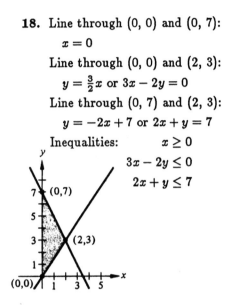

19. Vertices: $(0, 0)$, $(0, 7)$, $(6, 0)$, $(3, 5)$

$\qquad C = 30x + 26y$

At $(0, 0)$, $C = 0$

At $(0, 7)$, $C = 182$

At $(6, 0)$, $C = 180$

At $(3, 5)$, $C = 220$

The maximum value of C is 220.

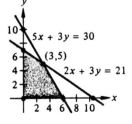

20. $\qquad x^2 + y^2 \leq 4$

$\qquad (x - 2)^2 + y^2 \geq 4$

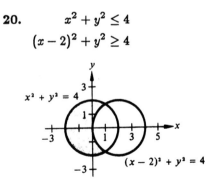

CHAPTER 8

Practice Test Solutions

1. $\begin{bmatrix} 1 & -2 & 4 \\ 3 & -5 & 9 \end{bmatrix} - 3R_1 + R_2 \rightarrow \begin{bmatrix} 1 & -2 & 4 \\ 0 & 1 & -3 \end{bmatrix} 2R_2 + R_1 \rightarrow \begin{bmatrix} 1 & 0 & -2 \\ 0 & 1 & -3 \end{bmatrix}$

2.
$$\begin{aligned} 3x + 5y &= 3 \\ 2x - y &= -11 \end{aligned} \quad \begin{bmatrix} 3 & 5 & \vdots & 3 \\ 2 & -1 & \vdots & -11 \end{bmatrix} -R_2 + R_1 \rightarrow \begin{bmatrix} 1 & 6 & \vdots & 14 \\ 2 & -1 & \vdots & -11 \end{bmatrix}$$

$$-2R_1 + R_2 \rightarrow \begin{bmatrix} 1 & 6 & \vdots & 14 \\ 0 & -13 & \vdots & -39 \end{bmatrix}$$

$$-\tfrac{1}{13}R_2 \rightarrow \begin{bmatrix} 1 & 6 & \vdots & 14 \\ 0 & 1 & \vdots & 3 \end{bmatrix}$$

$$-6R_2 + R_1 \rightarrow \begin{bmatrix} 1 & 0 & \vdots & -4 \\ 0 & 1 & \vdots & 3 \end{bmatrix}$$

Solution: $x = -4$, $y = 3$

3.
$$\begin{aligned} 2x + 3y &= -3 \\ 3x + 2y &= 8 \\ x + y &= 1 \end{aligned} \quad \begin{bmatrix} 2 & 3 & \vdots & -3 \\ 3 & 2 & \vdots & 8 \\ 1 & 1 & \vdots & 1 \end{bmatrix} \begin{matrix} \nearrow R_3 \\ \\ \searrow R_1 \end{matrix} \begin{bmatrix} 1 & 1 & \vdots & 1 \\ 3 & 2 & \vdots & 8 \\ 2 & 3 & \vdots & -3 \end{bmatrix}$$

$$\begin{matrix} -3R_1 + R_2 \rightarrow \\ 2R_1 + R_3 \rightarrow \end{matrix} \begin{bmatrix} 1 & 1 & \vdots & 1 \\ 0 & -1 & \vdots & 5 \\ 0 & -1 & \vdots & 5 \end{bmatrix}$$

$$\begin{matrix} R_2 + R_1 \rightarrow \\ -R_2 \rightarrow \\ -R_2 + R_3 \rightarrow \end{matrix} \begin{bmatrix} 1 & 0 & \vdots & 6 \\ 0 & 1 & \vdots & -5 \\ 0 & 0 & \vdots & 0 \end{bmatrix}$$

Solution: $x = 6$, $y = -5$

350

4.

$$\begin{aligned} x \quad\;\; + 3z &= -5 \\ 2x + y \quad\;\; &= 0 \\ 3x + y - z &= 3 \end{aligned}$$

$$\begin{bmatrix} 1 & 0 & 3 & \vdots & -5 \\ 2 & 1 & 0 & \vdots & 0 \\ 3 & 1 & -1 & \vdots & 3 \end{bmatrix} \begin{matrix} \\ -2R_1 + R_2 \to \\ -3R_1 + R_3 \to \end{matrix} \begin{bmatrix} 1 & 0 & 3 & \vdots & -5 \\ 0 & 1 & -6 & \vdots & 10 \\ 0 & 1 & -10 & \vdots & 18 \end{bmatrix}$$

$$-R_2 + R_3 \to \begin{bmatrix} 1 & 0 & 3 & \vdots & -5 \\ 0 & 1 & -6 & \vdots & 10 \\ 0 & 0 & -4 & \vdots & 8 \end{bmatrix}$$

$$\begin{matrix} -3R_3 + R_1 \to \\ 6R_3 + R_2 \to \\ -\frac{1}{4}R_4 \to \end{matrix} \begin{bmatrix} 1 & 0 & 0 & \vdots & 1 \\ 0 & 1 & 0 & \vdots & -2 \\ 0 & 0 & 1 & \vdots & -2 \end{bmatrix}$$

Solution: $x = 1$, $y = -2$, $z = -2$

5. $\begin{bmatrix} 1 & 4 & 5 \\ 2 & 0 & -3 \end{bmatrix} \begin{bmatrix} 1 & 6 \\ 0 & -7 \\ -1 & 2 \end{bmatrix} = \begin{bmatrix} -4 & -12 \\ 5 & 6 \end{bmatrix}$

6. $3A - 5B = 3\begin{bmatrix} 9 & 1 \\ -4 & 8 \end{bmatrix} - 5\begin{bmatrix} 6 & -2 \\ 3 & 5 \end{bmatrix}$

$$= \begin{bmatrix} 27 & 3 \\ -12 & 24 \end{bmatrix} - \begin{bmatrix} 30 & -10 \\ 15 & 25 \end{bmatrix}$$

$$= \begin{bmatrix} -3 & 13 \\ -27 & -1 \end{bmatrix}$$

7. $f(A) = \begin{bmatrix} 3 & 0 \\ 7 & 1 \end{bmatrix}^2 - 7\begin{bmatrix} 3 & 0 \\ 7 & 1 \end{bmatrix} + 8\begin{bmatrix} 1 & 0 \\ 0 & 1 \end{bmatrix}$

$$= \begin{bmatrix} 3 & 0 \\ 7 & 1 \end{bmatrix}\begin{bmatrix} 3 & 0 \\ 7 & 1 \end{bmatrix} - \begin{bmatrix} 21 & 0 \\ 49 & 7 \end{bmatrix} + \begin{bmatrix} 8 & 0 \\ 0 & 8 \end{bmatrix}$$

$$= \begin{bmatrix} 9 & 0 \\ 28 & 1 \end{bmatrix} - \begin{bmatrix} 21 & 0 \\ 49 & 7 \end{bmatrix} + \begin{bmatrix} 8 & 0 \\ 0 & 8 \end{bmatrix}$$

$$= \begin{bmatrix} -4 & 0 \\ -21 & 2 \end{bmatrix}$$

8. False since

$$(A + B)(A + 3B) = A(A + 3B) + B(A + 3B)$$
$$= A^2 + 3AB + BA + 3B^2$$

9. $\begin{bmatrix} 1 & 2 & \vdots & 1 & 0 \\ 3 & 5 & \vdots & 0 & 1 \end{bmatrix} \begin{matrix} \\ -3R_1 + R_2 \to \end{matrix} \begin{bmatrix} 1 & 2 & \vdots & 1 & 0 \\ 0 & -1 & \vdots & -3 & 1 \end{bmatrix}$

$$\begin{matrix} 2R_2 + R_1 \to \\ -R_2 \to \end{matrix} \begin{bmatrix} 1 & 0 & \vdots & -5 & 2 \\ 0 & 1 & \vdots & 3 & -1 \end{bmatrix}$$

$$A^{-1} = \begin{bmatrix} -5 & 2 \\ 3 & -1 \end{bmatrix}$$

10.

$$\begin{bmatrix} 1 & 1 & 1 & \vdots & 1 & 0 & 0 \\ 3 & 6 & 5 & \vdots & 0 & 1 & 0 \\ 6 & 10 & 8 & \vdots & 0 & 0 & 1 \end{bmatrix} \begin{matrix} \\ -3R_1 + R_2 \to \\ -6R_1 + R_3 \to \end{matrix} \begin{bmatrix} 1 & 1 & 1 & \vdots & 1 & 0 & 0 \\ 0 & 3 & 2 & \vdots & -3 & 1 & 0 \\ 0 & 4 & 2 & \vdots & -6 & 0 & 1 \end{bmatrix}$$

$$\begin{matrix} -R_2 + R_1 \to \\ \frac{1}{3}R_2 \to \\ -4R_2 + R_3 \to \end{matrix} \begin{bmatrix} 1 & 0 & \frac{1}{3} & \vdots & 2 & -\frac{1}{3} & 0 \\ 0 & 1 & \frac{2}{3} & \vdots & -1 & \frac{1}{3} & 0 \\ 0 & 0 & -\frac{2}{3} & \vdots & -2 & -\frac{4}{3} & 1 \end{bmatrix}$$

$$\begin{matrix} \frac{1}{2}R_3 + R_1 \to \\ R_3 + R_2 \to \\ -\frac{3}{2}R_3 \to \end{matrix} \begin{bmatrix} 1 & 0 & 0 & \vdots & 1 & -1 & \frac{1}{2} \\ 0 & 1 & 0 & \vdots & -3 & -1 & 1 \\ 0 & 0 & 1 & \vdots & 3 & 2 & -\frac{3}{2} \end{bmatrix}$$

$$A^{-1} = \begin{bmatrix} 1 & -1 & \frac{1}{2} \\ -3 & -1 & 1 \\ 3 & 2 & -\frac{3}{2} \end{bmatrix}$$

11. (a)
$$\begin{matrix} x + 2y = 4 \\ 3x + 5y = 1 \end{matrix} \begin{bmatrix} 1 & 2 & \vdots & 1 & 0 \\ 3 & 5 & \vdots & 0 & 1 \end{bmatrix} \begin{matrix} \\ -3R_1 + R_2 \to \end{matrix} \begin{bmatrix} 1 & 2 & \vdots & 1 & 0 \\ 0 & -1 & \vdots & -3 & 1 \end{bmatrix}$$

$$\begin{matrix} -2R_2 + R_1 \to \\ -R_2 \to \end{matrix} \begin{bmatrix} 1 & 0 & \vdots & -5 & 2 \\ 0 & 1 & \vdots & 3 & -1 \end{bmatrix}$$

$$X = A^{-1}B = \begin{bmatrix} -5 & 2 \\ 3 & -1 \end{bmatrix} \begin{bmatrix} 4 \\ 1 \end{bmatrix} = \begin{bmatrix} -18 \\ 11 \end{bmatrix}$$

$$x = -18, \ y = 11$$

(b)
$$\begin{matrix} x + 2y = 3 \\ 3x + 5y = -2 \end{matrix}$$

$$X = A^{-1}B = \begin{bmatrix} -5 & 2 \\ 3 & -1 \end{bmatrix} \begin{bmatrix} 3 \\ -2 \end{bmatrix} = \begin{bmatrix} -19 \\ 11 \end{bmatrix}$$

$$x = -19, \ y = 11$$

12. $\begin{vmatrix} 6 & -1 \\ 3 & 4 \end{vmatrix} = 24 - (-3) = 27$

13. $\begin{vmatrix} 1 & 3 & -1 \\ 5 & 9 & 0 \\ 6 & 2 & -5 \end{vmatrix} \begin{matrix} 1 & 3 \\ 5 & 9 \\ 6 & 2 \end{matrix} = (-45 + 0 - 10) - (-54 + 0 - 75) = 74$

14. $\begin{vmatrix} 1 & 4 & 2 & 3 \\ 0 & 1 & -2 & 0 \\ 3 & 5 & -1 & 1 \\ 2 & 0 & 6 & 1 \end{vmatrix} = \begin{vmatrix} 1 & 2 & 3 \\ 3 & -1 & 1 \\ 2 & 6 & 1 \end{vmatrix} + 2 \begin{vmatrix} 1 & 4 & 3 \\ 3 & 5 & 1 \\ 2 & 0 & 1 \end{vmatrix} = 51 + 2(-29) = -7$ Expansion along Row 2.

15. $\begin{vmatrix} 3 & 0 & 0 \\ 0 & 3 & 0 \\ 0 & 0 & 3 \end{vmatrix} = 3(3)(3) \begin{vmatrix} 1 & 0 & 0 \\ 0 & 1 & 0 \\ 0 & 0 & 1 \end{vmatrix} = -3^3 \begin{vmatrix} 1 & 0 & 0 \\ 0 & 0 & 1 \\ 0 & 1 & 0 \end{vmatrix}$

True

16. $\begin{vmatrix} 6 & 4 & 3 & 0 & 6 \\ 0 & 5 & 1 & 4 & 8 \\ 0 & 0 & 2 & 7 & 3 \\ 0 & 0 & 0 & 9 & 2 \\ 0 & 0 & 0 & 0 & 1 \end{vmatrix} = 6(5)(2)(9)(1) = 540$

17. $A = \begin{bmatrix} 1 & 3 & 0 \\ 0 & 4 & 5 \\ 0 & 1 & 2 \end{bmatrix}$ $|A| = 3$ $A^t = \begin{bmatrix} 1 & 0 & 0 \\ 3 & 4 & 1 \\ 0 & 5 & 2 \end{bmatrix}$

$$A^{-1} = \frac{1}{3} \begin{bmatrix} \begin{vmatrix} 4 & 1 \\ 5 & 2 \end{vmatrix} & -\begin{vmatrix} 3 & 1 \\ 0 & 2 \end{vmatrix} & \begin{vmatrix} 3 & 4 \\ 0 & 5 \end{vmatrix} \\ -\begin{vmatrix} 0 & 0 \\ 5 & 2 \end{vmatrix} & \begin{vmatrix} 1 & 0 \\ 0 & 2 \end{vmatrix} & -\begin{vmatrix} 1 & 0 \\ 0 & 5 \end{vmatrix} \\ \begin{vmatrix} 0 & 0 \\ 4 & 1 \end{vmatrix} & -\begin{vmatrix} 1 & 0 \\ 3 & 1 \end{vmatrix} & \begin{vmatrix} 1 & 0 \\ 3 & 4 \end{vmatrix} \end{bmatrix} = \frac{1}{3} \begin{bmatrix} 3 & -6 & 15 \\ 0 & 2 & -5 \\ 0 & -1 & 4 \end{bmatrix} = \begin{bmatrix} 1 & -2 & 5 \\ 0 & \frac{2}{3} & -\frac{5}{3} \\ 0 & -\frac{1}{3} & \frac{4}{3} \end{bmatrix}$$

18. $x = \dfrac{\begin{vmatrix} 4 & -7 \\ 11 & 5 \end{vmatrix}}{\begin{vmatrix} 6 & -7 \\ 2 & 5 \end{vmatrix}} = \dfrac{97}{44}$

19. $z = \dfrac{\begin{vmatrix} 3 & 0 & 1 \\ 0 & 1 & 3 \\ 1 & -1 & 2 \end{vmatrix}}{\begin{vmatrix} 3 & 0 & 1 \\ 0 & 1 & 4 \\ 1 & -1 & 0 \end{vmatrix}} = \dfrac{14}{11}$

20. $y = \dfrac{\begin{vmatrix} 721.4 & 33.77 \\ 45.9 & 19.85 \end{vmatrix}}{\begin{vmatrix} 721.4 & -29.1 \\ 45.9 & 105.6 \end{vmatrix}} = \dfrac{12,769.747}{77,515.530} \approx 0.1647$

CHAPTER 9

Practice Test Solutions

1. $a_n = \dfrac{2n}{(n+2)!}$

$a_1 = \dfrac{2(1)}{3!} = \dfrac{2}{6} = \dfrac{1}{3}$

$a_2 = \dfrac{2(2)}{4!} = \dfrac{4}{24} = \dfrac{1}{6}$

$a_3 = \dfrac{2(3)}{5!} = \dfrac{6}{120} = \dfrac{1}{20}$

$a_4 = \dfrac{2(4)}{6!} = \dfrac{8}{720} = \dfrac{1}{90}$

$a_5 = \dfrac{2(5)}{7!} = \dfrac{10}{5040} = \dfrac{1}{504}$

$\left\{\dfrac{1}{3}, \dfrac{1}{6}, \dfrac{1}{20}, \dfrac{1}{90}, \dfrac{1}{504}, \ldots\right\}$

2. $a_n = \dfrac{n+3}{3n}$

3. $\displaystyle\sum_{i=1}^{6}(2i-1) = 1 + 3 + 5 + 7 + 9 + 11 = 36$

4. $a_1 = 23, \ d = -2$

$a_2 = a_1 + d = 21$

$a_3 = a_2 + d = 19$

$a_4 = a_3 + d = 17$

$a_5 = a_4 + d = 15$

$\{23, \ 21, \ 19, \ 17, \ 15, \ \ldots\}$

5. $a_1 = 12, \ d = 3, \ n = 50$

$a_n = a_1 + (n-1)d$

$a_{50} = 12 + (50-1)3 = 159$

6. $a_1 = 1$

$a_{200} = 200$

$S_n = \dfrac{n}{2}(a_1 + a_n)$

$S_{200} = \dfrac{200}{2}(1 + 200) = 20,100$

7. $a_1 = 7, \ r = 2$

$a_2 = a_1 r = 14$

$a_3 = a_2 r = 28$

$a_4 = a_3 r = 56$

$a_5 = a_4 r = 112$

$\{7, \ 14, \ 28, \ 56, \ 112, \ \ldots\}$

8. $\displaystyle\sum_{n=0}^{9} 6\left(\dfrac{2}{3}\right)^n, \ a_1 = 6, \ r = \dfrac{2}{3}, \ n = 9$

$S_n = \dfrac{a_1(1 - r^n)}{1 - r}$

$= \dfrac{6\left(1 - \left(\frac{2}{3}\right)^9\right)}{1 - \frac{2}{3}} \approx 17.5318$

9. $\displaystyle\sum_{n=0}^{\infty}(0.03)^n, \ a_1 = 1, \ r = 0.03$

$S_n = \dfrac{a_1}{1 - r} = \dfrac{1}{1 - 0.03} = \dfrac{1}{0.97} = \dfrac{100}{97} \approx 1.0309$

10. For $n = 1$, $1 = \dfrac{1(1+1)}{2}$.

Assume that $1 + 2 + 3 + 4 + \cdots + k = \dfrac{k(k+1)}{2}$.

Now for $n = k + 1$,

$$1 + 2 + 3 + 4 + \cdots + k + (k+1) = \dfrac{k(k+1)}{2} + k + 1$$

$$= \dfrac{k(k+1)}{2} + \dfrac{2(k+1)}{2}$$

$$= \dfrac{(k+1)(k+2)}{2}.$$

Thus, $1 + 2 + 3 + 4 + \cdots + n = \dfrac{n(n+1)}{2}$ for all integers $n \geq 1$.

11. For $n = 4$, $4! > 2^4$.

Assume that $k! > 2^k$.

Then $(k+1)! = (k+1)(k!) > (k+1)2^k > 2 \cdot 2^k = 2^{k+1}$.

Thus, $n! > 2^n$ for all integers $n \geq 4$.

12. $_{13}C_4 = \dfrac{13!}{(13-4)!4!} = 715$

13. $(x+3)^5 = x^5 + 5x^4(3) + 10x^3(3)^2 + 10x^2(3)^3 + 5x(3)^4 + (3)^5$

$$= x^5 + 15x^4 + 90x^3 + 270x^2 + 405x + 243$$

14. $_{12}C_5 x^7 (-2)^5 = -25,344x^7$

15. $_{30}P_4 = \dfrac{30!}{(30-4)!} = 657,720$

16. $6! = 720$ ways

17. $_{12}P_3 = 1320$

18. $P(2) + P(3) + P(4) = \dfrac{1}{36} + \dfrac{2}{36} + \dfrac{3}{36}$

$$= \dfrac{6}{36} = \dfrac{1}{6}$$

19. $P(K,\ B10) = \dfrac{4}{52} \cdot \dfrac{2}{51} = \dfrac{2}{663}$

20. Let A = probability of no faulty units.

$$P(A) = \left(\dfrac{997}{1000}\right)^{50} \approx 0.8605$$

$$P(A') = 1 - P(A) \approx 0.1395$$